D1453297

THEORY AND APPLICATION
OF THE z-TRANSFORM METHOD

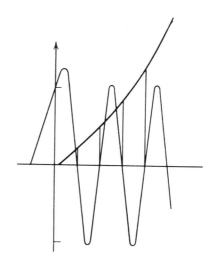

THEORY AND APPLICATION
OF THE *z*-TRANSFORM METHOD

E. I. JURY, DEPARTMENT OF ELECTRICAL ENGINEERING,

UNIVERSITY OF CALIFORNIA, BERKELEY, CALIFORNIA

ROBERT E. KRIEGER PUBLISHING CO.
HUNTINGTON, NEW YORK

Originally Published 1964
Reprinted With Corrections 1973

Published by Robert E. Krieger Publishing Co., Inc.
          P.O. Box 542
          Huntington, N.Y. 11743

LIBRARY OF CONGRESS CATALOG CARD NUMBER: 64-17145
ISBN NUMBER 0-88275-122-0

In memory of my uncle Murad

PREFACE

During the early fifties, considerable interest and activity arose among engineers and systems theorists in the relatively new area of discrete system theory. This activity and aroused interest were mainly motivated by the advancement made in digital computer technology and its widespread application in system analysis and design. Several methods of analysis of discrete systems were proposed and applied. Among them were the transform techniques and operators' methods. One transform method, which found wide application in the analysis, is the z-transform method. It represents the counterpart of the Laplace transform as applied to continuous system theory. In this text the z-transform method is extensively developed and applied to many areas of discrete system theory.

The subject matter is mainly addressed to engineers and systems theorists; however, some of the material developed would also be of interest to applied mathematicians. Whenever it is found necessary, most of the theorems and lemmas are proved on a somewhat rigorous mathematical basis. However, to limit the text and to place more emphasis on the applications, the rigor is sometimes sacrificed. Consequently, certain theorems are touched on briefly without proofs. Convergence problems are not vigorously pursued, but are left to the reader for further study. In most of the unproven material the pertinent references are cited so that the reader can easily find the rigorous derivations of the theory.

Chapter 1 discusses in detail the z-transform theory and its modifications and the modified z-transform. Extensive lists of theorems or rules are either derived or presented to acquaint the reader with the detailed use of this method.

In Chapter 2, the z-transform method is applied to the solution of linear difference or difference-differential equations. Several forms of difference equations are given with examples from network, circuit, and control theory.

The problem of stability of linear discrete systems and the root distribution within the unit circle are discussed in detail in Chapter 3. This stability discussion is not yet available in any other text; it also represents some of my original work that is available only in papers. Thus the contents of this chapter could be very useful to applied mathematicians as well as to engineers and systems theorists.

Further development of the z-transform theory is considered in Chapter 4, with the derivation of the convolution of the z-transform and the modified z-transform. The application of the convolution theorem, and of the two-sided z-transform to statistical study and design of discrete systems are demonstrated.

The application of the convolution z-transform to the solution of certain types of nonlinear discrete systems or nonlinear difference equations is emphasized in Chapter 5. Examples of the application of this method are also described.

In Chapter 6 the periodic modes of oscillation of certain nonlinear discrete systems are emphasized and applied. The stability study of limit cycles and their identification is also included.

The use of the z-transform method and its modification as applied to the approximate solution of differential equations or continuous systems is examined in Chapter 7. The methods developed are well suited for digital computer analysis.

Finally, in Chapter 8 are found various examples of areas in discrete system theory. These areas include nonlinear sampled-data feedback system, discrete antenna array theory, information and filtering theory, economic systems, sequential circuits, and discrete Markov processes. The main emphasis is the application of the z-transform theory, developed in the preceding chapters, to various disciplines of discrete system theory.

Extensive tables of z-transform, modified z-transforms, total square integrals, and summation of special series are in the Appendix. Furthermore, there are many problems that illustrate further the application of the z-transform theory and indicate the method of the proofs of certain theorems omitted from the text.

Some of the chapters have been taught at a graduate seminar for a one-unit, one-semester course at the University of California. The prerequisite is an undergraduate course in linear system analysis. If used as a text, I believe that all the material can be adequately covered in a two-unit, one-semester course at the graduate level.

The writing of this book was aided considerably by my students whose contributions and efforts are very much emphasized. To mention but a few, I would like to thank Professors M. A. Pai and S. C. Gupta, Doctors C. A. Galtieri and T. Nishimura, and Messrs. A. Chang, T. Pavlidis, and A. G. Dewey.

The suggestions and valuable comments of Professor W. Kaplan have led to much improvement in the mathematics and they are greatly appreciated.

Since the major part of this material grew both from my research activities and those of my students, I would like to thank the Air Force Office of Scientific Research for their generous support and interest in our group at the University of California. The patience and efforts of Mrs. L. Gilmore in typing this manuscript are gratefully appreciated and acknowledged.

I wish to acknowledge the very helpful private discussions by correspondence, over many years, with my colleague Professor Ya. Z. Tsypkin of the Institute of Automatics and Telemechanics in the U.S.S.R.

I hope that the contents will serve the useful purpose of providing a unified and integrated transform method which can be applied extensively and fruitfully by systems engineers and scientists for many years.

February 1964

E. I. JURY

CONTENTS

1

z-TRANSFORM DEFINITION

AND THEOREMS

The techniques of the z-transform method are not new, for they can be actually traced back as early as 1730 when DeMoivre[1] introduced the concept of the "generating function" (which is actually identical to the z-transform) to probability theory. The concept of the generating function was later extensively used in 1812 by Laplace[2] and others in probability theory. In a much later article by H. L. Seal,[3] a historical survey of the use of the generating function in probability theory was presented. Recently, the development and extensive applications of the z-transform[31,35] are much enhanced as a result of the use of digital computers in systems. These systems are referred to as discrete, because of the discrete nature of the signals or information flowing in them. Thus a new discipline of system theory is being developed, to be known as discrete system theory. The material here is devoted for the most part to discussing the various facets of this discrete theory.

The z-transform method constitutes one of the transform methods that can be applied to the solution of linear difference equations. It reduces the solutions of such equations into those of algebraic equations. The Laplace transform method, which is well developed for the solution of differential equations and extensively used in the literature, can be modified to extend its applicability to discrete systems. Such modifications have resulted in introducing the various associated transform techniques which are briefly discussed in the last section of this chapter.

This chapter is mainly devoted to the development of the theory of z-transform and the modified z-transform. Many useful theorems related to these transforms are either derived or stated. In addition, other theorems are introduced in the problem section related to this chapter.

1.1 Discrete time function and *z*-transform definitions[14–16,24–26]

In many discrete systems, the signals flowing are considered at discrete values of t, usually at nT, $n = 0, 1, 2, \ldots$, where T is a fixed positive number usually referred to as the sampling period. In Fig. 1.1, a continuous function of time $f(t)$ is shown where its values at $t = nT$ are indicated. The study of such discrete systems may be carried through by using the *z*-transform method. This method will be extensively developed in this and other chapters with its modifications, extensions, and applications.

Definition

Let T be a fixed positive number (it could be taken as unity). Let $f(t)$ be defined for this discussion for $t \geq 0$. This case will be extended in Chapter 4 to cover values of t which are also negative. The *z*-transform of $f(t)$ is the function

$$\mathcal{J}[f] = \mathcal{F}(z) = \sum_{n=0}^{\infty} f(nT)z^{-n}, \qquad \text{for } |z| > R = \frac{1}{\rho} \tag{1.1}$$

ρ = radius of convergence of the series

of the complex variable z. We use the symbol $\mathcal{J}$ to denote the *z*-transform of f.

Since only the values $f_n = f(nT)$ of f at nT are used, the *z*-transform is actually defined for the sequence $\{f_n\}$.

$$\mathcal{J}[\{f_n\}] = \sum_{n=0}^{\infty} f_n z^{-n} = \mathcal{F}(z) \tag{1.2}$$

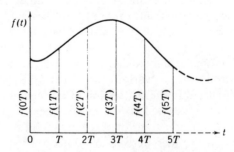

FIGURE 1.1 Discrete and continuous functions.

The series in equation (1.1) can always be considered as a formal series to be manipulated in certain ways and not necessarily to be summed.

If $f(t)$ has a jump discontinuity at a value nT, we shall always interpret $f(nT)$ as the limit of $f(t)$ as $t \to nT^+$, and we shall assume the existence of this limit, for $n = 0, 1, 2, \ldots$ for all $f(t)$ considered.

EXAMPLE

To obtain the z-transform of $f(t) = t$, we use equation (1.1) as follows:

$$\mathscr{F}(z) = \mathscr{J}[f] = \sum_{n=0}^{\infty} f(nT)z^{-n} = Tz^{-1} + 2Tz^{-2} + 3Tz^{-3} + \ldots$$

$$= Tz^{-1}[1 + 2z^{-1} + 3z^{-2} + \ldots] = \frac{Tz}{(z-1)^2},$$

$$\text{for } |z| > 1 \quad (1.3)$$

1.2 Properties of z-transforms[5,14,25,26]

In the following we shall show a few properties and theorems related to the z-transform. Some theorems will be presented whose proofs could be easily obtained as an exercise in the problem section. Their use will enable us to develop the z-transform method and indicate its applications in the following chapters.

Linearity of the z-transform

For all constants c_1 and c_2, the following property holds:

$$\mathscr{J}(c_1 f_1 + c_2 f_2) = \sum_{n=0}^{\infty} [c_1 f_1(nT) + c_2 f_2(nT)]z^{-n}$$

$$= c_1 \sum_{n=0}^{\infty} f_1(nT)z^{-n} + c_2 \sum_{n=0}^{\infty} f_2(nT)z^{-n}$$

$$= c_1 \mathscr{J}[f_1] + c_2 \mathscr{J}[f_2] \quad (1.4)$$

Thus $\mathscr{J}$ is a linear operator on the linear space of all z-transformable functions $f(t)$, $(t \geq 0)$.

Shifting theorem

If $\mathscr{J}[f] = \mathscr{F}(z)$,

$$\mathscr{J}[f(t + T)] = z[\mathscr{F}(z) - f(0^+)] \quad (1.5)$$

Proof: By definition

$$\mathscr{z}[f(t + T)] = \sum_{n=0}^{\infty} f[(n + 1)T]z^{-n}$$

$$= z\sum_{n=0}^{\infty} f[(n + 1)T]z^{-(n+1)} = z\sum_{k=1}^{\infty} f(kT)z^{-k} \quad (1.6)$$

where $k = n + 1$. By adding and substracting $f(0^+)$ term under the summation sign of equation (1.6), we can write the summation over the range from $k = 0$ to $k = \infty$. Thus

$$\mathscr{z}[f(t + T)] = z\left[\sum_{k=0}^{\infty} f(kT)z^{-k} - f(0^+)\right] = z[\mathscr{F}(z) - f(0^+)] \tag{1.7}$$

Extending these procedures, we can readily obtain for any positive integer m the following results:

$$\mathscr{z}[f(t + mT)] = z^m\left[\mathscr{F}(z) - \sum_{k=0}^{m-1} f(kT)z^{-k}\right] \tag{1.8}$$

COROLLARY: If $\mathscr{z}[f(t)] = \mathscr{F}(z)$, then

$$\mathscr{z}[f(t - nT)u(t - nT)] = z^{-n}\mathscr{F}(z) \text{ where } u(t)$$
$$= \text{unit step function} \quad \text{for } n = 0, 1, 2, \ldots \tag{1.9}$$

Proof: By definition

$$\mathscr{z}[f(t - nT)u(t - nT)] = \sum_{m=0}^{\infty} [f(m - n)Tu(m - n)T]z^{-m}$$

$$= z^{-n}\sum_{m=0}^{\infty} \{f[(m - n)T]u[(m - n)T]\}z^{-(m-n)} \tag{1.10}$$

Letting $m - n = k$, we obtain

$$\mathscr{z}[f(t - nT)u(t - nT)] = z^{-n}\sum_{k=-n}^{\infty} f(kT)u(kT)z^{-k}$$

$$= z^{-n}\sum_{k=0}^{\infty} f(kT)z^{-k} = z^{-n}\mathscr{F}(z) \tag{1.11}$$

The use of the shifting theorem is important in the solution of difference equations as indicated in Chapter 2. Following a similar procedure, we can easily obtain the z-transform of the forward difference as well as the backward difference as follows:

$$\mathscr{z}[\Delta^k f(nT)] = (z - 1)^k\mathscr{F}(z) - z\sum_{j=0}^{k-1}(z - 1)^{k-j-1}\Delta^j f(0T) \tag{1.12}$$

where

$$\Delta f(nT) = f(n + 1)T - f(nT) \tag{1.13}$$

Furthermore,

$$\mathscr{J}[\nabla^k f(nT)] = (1 - z^{-1})^k \mathscr{F}(z) \tag{1.14}$$

where

$$\nabla f(nT) = f(nT) - f(n-1)T \tag{1.15}$$

Complex scale change

If the z-transform of $f(t)$ is $\mathscr{F}(z)$,

$$\mathscr{J}[e^{-at}f(t)] = \mathscr{F}(e^{aT}z). \tag{1.16}$$

Proof: From the definition of the z-transform we have

$$\mathscr{J}[e^{-at}f(t)] = \sum_{n=0}^{\infty} e^{-anT}f(nT)z^{-n} = \sum_{n=0}^{\infty} f(nT)(e^{aT}z)^{-n} \tag{1.17}$$

$$= \mathscr{F}(e^{aT}z)$$

Finite summation[14,25,28]

To obtain the z-transform of

$$\mathscr{J}\left[\sum_{k=0}^{n} f(kT)\right] \tag{1.18}$$

first we define

$$\sum_{k=0}^{n} f(kT) \triangleq g[(nT)], \quad \text{or} \quad g[(n-1)T] = \sum_{k=0}^{n-1} f(kT) \tag{1.19}$$

We can write a relation between successive values of the sum by noting this definition and equation (1.19).

$$g(nT) = g(n-1)Tu(n-1)T + f(nT) \tag{1.20}$$

Applying the z-transform to this equation, we have

$$\mathscr{G}(z) = z^{-1}\mathscr{G}(z) + \mathscr{F}(z) \tag{1.21}$$

Solving for $\mathscr{G}(z)$, we finally obtain

$$\mathscr{G}(z) = \mathscr{J}\left[\sum_{k=0}^{n} f(kT)\right] = \frac{z}{z-1}\mathscr{F}(z). \quad \text{for } |z| > 1 \tag{1.22}$$

Initial and final values[14,24]

From the definition of the z-transform,

$$\mathscr{F}(z) = \sum_{n=0}^{\infty} f(nT)z^{-n} = f(0T) + \frac{f(1T)}{z} + \frac{f(2T)}{z^2} + \ldots \tag{1.23}$$

We readily notice that the initial value is obtained as:

$$f(0) = \lim_{z \to \infty} \mathscr{F}(z) \qquad (1.24)$$

If $f(0) = 0$, we can obtain $f(T)$ as the $\lim_{z \to \infty} z\mathscr{F}(z)$.
    For the final value, let us write

$$\mathscr{J}[f(t + T) - f(t)] = \lim_{n \to \infty} \sum_{k=0}^{n} [f(k + 1)T - f(kT)]z^{-k} \qquad (1.25)$$

The transform of the left-hand side is obtained from equation (1.4) and (1.5) thus

$$z\mathscr{F}(z) - zf(0T) - \mathscr{F}(z) = \lim_{n \to \infty} \sum_{k=0}^{n} [f(k + 1)T - f(kT)]z^{-k} \qquad (1.26)$$

We now let $z \to 1$ for both sides of equation (1.26), assuming the order of taking the limits may be interchanged.

$$\begin{aligned}
\lim_{z \to 1} (z - 1)\mathscr{F}(z) - f(0T) &= \lim_{n \to \infty} \sum_{k=0}^{n} [f(k + 1)T - f(kT)] \\
&= \lim_{n \to \infty} \{[f(1T) - f(0T)] \\
&\quad + [f(2T) - f(1T)] \\
&\quad + \ldots + [f(nT) - f(n - 1)T] \\
&\quad + [f(n + 1)T - f(nT)]\} \\
&= \lim_{n \to \infty} [-f(0T) + f(n + 1)T] \\
&= -f(0T) + f(\infty) \qquad (1.27)
\end{aligned}$$

so that we finally obtain

$$\lim_{n \to \infty} f(nT) = \lim_{z \to 1} (z - 1)\mathscr{F}(z) \qquad (1.28)$$

if the limit exists.

Complex multiplication (real convolution)

If f_1 and f_2 have the z-transform $\mathscr{F}_1(z)$ and $\mathscr{F}_2(z)$, then

$$\mathscr{F}_1(z)\mathscr{F}_2(z) = \mathscr{J}\left[\sum_{k=0}^{n} f_1(kT)f_2(n - k)T \right] \qquad (1.29)$$

Proof: By definition

$$\mathscr{F}_1(z)\mathscr{F}_2(z) = \sum_{k=0}^{\infty} f_1(kT)z^{-k}\mathscr{F}_2(z) \qquad (1.30)$$

but from equation (1.11)

$$z^{-k}\mathscr{F}_2(z) = \mathscr{J}[f_2(t - kT)] \qquad (1.31)$$

$$\text{if } f_2(n - k)T = 0, \text{ for } n < k$$

Hence

$$\mathscr{F}_1(z)\mathscr{F}_2(z) = \sum_{k=0}^{\infty} f_1(kT)\mathscr{J}[f_2(t - kT)]$$

$$= \sum_{k=0}^{\infty} f_1(kT) \sum_{n=0}^{\infty} f_2[(n - k)T]z^{-n}$$

$$= \sum_{n=0}^{\infty} \left\{ \sum_{k=0}^{\infty} f_1(kT)f_2[(n - k)T] \right\} z^{-n} \tag{1.32}$$

but $f_2(n - k)T = 0$, for $n < k$ and therefore

$$\mathscr{F}_1(z)\mathscr{F}_2(z) = \mathscr{J}\left[\sum_{k=0}^{n} f_1(kT)f_2(n - k)T \right] \tag{1.33}$$

Complex differentiation or multiplication by t

If $\mathscr{F}(z)$ is the z-transform of f, then

$$\mathscr{J}[tf] = -Tz\frac{d}{dz}\mathscr{F}(z) \tag{1.34}$$

Proof: By definition

$$\mathscr{J}[tf] = \sum_{n=0}^{\infty} (nT)f(nT)z^{-n} = -Tz\sum_{n=0}^{\infty} f(nT)[-nz^{-n-1}] \tag{1.35}$$

The term in the brackets is a derivative of z^{-n} with respect to z.

$$\mathscr{J}[tf] = -Tz\sum_{n=0}^{\infty} f(nT)\frac{d}{dz}z^{-n} = -Tz\frac{d}{dz}\sum_{n=0}^{\infty} f(nT)z^{-n}$$

$$= -Tz\frac{d}{dz}\mathscr{F}(z) \tag{1.36}$$

Similarly, we can write

$$\mathscr{J}[t^k f] = -Tz\frac{d}{dz}\mathscr{F}_1(z) \tag{1.37}$$

where

$$\mathscr{F}_1(z) = \mathscr{J}[t^{k-1}f], \qquad k > 0 \quad \text{and integer} \tag{1.38}$$

As a corollary to this theorem we can deduce

$$\mathscr{J}[n^{(k)}f(n)] = z^{-k}\frac{d^k\mathscr{F}(z)}{d(z^{-1})^k} \tag{1.39}$$

where the function $n^{(k)}$ is given by

$$n^{(k)} = n(n - 1)(n - 2)\ldots(n - k + 1) \tag{1.40}$$

As special cases of the preceding,

$$\mathscr{Y}[(-1)^k n^{(k)} f(n - k + 1)] = z \frac{d^k \mathscr{F}(z)}{dz^k} \tag{1.41}$$

and

$$\mathscr{Y}[n(n + 1)(n + 2) \ldots (n + k - 1) f(n)] = (-1)^k z^k \frac{d^k \mathscr{F}(z)}{dz^k} \tag{1.42}$$

Special summation theorem

If $\mathscr{F}(z) = \sum_{n=0}^{\infty} f(nT) z^{-n}$, then

$$\mathscr{F}(z^k) = \mathscr{Y}[\nabla f_1(nT)] \tag{1.43}$$

where

$$f_1(nT) = \sum_{m=0}^{[n/k]} f(mT), \qquad \nabla f_1(nT) = f_1(nT) - f_1(n - 1)T \tag{1.44}$$

and $[n/k]$ denotes the largest integer in n/k.

Proof: From the definition of the z-transform we can write

$$\mathscr{Y}\left[\sum_{m=0}^{[n/k]} f(mT)\right] \triangleq \sum_{n=0}^{\infty} z^{-n} \sum_{m=0}^{[n/k]} f(mT) = \sum_{n=0}^{\infty} \sum_{m=0}^{[n/k]} z^{-n} f(mT) \tag{1.45}$$

Since n varies in integer values from zero to infinity and m also varies in integer values, we can write for the right-hand side of this equation,

$$\mathscr{Y}\left[\sum_{m=0}^{[n/k]} f(mT)\right] = \sum_{m=0}^{\infty} \sum_{n=mk}^{\infty} f(mT) z^{-n} = \sum_{m=0}^{\infty} f(mT) \sum_{n=mk}^{\infty} z^{-n}$$

$$= \sum_{m=0}^{\infty} f(mT) z^{-mk} \sum_{n=0}^{\infty} z^{-n} \tag{1.46}$$

However,

$$\sum_{n=0}^{\infty} z^{-n} = \frac{z}{z - 1}, \qquad \text{for } |z| > 1$$

Therefore equation (1.46) can be written

$$\mathscr{Y}\left[\sum_{m=0}^{[n/k]} f(mT)\right] = \frac{z}{z - 1} \sum_{m=0}^{\infty} f(mT) z^{-mk} = \frac{z}{z - 1} \mathscr{F}(z^k) \tag{1.47}$$

From equation (1.14), we have for $k = 1$

$$\mathscr{Y}[\nabla f(nT)] = \frac{z - 1}{z} \mathscr{F}(z) \tag{1.48}$$

Using this equation in (1.47) we finally obtain

$$\mathscr{F}(z^k) = \mathscr{Y}[\nabla f_1(nT)] \tag{1.49}$$

This theorem is very important in obtaining the inverse z-transform of special functions of $\mathscr{F}(z)$ containing essential singularities. These functions are discussed in detail in the next section.

We introduce the following additional theorems whose proofs are left as an exercise to the reader.

Differentiation with respect to
second independent variable

$$\mathscr{J}\left[\frac{\partial}{\partial a} f(t, a)\right] = \frac{\partial}{\partial a} \mathscr{F}(z, a) \tag{1.50}$$

Second independent variable limit value

$$\mathscr{J}\left[\lim_{a \to a_0} f(t, a)\right] = \lim_{a \to a_0} \mathscr{F}(z, a) \tag{1.51}$$

Integration with respect to
second independent variable

$$\mathscr{J}\left[\int_{a_0}^{a_1} f(t, a)\, da\right] = \int_{a_0}^{a_1} \mathscr{F}(z, a)\, da \tag{1.52}$$

if the integral is finite.

1.3 Inverse z-transform and branch points[14,27]

The discrete function $f(t)$ at $t = nT$ or $f(nT)$ can be obtained from $\mathscr{F}(z)$ by a process called the inverse z-transform. This process is symbolically denoted as

$$f(nT) = \mathscr{J}^{-1}[\mathscr{F}(z)] \tag{1.53}$$

where $\mathscr{F}(z)$ is the z-transform of $f(t)$† or $f(nT)$.

In the following, we discuss the several methods from which we can obtain $f(nT)$ from $\mathscr{F}(z)$ or the inverse z-transform.

The power series method

When $\mathscr{F}(z)$ is given as a function analytic for $|z| > R$ (and at $z = \infty$), the value of $f(nT)$ can be readily obtained as the coefficient of z^{-n} in the power series expansion (Taylor's series) of $\mathscr{F}(z)$ as a function of z^{-1}.

---

† It may also be written as f.

From equation (1.1) it is observed that

$$\mathcal{F}(z) = f(0T) + f(T)z^{-1} + \ldots f(kT)z^{-k} + \ldots f(nT)z^{-n} + \ldots$$

(1.54)

Thus it is noticed that $f(nT)$ can be read off as the coefficient of z^{-n} and so can values of f at other instants of time.

If $\mathcal{F}(z)$ is given as a ratio of two polynomials in z^{-1}, the coefficients $f(0T), \ldots, f(nT)$ are obtained as follows:

$$\mathcal{F}(z) = \frac{p_0 + p_1 z^{-1} + p_2 z^{-2} + \ldots + p_n z^{-n}}{q_0 + q_1 z^{-1} + q_2 z^{-2} + \ldots + q_n z^{-n}}$$

$$= f(0T) + f(1T)z^{-1} + f(2T)z^{-2} + \ldots$$

(1.55)

where

$$p_0 = f(0T)q_0$$

$$p_1 = f(1T)q_0 + f(0T)q_1$$

$$\cdot \qquad \cdot \qquad \cdot$$
$$\cdot \qquad \cdot \qquad \cdot$$
$$\cdot \qquad \cdot \qquad \cdot$$

(1.56)

$$p_n = f(nT)q_0 + f(n-1)Tq_1 + f(n-2)Tq_2 + \ldots + f(0T)q_n$$

It is also observed that $f(nT)$ can be obtained by a synthetic division of the numerator by the denominator.

Partial fraction expansion

If $\mathcal{F}(z)$ is a rational function of z, analytic at ∞, it can be expressed by a partial fraction expansion,

$$\mathcal{F}(z) = \mathcal{F}_1(z) + \mathcal{F}_2(z) + \mathcal{F}_3(z) + \ldots$$

(1.57)

The inverse of this equation $f(nT)$ can be obtained as the sum of the individual inverses obtained from the expansion, that is,

$$f(nT) = \mathcal{J}^{-1}\mathcal{F}(z) = \mathcal{J}^{-1}[\mathcal{F}_1(z)] + \mathcal{J}^{-1}[\mathcal{F}_2(z)] + \ldots$$

(1.58)

We can easily identify the inverse of a typical $\mathcal{F}_k(z)$, from tables† or power series and thus obtain $f(nT)$.‡

---

† See Appendix, Table 1.
‡ A determinant method for obtaining $f(nT)$ from equation (1.55) is in the Appendix of this chapter.

Complex integral formula

We can also represent the coefficient $f(nT)$ as a complex integral. Since $\mathscr{F}(z)$ can be regarded as a Laurent series, we can multiply $\mathscr{F}(z)$ in equation (1.54) by z^{n-1} and integrate around a circle Γ on which $|z| = R_0$, $R_0 > R$, or any simple closed path on or outside of which $\mathscr{F}(z)$ is analytic. This integral yields $2\pi j$ times the residue of the integrand, which is, in this case, $f(nT)$, the coefficient of z^{-1}. Hence

$$\oint_{\Gamma} \mathscr{F}(z)z^{n-1}\, dz = f(nT) \cdot 2\pi j \tag{1.59}$$

or

$$f(nT) = \frac{1}{2\pi j} \oint_{\Gamma} \mathscr{F}(z)z^{n-1}\, dz, \qquad (n = 0, 1, 2, \dots) \tag{1.60}$$

The contour Γ encloses all singularities of $\mathscr{F}(z)$ as shown in Fig. 1.2.

The contour integral in equation (1.60) can be evaluated when $\mathscr{F}(z)$ has only isolated singularities by using Cauchy's integral formula,

$$f(nT) = \frac{1}{2\pi j} \oint_{\Gamma} \mathscr{F}(z)z^{n-1}\, dz = \text{sum of the residues of } \mathscr{F}(z)z^{n-1}$$

$$\tag{1.61}$$

The following cases are discussed for the inversion formula.

THE POLES OF $\mathscr{F}(z)$ ARE SIMPLE.   Assume that

$$\mathscr{F}(z) = \frac{\mathscr{H}(z)}{\mathscr{G}(z)} \tag{1.62}$$

When $\mathscr{G}(z)$ has simple zeros only, the residue at a simple singularity a is given by

$$\lim_{z \to a} (z - a)\mathscr{F}(z)z^{n-1} = \lim_{z \to a} \left[(z - a) \frac{\mathscr{H}(z)}{\mathscr{G}(z)} z^{n-1} \right] \tag{1.63}$$

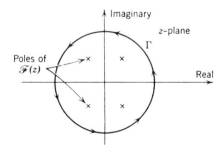

FIGURE 1.2   Contour integration in the z-plane.

POLES OF $\mathcal{F}(z)$ ARE NOT GIVEN IN A FACTORED FORM, BUT ARE SIMPLE. The residue at the singularity a_m is

$$\left[\frac{\mathcal{H}(z)}{\mathcal{G}'(z)} z^{n-1} \right]_{z=a_m} \tag{1.64}$$

where

$$\mathcal{G}'(z) = \frac{d\mathcal{G}(z)}{dz} \tag{1.65}$$

$\mathcal{F}(z)$ HAS MULTIPLE POLES. The residue at a kth-order pole of $\mathcal{F}(z)$ is given by the following expression: residue at kth-order pole at a,

$$b_1 = \frac{1}{k-1!} \frac{d^{k-1}}{dz^{k-1}} [\mathcal{F}(z)(z-a)^k z^{n-1}] \Big|_{z \to a} \tag{1.66}$$

$\mathcal{F}(z)$ has essential singularities[37]

In some cases when $\mathcal{F}(z)$ has an essential singularity at z other than infinity, we can utilize the preceding theorems of the z-transform to obtain the inverse without power series expansion. This is best illustrated by the following examples.

If $\mathcal{F}(z)$ is given as

$$\mathcal{F}(z) = e^{-(x/z)-1/2z^2} \tag{1.67}$$

to obtain its inverse, that is, $f(nT) = \mathcal{J}^{-1}[\mathcal{F}(z)]$.

We let $\mathcal{G}(z) = e^{-x/z}$ and $\mathcal{H}(z) = e^{-1/2z^2}$; then by using the real convolution theorem on p. 6,

$$f(nT) = \mathcal{J}^{-1}[\mathcal{G}(z)\mathcal{H}(z)] = \sum_{k=0}^{n} h(kT)g[(n-k)T] \tag{1.68}$$

The inverse of $e^{-x/z}$ can be readily obtained from the series expansion

$$g(nT) = \mathcal{J}^{-1}[\mathcal{G}(z)] = \frac{(-x)^n}{n!} \tag{1.69}$$

Furthermore, from the theorem on p. 8, we have for $k = 2$,

$$\mathcal{J}^{-1}[e^{-1/2z^2}] = h(nT) = \nabla \sum_{m=0}^{[n/2]} \frac{(-1)^m}{2^m m!} \tag{1.70}$$

Using equations (1.69) and (1.70) in equation (1.68), we obtain (replacing k by s)

$$f(nT) = \mathcal{J}^{-1}[e^{-x/z}e^{-1/2z^2}] = \sum_{s=0}^{n} \left[\nabla \sum_{m=0}^{[s/2]} \frac{(-1)^m}{2^m m!} \right] \frac{(-x)^{n-s}}{(n-s)!} \tag{1.71}$$

The expression in the bracketed term of equation (1.71) is different from zero only for s even, and then it is equal to

$$\frac{(-1)^{s/2}}{2^{s/2}(s/2)!} \qquad (1.72)$$

Putting $s = 2k$ in equation (1.71) and using (1.72), we finally obtain for the inverse z-transform

$$f(nT) = \mathcal{Z}^{-1}[e^{-x/z}e^{-1/2z^2}] = \sum_{k=0}^{[n/2]} \frac{(-1)^{n-k}}{k!} \frac{x^{n-2k}}{(n-2k)! \, 2^k} = \frac{H_n(x)}{n!} \qquad (1.73)$$

where H_n is the Hermite polynomial of degree n.

$\mathcal{F}(z)$ is irrational function of "z"[37]

The inverse z-transform can be obtained either by power series expansion or the integral formula. If we use the latter form, we must be specially careful in the integration because of branch points in the integrand. As in the previous case, we shall illustrate the procedure by using the following example.

Let $\mathcal{F}(z)$ be given as

$$\mathcal{F}(z) = \left(\frac{z+b}{z}\right)^{\alpha} \qquad (1.74)$$

where α can be any real value and assumed to be noninteger.

To obtain $f(nT)$ we use the two procedures of contour integration and power series expansion. To simplify the integration process we introduce a change of variable to normalize the constant b to be unity.

Let

$$z = by \qquad (1.75)$$

Then $\mathcal{F}(z)$ becomes

$$\mathcal{F}(by) = \left(\frac{y+1}{y}\right)^{\alpha} \qquad (1.76)$$

The function $\mathcal{F}(by)$ has a branch cut in the y-plane that extends from zero to minus unity as shown in Fig. 1.3. By using equation (1.60), the inverse is given

$$f(nT) = \mathcal{Z}^{-1}[\mathcal{F}(by)] = \frac{b^n}{2\pi j} \int_{\Gamma} \left(\frac{y+1}{y}\right)^{\alpha} y^{n-1} \, dy \qquad (1.77)$$

where the closed contour Γ is as shown in Fig. 1.3.

We can easily show that at the limit $y \to 0$ the integral around the small circle BCD is zero. Furthermore, the integral along EA is also zero.

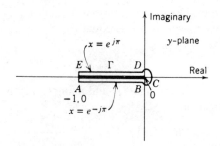

FIGURE 1.3   Contour integration enclosing branch point of $\mathscr{F}(by)$.

Therefore $f(nT)$ can be obtained by integrating around the barrier.

$$f(nT) = \frac{b^n}{2\pi j}\left[\int_1^0 \left(\frac{xe^{-j\pi}+1}{xe^{-j\pi}}\right)^\alpha x^{n-1}e^{-j\pi n}\,dx\right.$$

$$\left. + \int_0^1 \left(\frac{xe^{j\pi}+1}{xe^{j\pi}}\right)^\alpha x^{n-1}e^{j\pi n}\,dx\right] \quad (1.78)$$

This equation can also be written as

$$f(nT) = \frac{b^n}{2\pi j}\left[\int_0^1 x^{n-1-\alpha}(1-x)^\alpha e^{j\pi(n-\alpha)}\,dx\right.$$

$$\left. - \int_0^1 x^{n-1-\alpha}(1-x)^\alpha e^{-j\pi(n-\alpha)}\,dx\right]$$

$$= b^n \frac{\sin(n-\alpha)\pi}{\pi}\int_0^1 x^{n-1-\alpha}(1-x)^\alpha\,dx \quad (1.79)$$

By utilizing the following identity,

$$B(m,k) = \frac{\Gamma(m)\Gamma(k)}{\Gamma(m+k)} = \int_0^1 x^{m-1}(1-x)^{k-1}\,dx \quad (1.80)$$

we obtain for $f(nT)$

$$f(nT) = b^n \frac{\sin(n-\alpha)\pi}{\pi}\frac{\Gamma(n-\alpha)\Gamma(\alpha+1)}{\Gamma(n+1)} \quad (1.81)$$

By using the identity

$$\Gamma(m)\Gamma(1-m) = \frac{\pi}{\sin\pi m} \quad (1.82)$$

we finally obtain

$$f(nT) = b^n \frac{\Gamma(\alpha+1)}{\Gamma(n+1)\Gamma(\alpha-n+1)} = \binom{\alpha}{n}b^n \quad (1.83)$$

and for α negative integer

$$\binom{\alpha}{n} = \frac{\Gamma(n-\alpha)}{\Gamma(n+1)\Gamma(-\alpha)}(-1)^n \quad (1.84)$$

We can also obtain $f(nT)$ from the Taylor's series expansion of $\mathscr{F}(z)$ as follows:

$$\mathscr{F}(z) = \left(\frac{z + b}{z}\right)^{\alpha} = (1 + bz^{-1})^{\alpha}$$

$$= \sum_{n=0}^{\infty} \frac{1}{n!} \frac{d^n(1 + bz^{-1})^{\alpha}}{(dz^{-1})^n}\bigg|_{z^{-1}=0} z^{-n} \qquad (1.85)$$

Equation (1.85) yields

$$\mathscr{F}(z) = \sum_{n=0}^{\infty} \frac{1}{n!} \alpha(\alpha - 1)(\alpha - 2)\ldots(\alpha - n + 1)b^n z^{-n} \qquad (1.86)$$

We know that

$$\Gamma(\alpha + 1) = \alpha(\alpha - 1)(\alpha - 2)\ldots(\alpha - n + 1)\cdot\Gamma(\alpha - n + 1) \qquad (1.87)$$

and

$$\Gamma(n + 1) = n! \qquad (1.88)$$

By using equations (1.87) and (1.88) in equation (1.86),

$$\mathscr{F}(z) = \left(\frac{z + b}{z}\right)^{\alpha} = \sum_{n=0}^{\infty} \frac{\Gamma(\alpha + 1)b^n}{\Gamma(n + 1)\Gamma(\alpha - n + 1)} z^{-n}$$

$$= \sum_{n=0}^{\infty} \binom{\alpha}{n} b^n z^{-n} \qquad (1.89)$$

From the definition of the z-transform we readily ascertain

$$f(nT) = \binom{\alpha}{n} b^n \qquad (1.90)$$

The entries of Table I in the Appendix readily yield the inverse z-transforms of $f(nT)$. They have been obtained by using the theorems and properties of the z-transforms discussed in the preceding sections.

It should be noted from the inverse theorem that $f(nT)$ can be obtained from the power series expansion without having to evaluate the poles of $\mathscr{F}(z)$. This feature offers a decisive advantage over the continuous case using the Laplace transform. Thus the z-transform is used for approximating a continuous function, which will be discussed in Chapter 7.

1.4 The modified z-transform[14,28,31,32]

In many applications of discrete systems and particularly in the use of digital computers in control systems, the output between the sampling instants is very important. In studying hybrid systems (mixed digital and analog systems) the output is a continuous function of time, and thus the z-transform method is not quite adequate for a critical study of such

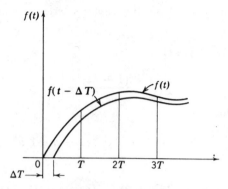

FIGURE 1.4 A fictitiously delayed output to scan values of $f(t)$ other than at $t = nT$.

systems. However, the z-transform can be easily modified to cover the system behavior at all instants of time; The extension of this method is called the modified z-transform method.

The modified z-transform is also important in the study of linear systems for periodic inputs, in sampled-data systems with pure delay, in limit cycle analysis of discrete systems, in the solution of difference equations whose coefficients are periodic functions (with period equal to unity), in the solution of mixed difference-differential equations, in approximation techniques for continuous systems, and in summing up of infinite convergent series. The introduction of the modified z-transform as well as its applications will be discussed both in the remainder of this chapter and in the following chapters.

Modified z-transform definition[14,28]

To obtain the values of $f(t)$ other than at $t = nT$, $(n = 0, 1, 2, \ldots)$ we can delay the function $f(t)$ by a fictitious negative delay ΔT as shown in Fig. 1.4. By letting Δ vary between zero and unity we obtain all the points of $f(t)$ for $t = (n - \Delta)T$, $n = 0, 1, 2, \ldots$ and $0 \leq \Delta \leq 1$. As will be shown in Section 1.5 in order to avoid any convergence problem in the integral evaluation of the modified z-transform from the Laplace transform of $f(t)$, and also in order to utilize the existing extensive tables of the modified z-transform, we make the following change of variable:

$$\Delta = 1 - m, \qquad 0 \leq m \leq 1$$

With this change of variable, t becomes

$$t = (n - 1 + m)T, \qquad n = 0, 1, 2, \ldots, \qquad 0 \leq m \leq 1 \quad (1.91)$$

We can also scan the values of the continuous function between the sampling instants by fictitiously advancing the function $f(t)$ by the amount ηT, such that

$$t = (n + \eta)T, \qquad 0 \le \eta \le 1, \qquad n = 0, 1, 2, \ldots \qquad (1.92)$$

The preceding description of the time is utilized in some other works, thus avoiding any convergence difficulties in the integration process as will be explained in Section 1.5.

The modified z-transform of f is defined as follows:

$$\mathscr{F}(z, m) \triangleq \mathfrak{z}_m(f) = \sum_{n=0}^{\infty} [f(n - 1 + m)T]z^{-n},$$

$$0 \le m \le 1 \qquad (1.93)$$

This definition also relates to the modified z-transform of the function $f[(n - 1 + m)T]$.

By using equation (1.9), the preceding equation can be written as

$$\mathscr{F}(z, m) = z^{-1} \sum_{n=0}^{\infty} [f(n + m)T]z^{-n}, \qquad 0 \le m \le 1 \qquad (1.94)$$

From this equation by letting $m = 0$, we readily deduce

$$z\mathscr{F}(z, m)\big|_{m=0} = \sum_{n=0}^{\infty} f(nT)z^{-n} = \mathscr{F}(z) \qquad (1.95)$$

Therefore the z-transform is obtained as a special case from the modified z-transform. Furthermore, if $f(t)$ has no discontinuity at the sampling instants (or jumps), the z-transformation can also be obtained as follows:

$$\mathscr{F}(z) = \mathscr{F}(z, m)\big|_{m-1} \qquad (1.96)$$

When $f(t)$ has a discontinuity at the sampling instants, the time function related to this equation yields the value at the left side of the discontinuity, that is, at $t = nT^-$, for $n = 1, 2, \ldots$ and the value zero at $n = 0$. This can be readily ascertained by noting equation (1.7).

Similar to the z-transform we can derive several properties of the modified z-transform. These properties and important theorems only are stated in the following discussions and the proofs can be easily derived by the reader. The steps for the derivation follows exactly as for the z-transform.

Theorems related to the modified z-transform[14,27]

INITIAL VALUE THEOREM

$$\lim_{\substack{n \to 0 \\ m \to 0}} f(n + m)T = \lim_{\substack{z \to \infty \\ m \to 0}} z\mathscr{F}(z, m) \qquad (1.97)$$

Special case, the response over the first interval, $n = 0$, $0 \le m \le 1$, is

$$\lim_{\substack{n \to 0 \\ 0 \le m \le 1}} f(n + m)T = \lim_{\substack{z \to \infty \\ 0 \le m \le 1}} z\mathscr{F}(z, m) \tag{1.98}$$

FINAL VALUE

$$\lim_{n \to \infty} f(n, m)T = \lim_{z \to 1} (z - 1)\mathscr{F}(z, m) \tag{1.99}$$

if the limit exists.

REAL TRANSLATION

$$\mathscr{Z}_m[f(t - kT)] = z^{-k}\mathscr{F}(z, m), \qquad k = 0, 1, 2, \ldots \tag{1.100}$$

$$\mathscr{Z}_m[f(t - \Delta T)] = z^{-1}\mathscr{F}[z, m + 1 - \Delta], \qquad 0 \le m \le \Delta$$
$$= \mathscr{F}(z, m - \Delta), \qquad \Delta \le m \le 1 \tag{1.101}$$

where

$$0 < \Delta < 1, \text{ and zero initial conditions of } f.$$

LINEARITY

$$\mathscr{Z}_m\left[\sum_{l=0}^{k} a_l f_l(t) \right] = \sum_{l=0}^{k} a_l \mathscr{F}_l(z, m), \qquad \begin{array}{l} \text{where } a_l \text{ are constants} \\ \text{independent of } t \end{array} \tag{1.102}$$

COMPLEX SCALE CHANGE

$$\mathscr{Z}_m[e^{\pm bT}f(t)] = e^{\pm bT(m-1)}\mathscr{F}(ze^{\pm bT}, m) \tag{1.103}$$

DIFFERENTIATION WITH RESPECT TO m

$$\mathscr{Z}_m\left[\frac{\partial}{\partial m} f(n, m)T \right] = \frac{\partial}{\partial m} \mathscr{F}(z, m) \tag{1.104}$$

MULTIPLICATION BY t^k

$$\mathscr{Z}_m[t^k f(t)] = T\left[(m - 1)\mathscr{F}_1(z, m) - z\frac{\partial}{\partial z} \mathscr{F}_1(z, m) \right] \tag{1.105}$$

where

$$\mathscr{F}_1(z, m) = \mathscr{Z}_m[t^{k-1}f(t)] \tag{1.106}$$

and k integer larger than zero.

DIVISION BY t

$$\mathscr{Z}_m\left[\frac{f(t)}{t} \right] = \frac{1}{T} z^{m-1} \int_z^{\infty} z^{-m}\mathscr{F}(z, m)\, dz + \lim_{t \to 0} \frac{f(t)}{t},$$

$$0 \le m \le 1 \tag{1.107}$$

INTEGRATION WITH RESPECT TO t

$$\mathscr{Z}_m\left[\int_0^t f(t)\, dt \right] = \frac{T}{z - 1} \int_0^1 \mathscr{F}(z, m)\, dm + T\int_0^m \mathscr{F}(z, m)\, dm \tag{1.108}$$

SUMMATION OF SERIES

$$\sum_{n=0}^{\infty} f(n + m)T = \lim_{z \to 1} z\mathscr{F}(z, m), \qquad 0 \le m \le 1 \qquad (1.109)$$

if the sum exists.

INVERSE MODIFIED z-TRANSFORM. The continuous time function $f(t)|_{t=(n-1+m)T}$ can be obtained from the modified z-transform by a process called inverse modified z-transformation, that is,

$$f(t)|_{t=(n-1+m)T} = f(n, m)T = \mathscr{Z}_m^{-1}[\mathscr{F}(z, m)] \qquad (1.110)$$

Methods similar to those for the inverse z-transform exist for the inverse modified z-transform, namely the integral formula and the power series. The integral formula yields the time function in a closed form,

$$f(t)|_{t=(n-1+m)T} = \frac{1}{2\pi j} \oint_{\Gamma} \mathscr{F}(z, m)z^{n-1} dz, \qquad 0 \le m \le 1$$

$$t = (n - 1 + m)T \quad (1.111)$$

where the closed contour Γ encloses in a counterclockwise direction the poles of $\mathscr{F}(z, m)$.

The power series method yields the continuous function in a piecewise form,

$$z\mathscr{F}(z, m) = f_0(m) + f_1(m)z^{-1} + f_2(m)z^{-2} + \ldots$$

$$+ f_n(m)z^{-n} + \ldots, |z| > R \quad 0 \le m \le 1 \quad (1.112)\dagger$$

where $f_0(m)$ with $0 \le m \le 1$ represent the continuous time function in the first sampling interval, $f_1(m)$ represents the same function in the second interval, and so forth. Actually, the time function is related to $f_n(m)$ as follows:

$$f(t) = f(n + m)T = f_n(m) \qquad (1.113)$$

It should be noted that since m can be considered as a constant in the contour integration of equation (1.111), the same tables for the inverse z-transform are readily applicable to the inverse modified z-transform.

MAXIMUM OR MINIMUM POINTS OF $f(t) = f_n(m)$. To obtain the maxima or minima points we can differentiate the modified z-transform with respect to m to obtain, using the power series form,

$$\frac{\partial z\mathscr{F}(z, m)}{\partial m} = f_0'(m) + f_1'(m)z^{-1} + f_2'(m)z^{-2}$$

$$+ \ldots + f_n'(m)z^{-n} + \ldots \quad (1.114)$$

---

† The general form of $f_n(m)$ is obtained using the determinant form discussed in the Appendix to this chapter.

If we let

$$f_0'(m) = 0, f_1'(m) = 0, \ldots, f_n'(m) = 0 \tag{1.115}$$

the solution of this equation for $0 < m < 1$ yields the maxima or minima points. The sign of the second derivative determines which points are maxima and which are minima. The preceding theorem is very important in determining the quality of response in discrete systems.

MODIFIED z-TRANSFORM OF A kth DERIVATIVE

$$\mathcal{Z}_m[f^{(k)}(t)] = \frac{1}{T^k} \frac{\partial^k}{\partial m^k} \mathcal{F}(z, m), \qquad \text{provided that} \atop \lim_{t \to 0} f^{(n)}(t) = 0 \text{ for} \tag{1.116}$$

$$0 \le n \le k - 1$$

and

$$\mathcal{Z}_m[f^{(k)}(t + hT)] = \frac{1}{T^k} \frac{\partial^k}{\partial m^k}$$

$$\times \left\{ z^{h-1} \left[z\mathcal{F}(z, m) - \sum_{p=0}^{h-1} f_p(m)z^{-p} \right] \right\} \tag{1.117}$$

where h is a positive integer and $\lim_{t \to 0} f^{(n)}(t) = 0$ for $0 \le n \le k - 1$.

1.5 Relationship between Laplace and z-transforms[14,29,34]

The one-sided Laplace transform of a function "f" is defined as follows:

$$F(s) \triangleq \mathcal{L}[f] = \int_0^\infty f(t)e^{-st} \, dt, \qquad \text{Re}\,[s] > \sigma_a \tag{1.118}$$

where σ_a is the abscissa of absolute convergence associated with $f(t)$.

The inverse Laplace transform is represented by the following Bromwitch integral, that is,

$$f(t) = \mathcal{L}^{-1}[F(s)] = \frac{1}{2\pi j} \int_{c-j\infty}^{c+j\infty} F(s)e^{ts} \, ds, \qquad c > \sigma_a,$$

$$\text{for } t > 0 \tag{1.119}$$

We can obtain both $\mathcal{F}(z, m)$ and $\mathcal{F}(z)$ directly from $F(s)$ by an integral transformation symbolically denoted as follows:

$$\mathcal{F}(z, m) \triangleq \mathcal{Z}_m[F(s)] \tag{1.120}$$

and

$$\mathcal{F}(z) \triangleq \mathcal{Z}[F(s)] \tag{1.121}$$

The purpose of this section is to show the preceding relationship and develop the required transformation to enable us to obtain the z-transform directly from the Laplace transform.

The function $f(nT)$ shown in Fig. 1.1 can be considered as a sum of rectangular pulses of area $hf(nT)$, where h is the width of the rectangle (or pulse). Such a sum approximates $\Sigma\, hf(nT)\, \delta(t - nT)$, since $\delta(t - nT)$ should be considered as the limit of a pulse of unit area. Thus to convert $f(nT)$ into a train of pulses

$$f(0)\, \delta(t), f(T)\, \delta(t - T), f(2T)\, \delta(t - 2T), \ldots, f(nT)\, \delta(t - nT)$$

$$(1.122)$$

a scale factor $1/h$ is needed for such a conversion. Therefore we can replace the sampled function $f(nT)$ by the impulse function $f^*(t)$ provided the scale factor (or pulse width) is accounted for. The definition of such an impulse function is given (assuming a full impulse occurring at $t = 0^+$).

$$f^*(t) = f(t) \sum_{n=0}^{\infty} \delta(t - nT) = \sum_{n=0}^{\infty} f(nT)\, \delta(t - nT) \qquad (1.123)$$

Taking the Laplace transform of this equation and noting that

$$\delta(t) = 0, \qquad t \neq 0, \quad \text{and} \quad \int_{a}^{b} \delta(t)\, dt = 1,$$

$$\text{for } a < 0 < b \quad (1.124)$$

and

$$\mathscr{L}[\delta(t - kT)] = \int_{0}^{\infty} \delta(t - kT) e^{-st}\, dt = e^{-ksT} \qquad (1.125)$$

we obtain

$$F^*(s) \triangleq \mathscr{L}[f^*(t)] = \sum_{n=0}^{\infty} f(nT) e^{-nTs} \qquad (1.126)$$

This equation is readily recognized as the z-transform of f, if we replace e^{Ts} by z. Hence we establish

$$\mathscr{F}(z) = F^*(s)\big|_{s = T^{-1}\ln z} \qquad (1.127)$$

If we denote $\displaystyle\sum_{n=-\infty}^{\infty} \delta(t - nT) = \delta_T(t)$, we readily establish the connection (using Eqs. 1.123 and 1.127) between the z-transform and the Laplace transform

$$\mathscr{F}(z)\big|_{z = e^{Ts}} = F^*(s) \triangleq \mathscr{L}[f^*(t)] = \mathscr{L}[f(t)\, \delta_T(t)] \qquad (1.128)$$

By using the convolution theorem for the Laplace transform and assuming that $f(t)$ contains no impulses and is initially zero, we obtain

$$F^*(s) = \mathscr{F}(z)\big|_{z=e^{Ts}} = \frac{1}{2\pi j} \int_{c-j\infty}^{c+j\infty} F(p) \frac{1}{1 - e^{-T(s-p)}} \, dp \quad (1.129)$$

where

$$F(p) = F(s)\big|_{s=p} = \mathscr{L}[f(t)]\big|_{s=p} \quad (1.130)$$

$$\frac{1}{1 - e^{-Ts}} = 1 + e^{-Ts} + e^{-2Ts} + \ldots e^{-nTs} + \ldots$$

$$= \mathscr{L}[\delta_T(t)], \quad \text{for } |e^{-Ts}| < 1 \quad (1.131)$$

and

$$\sigma_{a_2} < c < \sigma - \sigma_{a_1}, \quad \max(\sigma_{a_1}, \sigma_{a_2}, \sigma_{a_1} + \sigma_{a_2}) < \sigma \quad (1.131a)\dagger$$

For the case $F(s)$ has only one degree higher denominator than numerator, Eq. 1.129 should be modified,[40]

$$F^*(s) = \mathscr{F}(z)\big|_{z=e^{Ts}} = \frac{1}{2\pi j} \int_{c-j\infty}^{c+j\infty} F(p) \frac{1}{1 - e^{-T(s-p)}} \, dp + \tfrac{1}{2}f(0^+) \quad (1.132)$$

The addition of $\tfrac{1}{2}f(0^+)$ is required in view of our definition that a full impulse occurs at $t = 0^+$.

Both equations (1.129) and (1.132) yield a relationship between $\mathscr{F}(z)$ and $F(s)$, hence we define the following transformation:[40]

$$\mathscr{F}(z) \triangleq \mathcal{Z}[F(s)]$$

$$= \left[\frac{1}{2\pi j} \int_{c-j\infty}^{c+j\infty} F(p) \frac{1}{1 - e^{-T(s-p)}} \, dp + \tfrac{1}{2}f(0^+)\right]_{e^{Ts}=z} \quad (1.133)$$

Evaluation of $\mathcal{Z}[F(s)]$

To evaluate $\mathscr{F}(z)$, we assume first that $F(s)$ has two degrees in s higher denominator than numerator; thus we can use equation (1.129). The path of integration in equation (1.129) should lie in an analytic strip which does not enclose or pass through the poles of the integrand. This is assured in view of the restriction imposed on c.

In effecting the line integral, we can readily enclose in a negative sense (clockwise direction) the poles of $1/1 - e^{-T(s-p)}$ in the right half of the p-plane, or alternatively we may enclose in a positive sense the left half of

---

† Where $\sigma = \text{Re}[s]$, σ_{a_2} = abscissa of absolute convergence of $f(t)$, σ_{a_1} = abscissa of absolute convergence of $\delta_T(t)$. Here $\sigma_{a_1} = 0$, $c = \text{Re}[p]$.

the plane. Because of the assumed form of $F(s)$ the integrals on both the infinite semicircles are zero.

If we integrate along the left half p-plane as shown in Fig. 1.5 equation (1.129) becomes

$$\mathscr{F}(z)\big|_{z=e^{Ts}} = \frac{1}{2\pi j} \oint F(p) \frac{1}{1 - e^{-T(s-p)}} \, dp \qquad (1.134)$$

If $F(s)$ has only simple poles, the integral using Cauchy's formula yields the sum of the residue of the function in the closed path, that is,

$$\mathscr{F}(z) = \sum_{\substack{\text{roots of} \\ B(p)}} \text{residue of } \frac{A(p)}{B(p)} \frac{1}{1 - e^{Tp}e^{-Ts}} \bigg|_{z=e^{Ts}} \qquad (1.135)$$

where

$$F(p) = F(s)\big|_{s=p} = \frac{A(p)}{B(p)} \qquad (1.136)$$

When $B(s)\big|_{s=p} = 0$ has simple roots only, this equation becomes

$$\mathscr{F}(z) = \sum_{n=1}^{n} \frac{A(s_n)}{B'(s_n)} \frac{1}{1 - e^{Ts_n}z^{-1}} \qquad (1.137)$$

where $s_1, s_2, s_3, \ldots, s_n$ are the simple roots of $B(s) = 0$, and

$$B'(s_n) = \frac{dB}{ds}\bigg|_{s=s_n} \qquad (1.138)$$

Where $F(s)$ has branch points in addition to regular singularities, the z-transform can also be obtained using equation (1.129); however, here

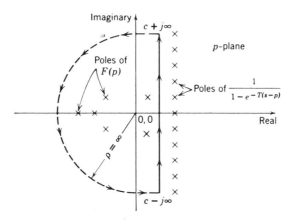

FIGURE 1.5   Path of integration in the left half of the p-plane.

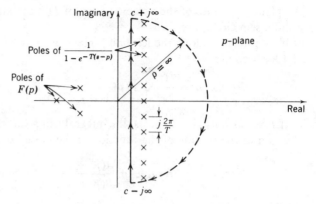

FIGURE 1.6   Path of integration in the right half of the p-plane.

special care is required to evaluate the line integral. An example will be presented later.

The integral in equation (1.129) can also be evaluated by the contour integration which encloses only the poles of $1/1 - e^{-T(s-p)}$ in the right half of the p-plane as shown in Fig. 1.6.

Thus equation (1.129) can be represented by

$$F^*(s) = \mathscr{L}[f^*(t)] = \frac{1}{2\pi j} \oint F(p) \frac{1}{1 - e^{-T(s-p)}} \, dp \qquad (1.139)$$

The integral of equation (1.139) is equivalent to the negative sum of the residue according to Cauchy's theorem,

$$F^*(s) = -(\text{sum of the residue of the integrand at the poles enclosed}) \quad (1.140)$$

By evaluating the residues at the infinite poles of $1/1 - e^{-T(s-p)}$, we finally obtain

$$F^*(s) = \frac{1}{T} \sum_{k=-\infty}^{k=\infty} F(s + jk\omega_r) \qquad (1.141)$$

where

$$\omega_r = \frac{2\pi}{T} \qquad (1.142)$$

If we replace in this equation $e^{Ts} = z$, we readily obtain the z-transform $\mathscr{F}(z) = \mathscr{Z}[F(s)]$. The two forms of (1.135 and 1.141) are equivalent can be readily verified for specific examples of $F(s)$.

For $F(s)$ has one degree in s higher denominator than numerator, the integral along the infinite semicircle in the left-half plane is no longer zero, whereas in the right-half plane it is still zero. There equation (1.132) should be used, which yields on the left-half plane the same as equation (1.135), whereas for integration in the right-half plane we obtain[14,40]

$$F^*(s) = \frac{1}{T} \sum_{k=-\infty}^{k=\infty} F(s + jk\omega_r) + \tfrac{1}{2}f(0^+) \tag{1.143}$$

It should be noted that here the infinite summation is not absolutely convergent. However, if the sum is evaluated by taking pairs of terms corresponding to equal positive and negative values of the index k, the sum converges to a definite value.

EXAMPLE

Given $F(s) = \Gamma(1 - \beta)s^{\beta-1}e^{\alpha s}$, $\alpha > 0$, $\beta > 0$, and noninteger, we obtain $\mathscr{F}(z) \triangleq Z[F(s)]$ as follows:

Using the contour integration of equation (1.129), we can write for $T = 1$

$$\mathscr{F}(z) = Z[F(s)] = \frac{1}{2\pi j} \int_{c-j\infty}^{c+j\infty} \frac{e^{\alpha p}p^{\beta-1}\Gamma(1 - \beta)}{1 - z^{-1}e^p} \, dp \tag{1.144}$$

The integrand has a branch cut (for β not integer) in the left half of the plane. Using Cauchy's formula the integral of equation (1.144) is equivalent to integration around the branch cut as shown in Fig. 1.7. Hence

$$\mathscr{F}(z) = -\frac{\Gamma(1 - \beta)}{2\pi j} \int_{\Gamma_1+\Gamma_2} \frac{e^{\alpha p}p^{\beta-1}}{1 - z^{-1}e^p} \, dp \tag{1.145}$$

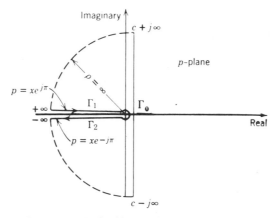

FIGURE 1.7 Path of integration around a branch cut.

Setting $p = xe^{j\pi}$ on Γ_1, and $p = xe^{-j\pi}$ on Γ_2, and noting that the integral around Γ_0 vanishes, we have

$$\mathscr{F}(z) = -\frac{\Gamma(1-\beta)}{2\pi j}\left[\int_\infty^0 \frac{e^{-\alpha x}x^{\beta-1}e^{j\beta\pi}}{1 - z^{-1}e^{-x}}\,dx + \int_0^\infty \frac{e^{-\alpha x}x^{\beta-1}e^{-j\beta\pi}}{1 - z^{-1}e^{-x}}\,dx\right]$$

$$= \frac{\Gamma(1-\beta)\sin\beta\pi}{\pi}\int_0^\infty \frac{e^{-\alpha x}x^{\beta-1}}{1 - z^{-1}e^{-x}}\,dx$$

$$= \frac{1}{\Gamma(\beta)}\int_0^\infty \frac{e^{-\alpha x}x^{\beta-1}}{1 - z^{-1}e^{-x}}\,dx \qquad (1.146)$$

We note from integral tables that

$$\int_0^\infty \frac{e^{-\alpha x}x^{\beta-1}}{1 - z^{-1}e^{-x}}\,dx = \Gamma(\beta)\Phi(z^{-1},\beta,\alpha), \qquad \beta > 0, \alpha > 0 \quad (1.147)$$

This equation is also defined for β integer. Therefore

$$\mathscr{F}(z) = \Phi(z^{-1},\beta,\alpha), \qquad \text{for } \alpha > 0 \text{ and } \beta > 0$$

$$\text{(and also integer)} \quad (1.148)$$

It is known that the definition of $\Phi(z^{-1},\beta,\alpha)$ is

$$\Phi(z^{-1},\beta,\alpha) = \sum_{n=0}^\infty \frac{1}{(n+\alpha)^\beta}z^{-n} \qquad (1.149)$$

which is the definition of the z-transform of $f(t) = 1/(t+\alpha)^\beta$, for $\beta > 0$, $\alpha > 0$, and $T = 1$. This result is expected because

$$f(t) = \mathscr{L}^{-1}[F(s)] = \mathscr{L}^{-1}[\Gamma(1-\beta)s^{\beta-1}e^{\alpha s}] = 1/(t+\alpha)^\beta$$

for all β's different from $1, 2, 3, \ldots$.

Although $\Phi(z^{-1}, \beta, \alpha)$ can be represented only in a summation form, however, if $z^{-1} = 1$, the function $\Phi(1, \beta, \alpha) = \zeta(\beta, \alpha)$ is tabulated for certain α and β. This function is referred to as generalized Riemann-zeta function. Therefore the z-transform does not exist in a closed form; however, the infinite summation $\sum_{n=0}^\infty 1/(n+\alpha)^\beta$ can be calculated numerically for certain α's and β's.

Evaluation of $\mathscr{F}(z, m) \triangleq \mathcal{Z}_m[F(s)]$

The relationship between the Laplace transform and the modified z-transform can be readily obtained similarly to the relationship of the z-transform. From equations (1.93) and (1.123), we can write

$$\mathscr{F}(z, m)\big|_{z=e^{Ts}} \triangleq F^*(s, m) = \mathscr{L}[f^*(t, m)]$$

$$= \mathscr{L}[f(t - T + mT)\,\delta_T(t)], \quad 0 \le m < 1$$

$$(1.150)$$

This equation can also be written as

$$\mathcal{F}(z, m)\big|_{z=e^{Ts}} = \mathcal{L}[f(t - T + mT)\,\delta_T(t - T)]$$
$$= e^{-Ts}\mathcal{L}[f(t + mT)\,\delta_T(t)], \quad 0 \leq m < 1 \quad (1.151)$$

From the convolution theorem of Laplace transform this equation is equivalent to

$$\mathcal{F}(z, m)\big|_{z=e^{Ts}} = \frac{1}{2\pi j}\,z^{-1}\int_{c-j\infty}^{c+j\infty} F(p)e^{mpT}\,\frac{1}{1 - e^{-T(s-p)}}\,dp,$$
$$0 \leq m < 1 \quad (1.152)$$

It is noticed from the preceding that to evaluate this integral we require the change of variable parameter from m through $\Delta = 1 - m$, so as to get the term e^{mpT} such that the integral vanishes on the left half infinite semi-circle. Furthermore, equation (1.152) constitutes the relationship between $\mathcal{F}(z, m)$ and $F(s)$; thus we define

$$\mathcal{F}(z, m) \overset{\Delta}{=} \mathcal{Z}_m[F(s)] = \frac{1}{2\pi j}\,z^{-1}\int_{c-j\infty}^{c+j\infty} F(p)e^{mpT}\,\frac{1}{1 - e^{-T(s-p)}}\,dp,$$
$$0 \leq m < 1 \quad (1.153)$$

Integrating in the left-half plane and assuming $F(s)$ has regular singularities, equation (1.153) becomes

$$\mathcal{F}(z, m) = z^{-1}\sum_{\substack{\text{poles of}\\F(p)}} \text{residue of }\frac{F(p)e^{mpT}}{1 - e^{pT}z^{-1}}, \quad 0 \leq m < 1$$
$$(1.154)$$

When $F(s) = A(s)/B(s)$ has simple poles, equation (1.154) can be expressed as

$$\mathcal{F}(z, m) = z^{-1}\left[\sum_{n=1}^{N} \frac{A(s_n)}{B'(s_n)}\,\frac{e^{ms_nT}}{1 - e^{-T(s-s_n)}}\right]_{z=e^{Ts}}, \quad 0 \leq m < 1$$
$$(1.155)$$

where $s_1, s_2, \ldots, s_N$ are the simple roots of $B(s) = 0$, and $B'(s_n) = \dfrac{dB}{ds}\bigg|_{s=s_n}$.

Table II of the Appendix lists extensive forms of the modified z-transform for various forms of $G(s)$ or $F(s)$. This table can also be used to obtain $\mathcal{G}(z) = \mathcal{Z}[G(s)]$ using the relationship in equation (1.157).

Equations (1.154) and (1.155) are also valid for $m = 1$, provided $F(s)$ has two degrees in s higher denominator than numerator. However, if $F(s)$ has only one degree in s higher denominator than numerator, equations (1.154) and (1.155) yield for their inverses, if discontinuities exist, the values at the left side of the discontinuities. The value at $t = 0$ should be taken as at $t = 0^-$, that is, zero.

Evaluating the integral of equation (1.152) in the right half of the p-plane, we (with due care for convergence) obtain similar to equation (1.141) the infinite series form

$$F^*(s, m) \triangleq \mathscr{L}[f^*(t, m)]$$

$$= \frac{1}{T} \sum_{k=-\infty}^{k=\infty} F\left(s + jk\frac{2\pi}{T}\right) e^{-[s+jk(2\pi/T)](1-m)T},$$

$$0 \leq m < 1\dagger \quad (1.156)$$

If $F(s)$ is of two degrees higher denominator than numerator, this equation can be extended for $m = 1$.

The z-transform can be obtained as a special case from the preceding by noting

$$\mathscr{F}(z) = z\mathscr{F}(z, m)\big|_{m=0} \quad (1.157)$$

and for $f(0^+) = 0$

$$\mathscr{F}(z) = \mathscr{F}(z, m)\big|_{m=1} \quad (1.158)$$

The conditions for obtaining $F(s)$ knowing either $\mathscr{F}(z, m)$ or $\mathscr{F}(z)$, that is, $\mathcal{Z}_m^{-1}$, $\mathcal{Z}^{-1}$, are discussed in Chapter 4.

1.6 Application to sampled-data systems[14-16,20]

One of the basic engineering applications of the z-transform theory is in the field of sampled-data or digital control systems. Such systems are used more and more often in modern technology. We shall briefly obtain the z-transforms of certain systems configurations.

1. Let the sampled data systems be presented as shown in Fig. 1.8. The z-transform of the output is readily obtained by applying the z-transform to $C(s)$ as follows:

$$C(s) = E^*(s)G(s) \quad (1.159)$$

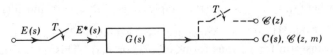

FIGURE 1.8   A sampled-data system.

---

† It should be noted that if we let $m = 1$ inside the summation and before summing, this equation should be modified as

$$F^*(s) = \frac{1}{T} \sum_{k=-\infty}^{k=\infty} F\left(s + jk\frac{2\pi}{T}\right) + \tfrac{1}{2}f(0^+).$$

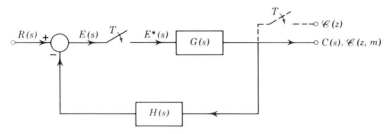

FIGURE 1.9 A sampled-data feedback control system.

or

$$\mathscr{C}(z) \triangleq \mathscr{Z}[C(s)] = \mathscr{E}(z)\mathscr{G}(z), \qquad \text{where } \mathscr{E}(z) = E^*(s)\big|_{s = T^{-1} \ln z}$$

$$(1.160)$$

The modified z-transform of equation (1.159) is

$$\mathscr{C}(z, m) \triangleq \mathscr{Z}_m[C(s)] = \mathscr{E}(z)\mathscr{G}(z, m) \tag{1.161}$$

2. Let the sampled-data feedback system be presented as shown in Fig. 1.9. The z-transform of the output transform $C(s)$ is given as

$$\mathscr{C}(z) \triangleq \mathscr{Z}[C(s)] = \mathscr{Z}[E^*(s)G(s)] = \mathscr{E}(z)\mathscr{G}(z) \tag{1.162}$$

$$\mathscr{E}(z) = \mathscr{Z}[E(s)] = \mathscr{Z}[R(s) - C(s)H(s)] = \mathscr{Z}[R(s) - E^*(s)$$
$$\times G(s)H(s)] = \mathscr{R}(z) - \mathscr{E}(z)\mathscr{G}\mathscr{H}(z)$$

$$(1.163)$$

Substituting the preceding in equation (1.162), we obtain

$$\mathscr{C}(z) = \mathscr{R}(z)\frac{\mathscr{G}(z)}{1 + \mathscr{H}\mathscr{G}(z)} \tag{1.164}$$

Similarly, for the modified z-transform of the output we obtain

$$\mathscr{C}(z, m) = \mathscr{Z}_m[C(s)] = \mathscr{R}(z)\frac{\mathscr{G}(z, m)}{1 + \mathscr{H}\mathscr{G}(z)} \tag{1.165}$$

We can also obtain the system transfer function of any configuration of sampled-data or digital control system. In later chapters some of these systems will be studied in more detail.

1.7 Mean square value theorem[14,37,38]

The following theorem with its extensions is very useful in the study of discrete systems. In particular, the mean square value of the continuous error in sampled-data control systems can be readily obtained.

THEOREM:

$$\mathcal{Z}[G(s) \cdot G(-s)]_{\substack{s=j\omega \\ z=e^{j\omega T}}} = T \overline{|\mathcal{G}(z, m)|_{z=e^{j\omega T}}}^2 \qquad (1.166)$$

Proof: From the infinite series form of the z-transform, we can write the following relations:

$$\mathcal{Z}[G(s)] = \frac{1}{T} \sum_{k=-\infty}^{k=\infty} G(s + jk\omega_r) + \tfrac{1}{2}g(0^+) \qquad (1.167)$$

$$\mathcal{Z}[G(s)G(-s)] = \frac{1}{T} \sum_{k=-\infty}^{k=\infty} G(s + jk\omega_r)G(-s - jk\omega_r) \qquad (1.168)$$

Letting $s \to j\omega$ in this expression and noting that $G(j\omega)$ is the conjugate of $G(-j\omega)$, we find that

$$\mathcal{Z}[G(s)G(-s)]_{s=j\omega} = \frac{1}{T} \sum_{k=-\infty}^{k=\infty} |G(j\omega + jk\omega_r)|^2 \qquad (1.169)$$

From the infinite series form of the modified z-transform, the following can be written:

$$G^*(j\omega, m) = \frac{1}{T} \sum_{n=-\infty}^{n=\infty} G(j\omega + jn\omega_r)e^{-j(1-m)(\omega+n\omega_r)T},$$
$$0 \leq m < 1 \quad (1.170)$$

Let

$$\hat{G}^*(j\omega, m) = \text{conjugate of } G^*(j\omega, m) \qquad (1.171)$$

Then

$$\hat{G}^*(j\omega, m) = \frac{1}{T} \sum_{k=-\infty}^{k=\infty} \hat{G}(j\omega + jk\omega_r)e^{j(1-m)(\omega+k\omega_r)T},$$
$$0 \leq m < 1 \quad (1.172)$$

Multiply equation (1.170) by (1.172) and note that since $G(j\omega)$ is the transform of a real valued function,

$$\hat{G}(j\omega) = G(-j\omega) \qquad (1.173)$$

Thus

$$|G^*(j\omega, m)|^2 = \frac{1}{T^2}\left[\sum_{n=-\infty}^{n=\infty} |G(j\omega + jn\omega_r)|^2 \right.$$
$$+ \sum_{\substack{n=-\infty \\ n \neq k}}^{n=\infty} \sum_{k=-\infty}^{k=\infty} G(j\omega + jn\omega_r)$$
$$\left. \times G(-j\omega - jk\omega_r)e^{-j(k-n)\omega_r(1-m)T}\right],$$
$$0 \leq m \leq 1 \quad (1.174)$$

The mean value of the second summation term, evaluated from $m = 0$ to $m = 1$, is zero since for $n \neq k$, $e^{-jk\omega_r(1-m)T}$ is orthogonal to $e^{-jn\omega_r(1-m)T}$ with respect to the interval $(0, 1)$ in m. Therefore

$$\overline{|G^*(j\omega, m)|^2} = \overline{|\mathscr{G}(z, m)|_{z=e^{j\omega T}}|^2} = \frac{1}{T^2} \sum_{n=-\infty}^{n=\infty} |G(j\omega + jn\omega_r)|^2$$

(1.175)

By noting equations (1.169) and (1.175), the following theorem is shown:

$$\mathscr{Z}[G(s)G(-s)] = T \int_0^1 |\mathscr{G}(z, m)|_{z=e^{j\omega T}}|^2 \, dm = T \overline{|\mathscr{G}(z, m)|_{z=e^{j\omega T}}|^2},$$

$$0 \leq m \leq 1 \quad (1.176)$$

The following two corollaries can be shown similar to the preceding proof:

$$\mathscr{Z}[F(s)F(-s)] = T \int_0^1 \mathscr{F}(z, m)\mathscr{F}(z^{-1}, m) \, dm, \qquad 0 \leq m \leq 1$$

(1.177)

and

$$\mathscr{Z}[F(s)H(-s)] = T \int_0^1 \mathscr{F}(z, m)\mathscr{H}(z^{-1}, m) \, dm, \qquad 0 \leq m \leq 1$$

(1.178)

The use of the extension of this theorem will be demonstrated in Chapter 4.

1.8 Equivalence between inverse Laplace and modified z-transforms[14,39]

From equation (1.111), it has been indicated that we can obtain the continuous time function from the modified z-transform as follows:

$$f(n, m)T \triangleq \mathscr{Y}_m^{-1}[\mathscr{F}(z, m)] = \frac{1}{2\pi j} \int_\Gamma \mathscr{F}(z, m)z^{n-1} \, dz,$$

$$t = (n - 1 + m)T, \quad (1.179)$$

$$0 \leq m \leq 1, \qquad n = \text{integer}$$

where

$$\mathscr{F}(z, m) \triangleq \mathscr{Y}_m[f(t)] \triangleq \mathscr{Z}_m[F(s)] \quad (1.180)$$

Furthermore, the same function can be obtained from equation (1.118) by using the inverse Laplace transform. Hence we have the following identity:

$$f(t)|_{t=(n-1+m)T} = \mathscr{L}^{-1}[F(s)] \triangleq \mathscr{Y}_m^{-1}[\mathscr{F}(z, m)],$$

$$0 \leq m \leq 1, \qquad n = \text{integer} \quad (1.181)$$

In some practical situations the form of $F(s)$ contains combinations of both e^{Ts} and s (mixed form), and thus the inverse Laplace transform yields the time function as an infinite series. However, by using the inverse modified z-transform, we obtain a closed form for the time function.

This procedure is advantageously utilized to obtain (1) a closed form for a convergent infinite Fourier series, (2) a closed form solution for the response of a linear time invariant circuit to general periodic inputs, and (3) the steady-state response (in a closed form) of such circuits by applying the final value theorem for the modified z-transform. To explain in detail these applications, we shall discuss the following three cases.

Summation of a Fourier series

Assume $F(s)$ as follows:

$$F(s) = \frac{1}{1 - e^{-Ts}} \frac{1}{s + a} \tag{1.182}$$

The inverse Laplace transform is expressed as

$$c(t) = \frac{1}{2\pi j} \int_{c-j\infty}^{c+j\infty} \frac{e^{st}}{(1 - e^{-Ts})(s + a)} \, ds \qquad \text{for } t > 0 \tag{1.183}$$

The integrand in this equation has simple poles at $s = -a$ and $s = \pm j(2\pi k/T)$, $k = 0, 1, 2, \ldots$. Evaluating the integral by the sum of the residues, we obtain

$$c(t) = \frac{e^{-at}}{1 - e^{aT}} + \frac{1}{aT} + \frac{2}{T} \sum_{k=1}^{\infty}$$
$$\times \frac{a \cos (2\pi k/T)t + (2\pi k/T) \sin (2\pi k/T)t}{a^2 + (2\pi k/T)^2} \tag{1.184}$$

The steady-state part of this equation is

$$c(t)_{ss} = \frac{1}{aT} + \frac{2}{T} \sum_{k=1}^{\infty} \frac{a \cos (2\pi k/T)t + (2\pi k/T) \sin (2\pi k/T)t}{a^2 + (2\pi k/T)^2} \tag{1.185}$$

If the substitution $t = (n - 1 + m)T$ is inserted in this equation, the expression is

$$c(t)_{ss} = \frac{1}{aT} + \frac{2}{T} \sum_{k=1}^{\infty} \frac{a \cos 2\pi km + (2\pi k/T) \sin 2\pi km}{a^2 + (2\pi k/T)^2} \tag{1.186}$$

On the other hand, the modified z-transform of $F(s)$ is readily obtained as

$$\mathscr{F}(z, m) = \mathcal{Z}_m[F(s)] = \frac{1}{1 - z^{-1}} \mathcal{Z}_m \left(\frac{1}{s + a} \right) = \frac{z}{z - 1} \frac{e^{-amT}}{z - e^{-aT}},$$
$$0 < m < 1 \tag{1.187}$$

The steady-state response is obtained by applying the final value theorem

$$c(t)_{ss} = \lim_{z \to 1} (z - 1)\mathscr{F}(z, m) = \frac{e^{-amT}}{1 - e^{-aT}}, \qquad 0 < m < 1$$

(1.188)

Multiplying the numerator and denominator respectively by e^{aT}, we get

$$c(t)_{ss} = \frac{e^{aT(1-m)}}{e^{aT} - 1}$$

(1.189)

By equating the steady-state part of this equation to the steady-state part of the inverse Laplace transform, we obtain

$$\sum_{k=1}^{\infty} \frac{a \cos 2\pi km + (2\pi k/T) \sin 2\pi km}{a^2 + (2\pi k/T)^2} = \frac{T}{2} \frac{e^{aT(1-m)}}{e^{aT} - 1} - \frac{1}{2a},$$

$$0 < m < 1 \quad (1.190)$$

Thus a closed form of a convergent infinite series is obtained by the final value theorem of the modified z-transform.

Response of a linear circuit for periodic input[39]

Derive the general equation for $i(t)$, the current in the RL circuit shown in Fig. 1.10 when $e(t)$, the applied voltage, is the periodic saw tooth voltage shown in Fig. 1.11. Assume zero initial conditions. The Laplace transform of the voltage $E(s)$ is given as

$$E(s) = \frac{1}{1 - e^{-Ts}}\left[\frac{k}{s^2}(1 - e^{-hs}) - \frac{khe^{-hs}}{s}\right]$$

$$= \frac{1}{1 - e^{-Ts}} \frac{1 - (1 + 0.4s)e^{-0.4s}}{s^2}$$

(1.191)

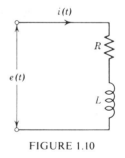

FIGURE 1.10

The current transform $I(s)$ is

$$I(s) = \frac{E(s)}{R + Ls} = \frac{0.5}{1 - e^{-Ts}} \frac{1 - (1 + 0.4s)e^{-0.4s}}{s^2(s + 0.5)}$$

(1.192)

We apply the modified z-transform to this equation to get

$$\mathscr{F}(z, m) = \mathcal{Z}_m[I(s)] = \frac{0.5z}{z - 1} \mathcal{Z}_m \frac{1 - (1 + 0.4s)e^{-0.4s}}{s^2(s + 0.5)}$$

$$= \frac{0.5z}{z - 1}\left[\mathcal{Z}_m\left(\frac{1}{s^2(s + 0.5)}\right) - \mathcal{Z}_m\left(\frac{(1 + 0.4s)e^{-0.4s}}{s^2(s + 0.5)}\right)\right]$$

(1.193)

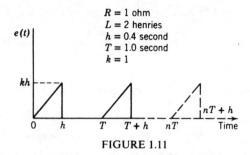

$R = 1$ ohm
$L = 2$ henries
$h = 0.4$ second
$T = 1.0$ second
$k = 1$

FIGURE 1.11

In view of the convergence required for the modified z-transform of the last term in this equation for $m < 0.4$, we have to divide the response into the following two regions:

1. $0 \leq m \leq 0.4$ (1.194)

In this region the modified z-transform $\mathscr{I}(z, m)$ is readily obtained by utilizing equation (1.101) as follows:

$$\mathscr{I}(z, m) = \frac{1}{z - 1}\left[\frac{(2z - 1.185)}{z - 0.607}e^{-m/2} + m - 2\right]$$

$$= \frac{1}{z - 1}\mathscr{I}_0(z, m)$$ (1.195)

The steady-state current for region 1 is

$$i_{ss} = \lim_{z \to 1} \mathscr{I}_0(z, m) = 2.07e^{-m/2} + m - 2$$ (1.196)

The total response for region 1 is obtained by using the inverse modified z-transform as follows:

$$i(n, m)T = \frac{1}{2\pi j}\int_\Gamma \frac{z^{n-1}}{z - 1}\left(\frac{2z - 1.185}{z - 0.607}e^{-m/2} + m - 2\right)dz$$

$$= 2.071e^{-m/2} + m - 2 - 0.07(0.607)^{n-1}e^{-m/2},$$

$$t = n - 1 + m, \quad 0 \leq m \leq 0.4$$

$$n = \text{integer}$$ (1.197)

2. $0.4 \leq m \leq 1$ (1.198)

In this region we obtain

$$i_{ss} = 0.114\,e^{-m/2}$$ (1.199)

$$i(n, m)T = 0.114\,e^{-m/2}[1 - (0.607)^n], \quad t = (n - 1 + m),$$

$$0.4 \leq m \leq 1 \quad (1.200)$$

Therefore, by using the modified z-transform and dividing the inverse into two regions, we obtain the solution in a closed form. However, if we had applied the inverse Laplace transform to $I(s)$, the response would be obtained as infinite series which is difficult to plot and calculate exactly.

Steady-state response of a linear time-invariant circuit[39]

Consider the steady-state voltage of $v_0(t)$ across the condenser in Fig. 1.12a for an input of the form of rectified sine wave shown in Fig. 1.12b. $V_0(s)$ in this example equals

$$V_0(s) = \frac{k}{s^2 + (\pi/T)^2} \frac{1 + e^{-Ts}}{1 - e^{-Ts}} \frac{1}{s + a} = \frac{1}{1 - e^{-Ts}} V_{01}(s) \quad (1.201)$$

where

$$k = \frac{\pi E}{TR_1C}, \qquad a = \frac{R_1 + R_2}{R_1 R_2 C} \quad (1.202)$$

The steady-state voltage is given by

$$v_{0ss} = \lim_{z \to 1} \mathcal{Z}_m[V_{01}(s)] = \lim_{z \to 1} 2k\mathcal{Z}_m\left[\frac{1}{(s^2 + (\pi/T)^2)(s + a)}\right]$$

$$(1.203)$$

By using partial fraction expansion of $1/[s^2 + (\pi/T)^2](s + a)$ or available tables of modified z-transforms, $\mathcal{Z}_m[1/(s^2 + (\pi/T)^2)(s + a)]$, can be readily obtained.

Thus the steady-state voltage is obtained as follows

$$v_{0ss} = \left[\frac{k}{a^2 + (\pi/T)^2}\right]\left[\frac{2e^{-amT}}{1 - e^{-aT}} - \cos \pi m + \frac{aT}{\pi} \sin \pi m\right],$$

$$0 \leq m \leq 1 \quad (1.204)$$

In summarizing the application of the final value theorem of the modified z-transform to obtain the steady-state response, the following two cases are discussed.

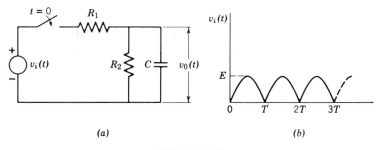

(a)   (b)

FIGURE 1.12

CASE 1

$$F(s) = F_1(s) + F_2(s) \frac{1}{1 - e^{-Ts}} \tag{1.205}$$

where $F_1(s)$ is a rational function of s and has a final value f_{1ss} that can be obtained from the $\lim\limits_{s \to 0} sF(s)$. Hence the steady-state response

$$f_{ss} = f_{1ss} + \lim\limits_{z \to 1} Z_m[F_2(s)] \tag{1.206a}$$

CASE 2

$$F(s) = F_1(s) \frac{F_2(e^{\tau_n s})}{1 - e^{-Ts}} = F_3(s) \frac{1}{1 - e^{-Ts}} \tag{1.206b}$$

The sum of all τ_n is less than T.

In general, the steady-state f_{ss} of this equation is composed of several regions depending on (τ_n); thus in obtaining the modified z-transform of $F_3(s)$ the several regions should be observed. Mathematically, this indicates that care should be taken in observing the convergence of the integral along the infinite semicircle in evaluating the modified z-transform. The example on p. 33 illustrates such a case where equation (1.101) can be readily applied in calculating the modified z-transform for the various regions.

1.9 Other transform methods

In this section various transform methods or operators other than the z-transform which have been used in the analysis of discrete systems are briefly discussed and enumerated. Pertinent references are given for each of these methods and the reader can pursue further study as needed. The close relationship between some of these methods and the z-transform can be readily ascertained after digesting the material of this chapter. Finally, this section will serve as an historical background to the z-transform and other associated transform methods.

Laplace-Stieltjes integral[4,5]

This transform integral is defined as

$$L_s[f(t)] = F(e^{sT}) \triangleq \int_0^\infty f(t)e^{-sT}\, d\alpha(t) \tag{1.207}$$

where $\alpha(t)$ is the staircase function shown in Fig. 1.13.

The integral in equation (1.207) can be rewritten as

$$L_s[f(t)] = \int_0^\infty f(t)e^{-st}\, d\alpha(t) = \sum_{n=0}^\infty f(nT)e^{-nTs},$$

$$s = \sigma + j\omega \tag{1.208}$$

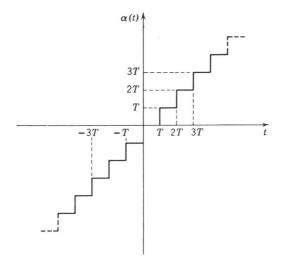

FIGURE 1.13   Staircase function $\alpha(t)$.

In this method, absolute convergence of the series is assumed, that is,

$$\sum_{n=0}^{\infty} |f(nT)z^{-n}|_{z=e^{Ts}} \leq M \tag{1.209}$$

where M is finite. This condition is satisfied, for example, if $f(t)$ is a polynomial, but not if $f(t) = e^{t^2}$. The magnitude of $|z^{-n}|$ is $e^{-nT\sigma}$, and if (1.209) holds for some σ, say σ_0, it would hold for any $\sigma > \sigma_0$.

Based on this definition, the use of Dirac (delta) function in the definition of the z-transform could be bypassed and thus retain a certain rigor in the mathematics of this transform. It may be noted that the Laplace-Stieltjes integral reduces to the one-sided Laplace transform when $\alpha(t) = t$.

The generalized Laplace transform[6]

This method, which has been introduced by W. M. Stone for the operational solution of difference equations, is defined as follows:

$$L[F(t)]_E \triangleq f(s) = \sum_{n=0}^{\infty} \frac{F(n)}{s^{n+1}} \tag{1.210}$$

with the condition $\lim_{s \to \infty} f(s) = 0$. The symbol E denotes a shifting operator defined by the relation $F(k + 1) = EF(k)$.

By using this transform, Stone has developed an extensive list of transform pairs $[F(k) - f(s)]$, which are closely related to the z-transform tables, except for a factor $z = e^{Ts}$.

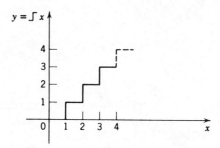

FIGURE 1.14   A jump function.

The jump function method[7]

This method was introduced by Gardner and Barnes and is similar to the Laplace-Stieltjes integral discussed earlier. The transform in this case is defined as

$$Y(s) = \mathcal{L}[\int y(x)] \triangleq \int_0^\infty \int y(x)e^{-sx}\,dx \tag{1.211}$$

where $\int y(x)$ denotes the jump function of $y(x)$. If $y(x) = x$, the jump function of $y(x)$ is as shown in Fig. 1.14 and gives

$$\int y(x) = \int x = \sum_{r=1}^\infty rp(x - r) \tag{1.212}$$

where $p(x)$ denotes a unit pulse of duration one, that is,

$$p(x) = u(x) - u(x - 1) \tag{1.213}$$

where $u(x)$ is the unit step function.
In general, the jump function $\int y(x)$ can be written as

$$\int y(x) = \sum_{r=0}^\infty y(r)p(x - r),$$
$$\text{where } p(x - r) \triangleq u(x - r) - u(x - r - 1) \quad (1.214)$$

Dirichlet series transform[8]

This transform has been proposed by T. Fort and has the following definition:

$$f(s) \triangleq D[a(t)] = \sum_{t=0}^\infty m^{-st}a(t),$$
$$\text{for } m > 1, s > 1, \quad t = \text{integer} \quad (1.215)$$

It is of interest to note that this transform reduces to the z-transform when $m = e$, $t = nT$, that is,

$$f(s) = \sum_{n=0}^{\infty} a(nT)z^{-n} \triangleq \mathscr{F}(z)\Big|_{z=e^{Ts}} = \mathscr{J}[a(nT)]$$ (1.216)

This change of notation could also be performed without influencing the application of the method.

Discrete Laplace transform[9,41]

The discrete Laplace transformation, which is denoted by the operator symbol $\mathscr{D}$, is a transformation applied to the sequence $\{f_n\}$, that is,

$$\mathscr{D}\{f_n\} \triangleq \sum_{n=0}^{\infty} f_n e^{-ns} = F^*(s)$$ (1.217)

This transformation can also be described as a Laplace transformation applied to a certain pseudofunction $f^*(t)$ described as

$$f^*(t) = f(t) \sum_{n=0}^{\infty} \delta(t - nT)$$ (1.218)

Therefore the $\mathscr{D}$ transformation may be considered as a special case of the Laplace transformation.

The discrete Laplace transformation has been applied extensively to discrete system theory by Tsypkin and his colleagues in the U.S.S.R. More recently, Doetsch[41] has presented an illuminating exposition of this method and its relationship with both Laplace transform and the z-transform methods.

Laurent-Cauchy's transform[10]

This transform is again related to the z-transform or the generating function method and is defined as

$$\mathscr{L}_c[h_k(t)] \triangleq \sum_{k=0}^{\infty} h_k(t)\rho^{-k}$$ (1.219)

where $h_k(t) = h(t + kT)$ and $0 \leq t \leq T$.

Shift operator[11,44]

A useful operator on sequences is the shift operator E, defined by the relations $u_{r+1} = Eu_r$. Then $u_{r+2} = Eu_{r+1} = E^2u_r$. In general,

$$E^n u_r = u_{r+n}$$ (1.220)

If $u(t)$ is a function of the continuous variable t and if T is a given constant, we define the shift operator E here by the formula

$$Eu(t) = u(t + T) \tag{1.221}$$

or, more generally,

$$E^n u(t) = u(t + nT) \tag{1.222}$$

In applications to difference equations, the shift operator plays the same role as the differentiation operator D in differential equations. B. M. Brown has applied this method extensively to the analysis and design of discrete systems.

ζ-Transform method[13]

This transform, which is applicable to sampled-data systems and to certain difference equations, is defined as

$$Y(\zeta, \varepsilon) = \mathscr{D}\{y_{n+\varepsilon}\} = \sum_{n=0}^{\infty} y_{n+\varepsilon}(1 + \zeta)^{-n},$$

$$\zeta = e^{Ts} - 1, \qquad 0 \le \varepsilon \le 1 \qquad n = 0, 1, 2, \ldots \tag{1.223}$$

The inverse integral transform is given by

$$y_{n+\varepsilon} = \frac{1}{2\pi j} \oint_{\substack{\text{poles of the} \\ \text{integrand}}} Y(\zeta, \varepsilon)(1 + \zeta)^{n-1}\, d\zeta,$$

$$0 \le \varepsilon \le 1, \qquad n = 0, 1, 2, \ldots \tag{1.224}$$

The advantage of this transform is that the Laplace transform is readily obtainable as a limiting process, that is,

$$Y(s) = \mathscr{L}[y(t)] = \int_0^{\infty} y(t)e^{-st}\, dt = \lim_{T \to 0} T\,Y(\zeta, 0) \tag{1.225}$$

Mikusinski's operational calculus[42,43]

Mikusinski's operational calculus is the most general method that encompasses both the continuous and the discrete theory. The z-transform method can be obtained as a special case of a series of the translation operator defined by Mikusinski. In this operator the numerical coefficients are the values of the function at the sampling instants and the exponents are $0, T, 2T, \ldots, nT, \ldots$. We can define for the function $[f(t)]$ the operator

$$f^* = \sum_{n=0}^{\infty} f(nT)h^{nT} \tag{1.226}$$

For h^{nT} we can write e^{-nTs}, and thus the identity between the operator $f*$ and the z-transform can be established. The modified z-transform can be also obtained from Mikusinski's calculus by introducing a parametric operator with respect to the parameter $\Delta = 1 - m$. This operator is defined in the whole domain $0 \leq \Delta < 1, 0 \leq t < \infty$.

In concluding this section of the survey of the various transform methods, we may mention that any of the methods could be effectively used in the treatment of discrete systems. They represent one and the same thing with different form or notation. Which method is preferred depends on the ease and familiarity to the reader.

*Appendix. A method of determining the
coefficients of the z-transform expansion*[9,47]

From equations (1.55) and (1.56), (letting $q_0 = 1$), we obtain the time coefficients $f(nT)$ as follows:

$$f(0T) = p_0$$
$$f(1T) = p_1 - f(0T)q_1$$
$$f(2T) = p_2 - q_1 f(1T) - q_2 f(0T) \tag{1}$$

$$\vdots$$

$$f(nT) = p_n - \sum_{i=1}^{n} f[(n-i)T]q_i$$

Equation (1) can be written in a determinant form as follows:

$$f(nT) = \begin{vmatrix} 1 & 0 & 0 & . & . & . & . & p_0 \\ q_1 & 1 & 0 & . & . & . & . & p_1 \\ q_2 & q_1 & 1 & 0 & . & . & . & p_2 \\ . & & & & & & & \\ . & & & & & & & \\ . & & & & & & & \\ q_n & q_{n-1} & . & . & . & q_2 & q_1 & p_n \end{vmatrix}, \quad \text{for } n \geq 1 \tag{2}$$

and $f(0T) = p_0$.

Equation (2) is readily used for $f_n(m)$ by substituting for p_n, $p_n(m)$. Furthermore, the coefficient $f_{n+k}(k \geq 1)$ can be obtained as

$$f_{n+k} = -\sum_{i=1}^{n} f_{n+k-i} q_i \tag{3}$$

(noting that $p_{n+k} = 0$ and $q_{n+k} = 0$) for $k \geq 1$ and $f_{n+k} = f[(n+k)T]$.

REFERENCES

1. DeMoivre, *Miscellanes Analytica de Seriebus et Quatratoris*, London, 1730.

2. Laplace, P. S., *Theorie Analytique de Probabilities, Part I: Du Calcul des Functions Generatrices*, Paris, 1812.

3. Seal, H. L., "The Historical Development of the Use of Generating Functions in Probability Theory," *Mitteilungen der Vereinigung Schweizerincher Verischerungs Mathematiker*, Bern, Switzerland, Vol. 49, 1949, pp. 209–228.

4. Widder, D. V., *The Laplace Transform*, Princeton University Press, Princeton, New Jersey, 1946.

5. Helm, H. A., "The z-Transformation," *B.S.T. Journal*, Vol. 38, No. 1, 1956, pp. 177–196.

6. Stone, W. M., "A List of Generalized Laplace Transforms," *Iowa State College Journal of Science*, Vol. 22, 1948, p. 215.

7. Gardner, M. F., and J. L. Barnes, *Transients in Linear Systems*, John Wiley and Sons, New York, 1942, Chapter 9.

8. Fort, T., "Linear Difference Equations and the Dirichlet Series Transform," *Am. Math. Monthly*, Vol. 62, No. 9, 1955, p. 241.

9. Tsypkin, Y. Z., *Theory of Pulse Systems*, State Press for Physics and Mathematical Literature, Moscow, 1958 (in Russian).

10. Ku, Y. H., and A. A. Wolf, "Laurent-Cauchy Transform for Analysis of Linear Systems Described by Differential-Difference and Sum Equations," *Proc. IRE*, Vol. 48, May 1960, pp. 923–931.

11. Brown, B. M., "Application of Operational Methods to Sampling and Interpolating Systems," *IFAC Proc.*, Vol. 3, pp. 1272–1276.

12. Van Der Pol, Balth, and H. Bremmer, *Operational Calculus Based on Two-Sided Laplace Integral*, Cambridge University Press, London, 1950.

13. Tschauner, J., *Einführung in die Theorie der Abtastsysteme*, Verlag R. Oldenbourg, Munich, 1960.

14. Jury, E. I., *Sampled-Data Control Systems*, John Wiley and Sons, New York, 1958.

15. Ragazzini, J. R., and G. F. Franklin, *Sampled-Data Control Systems*, McGraw-Hill Book Co., New York, 1959.

16. Tou, J. T., *Digital and Sampled-Data Control Systems*, McGraw-Hill Book Co., New York, 1959.

17. Jury, E. I., and F. J. Mullin, "A Note on the Operational Solution of Linear Difference Equations," *J.F.I.*, Vol. 266, No. 3, September 1958, pp. 189–205.

18. Neufeld, J., "On the Operational Solution of Linear Mixed Difference Differential Equations," *Cambridge Phil. Soc.*, Vol. 30, 1934, p. 289.

19. Bridgland, T. F., Jr., "A Linear Algebraic Formulation of the Theory of Sampled-Data Control," *J. Soc. Indust. Appl. Math.*, Vol. 7, No. 4, December 1959, p. 431.

20. James H., N. Nichols, and R. Phillips, *Theory of Servomechanisms*, M.I.T. Rad. Lab. Series No. 25, McGraw-Hill Book Co., New York, 1947, Ch. 5.

21. Meschkowski, H., *Differenzengleichungen*, Gottengen Vandenhoesch and Ruprecht, Basel und Stuttgart, 1959.

22. Montel, P., *Leçons sur les Recurrences et Leurs Applications*, Gauthier-Villars, Paris, 1957.

23. Miller, K. S., *An Introduction to the Calculus of Finite Difference and Differential Equations*, Henry Holt and Co., New York, 1960.

24. Kaplan, W., *Operational Methods for Linear Systems*, Addison-Wesley Publishing Co., Reading, Massachusetts, 1962.

25. Aseltine, John A., *Transform Method in Linear Systems*, McGraw-Hill Book Co., New York, 1958.

26. Cheng, D. K., *Analysis of Linear Systems*, Addison-Wesley Publishing Co., Reading, Massachusetts, 1959.

27. Jury, E. I., "Contribution to the Modified z-Transform Theory," *J. Franklin Inst.*, Vol. 270, No. 2, 1960, pp. 114–124.

28. Tsypkin, Y. Z., *Differenzenleichungen der Impuls-und Regeltchnik*, Veb Verlag Technik, Berlin, 1956.

29. Doetsch, G., *Handbuch der Laplace Transformation*, Birkhauser Verlag, Basel and Stuttgart, 1956.

30. Friedland, B., "Theory of Time-Varying Sampled-Data Systems," Dept. of Electrical Engineering Technical Report T-19/B, Columbia University, New York, 1956.

31. Barker, R. H., "The Pulse Transfer Function and its Application to Sampling Servo Systems," *Proc. I.E.E.*, *(London)*, Vol. 99, Part IV, 1952, pp. 202–317.

32. Lago, G. V., "Additions to z-Transformation Theory for Sampled-Data Systems," *Trans. A.I.E.E.*, Vol. 74, Part II, 1955, pp. 403–408.

33. Truxal, J. G., *Automatic Feedback System Synthesis*, McGraw-Hill Book Co., New York, 1955.

34. Lawden, D. F., "A General Theory of Sampling Servo Systems," *Proc. I.E.E. (London)*, Vol. 98, Part IV, 1951, pp. 31–36.

35. Ragazzini, J. R., and L. A. Zadeh, "Analysis of Sampled-Data Systems," *Trans. A.I.E.E.*, Vol. 71, Part II, 1952, pp. 225–232.

36. Freeman, H., and O. Lowenschuss, "Bibliography of Sampled-Data Control Systems and z-Transform Applications," *I.R.E. Trans. Automatic Control (PGAC)*, March 1958, pp. 28–30.

37. Jury, E. I., and C. A. Galtieri, "A Note on the Inverse z-Transform," *I.R.E. Trans. Circuit Theory (Correspondence)*, Vol. CT-9, September 1961, pp. 371–374.

38. Mori, M., "Statistical Treatment of Sampled-Data Control Systems for Actual Random Inputs," *Trans. ASME*, Vol. 80, No. 2, February 1958.

39. Jury, E. I., "A Note on the Steady-State Response of Linear Time-Invariant Systems," *I.R.E. Proc. (Correspondence)*, Vol. 48, No. 5, May 1960.

40. Wilts, C. H., *Principles of Feedback Control*, Addison-Wesley Publishing Co. Reading, Massachusetts, 1960 (Appendix B, p. 261).

41. Doetsch, Gustav, *Guide to the Applications of Laplace Transform*, D. Van Nostrand Co., 1961, Ch. 4.

42. Mikusinski, Jan, *Operational Calculus*, Pergamon Press, New York, Vol. 8, 1959.

43. Pasteur, Franceline, "Relationship between Mikusinski's Operational Calculus and the Modified z-Transform," Master of Science Project, Dept. of E.E., University of California, Berkeley, June 1963 (under supervision of the author).

44. Brown, B. M., *The Mathematical Theory of Linear Systems*, John Wiley and Sons, New York, 1961, Ch. 13.

45. Volgin, L. N., *Elements of the Theory of Control Machines*, Soviet Series, Moscow, 1962.

46. Kuo, B. C., *Analysis and Synthesis of Sampled-Data Control Systems*, Prentice-Hall, Englewood Cliffs, New Jersey, 1963.

47. Tsypkin, Y. Z., *Theory of Linear Sampled-Data Systems*, State Press for Physics and Mathematical Literature, Moscow, 1963 (in Russian).

48. Tamburelli, G., Alternate z-Transform, *Alta Frequenza*, Vol. 30. No. 10, October 1961, pp. 745–750.

2

z-TRANSFORM METHOD OF

SOLUTION OF LINEAR

DIFFERENCE EQUATIONS

The field of linear difference equations has been studied extensively by many mathematicians in the last century or more. Several excellent textbooks[1-8] have been written on this subject that can be studied by the interested reader. Several methods exist for solution of difference equations such as the classical method, the matrix method, the recurrence method, and the transform methods. In this chapter we shall apply the z-transform method (or widely known among mathematicians as the generating function method) for the solution of only certain types of linear difference equations. The formulation of the difference equation can be expressed in several forms such as the backward and forward difference method or the translational form. The theorems developed in the preceding chapter will be readily applied to any of the several forms used in the mathematical formulation of these equations. Several examples from network and system theory will be presented and solved, using the difference equations as the basis of description.

Although this chapter is necessarily a brief study of difference equations, several types of linear difference or difference-differential equations, usually encountered in physical, economic, and physiological systems, will be studied. This study will be based primarily (although other methods exist) on the z-transform or the modified z-transform theory.

2.1 Linear difference equations
with constant coefficients[28,31]

Consider the following difference equation.

$$\sum_{i=0}^{p} a_i x_{n+i} = \sum_{i=0}^{q} b_i y_{n+i} \tag{2.1}$$

a_i and b_i are constants, y_n is the forcing function and is known for all values of $n \geq 0$. It is desired to find x_n. x_n and y_n are both functions of the parameter $t = nT$. Assuming $T = 1$ in all the discussions of this chapter, $t = n$, where n is an integer equal to or greater than zero.

Taking the z-transform of equation (2.1), we obtain

$$\sum_{i=0}^{p} a_i z^i \left[\mathscr{X}(z) - \sum_{j=0}^{i-1} x_j z^{-j} \right] = \sum_{i=0}^{q} b_i z^i \left[\mathscr{Y}(z) - \sum_{j=0}^{i-1} y_j z^{-j} \right] \qquad (2.2)$$

where $\mathscr{X}(z) \triangleq \mathscr{Y}[x_n]$, $\mathscr{Y}(z) \triangleq \mathscr{Y}[y_n]$, and x_j, y_j are the initial conditions. Solving equation (2.2) for $\mathscr{X}(z)$, we obtain

$$\mathscr{X}(z) = \frac{\mathscr{Y}(z) \sum_{i=0}^{q} b_i z^i + \sum_{i=0}^{p} a_i z^i \left(\sum_{j=0}^{i-1} x_j z^{-j} \right) - \sum_{i=0}^{q} b_i z^i \left(\sum_{j=0}^{i-1} y_j z^{-j} \right)}{\sum_{i=0}^{p} a_i z^i}$$

$$(2.3)$$

The inverse z-transformation $x_n \triangleq \mathscr{Y}^{-1}[\mathscr{X}(z)]$ can be accomplished by using Cauchy's integral formula, the power series expansion, the partial fraction expansion, or the available table of inverse z-transforms. It is apparent from the foregoing that initial conditions are readily inserted automatically at the start, thus avoiding evaluating the integration constants as in the classical solution of difference equations. This fact with the use of tables of z-transform pairs indicates that this method of solution has certain advantages over the other methods.

The extension of the z-transform to solution of simultaneous linear difference equations with constant coefficients can be performed in a similar fashion as for the preceding case.

ILLUSTRATIVE EXAMPLE[29]

It is required to find the current in the nth loop i_n for the ladder network shown in Fig. 2.1. Assume all the resistances except the load R_L have the same value R.

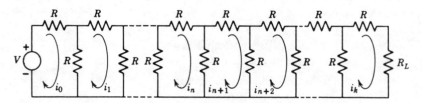

FIGURE 2.1 Ladder network.

The equation for the loop with current i_{n+1}

$$-Ri_n + 3Ri_{n+1} - Ri_{n+2} = 0 \qquad (2.4)$$

Equation 2.4 is true for any n except -1 and $k-1$ (the beginning and end loops). Equation (2.4) with end conditions is sufficient to describe the network.

Applying the z-transformation to equation (2.4) and dividing by R, we obtain

$$\mathscr{I}(z) - 3z\mathscr{I}(z) + 3zi_0 + z^2\mathscr{I}(z) - z^2i_0 - zi_1 = 0 \qquad (2.5)$$

Solving for $\mathscr{I}(z)$, we have

$$\mathscr{I}(z) = \frac{z(zi_0 - 3i_0 + i_1)}{z^2 - 3z + 1} \qquad (2.6)$$

We can eliminate one of the initial conditions by writing the equation for the first loop of Fig. 2.1.

$$2Ri_0 - Ri_1 = V \qquad (2.7)$$

or

$$i_1 = 2i_0 - \frac{V}{R} \qquad (2.8)$$

Thus $\mathscr{I}(z)$ becomes

$$\mathscr{I}(z) = \frac{z\{z - [1 + (V/Ri_0)]\}i_0}{z^2 - 3z + 1} \qquad (2.9)^*$$

From tables of inverse z-transform (Table 1) we readily obtain i_n as follows:

$$i_n = \mathscr{J}^{-1}[\mathscr{I}(z)] = i_0\left[\cosh \omega_0 n + \frac{\frac{1}{2} - (V/Ri_0)}{\frac{\sqrt{5}}{2}} \sinh \omega_0 n\right] \qquad (2.10)$$

where

$$\cosh \omega_0 = \frac{3}{2} \qquad (2.11)$$

and

$$\sinh \omega_0 = \frac{\sqrt{5}}{2} \qquad (2.12)$$

---

* This equation can be also written in a form suitable for table entries as

$$\mathscr{I}(z) = i_0 \frac{z(z - \frac{3}{2}) + z[\frac{1}{2} - (V/Ri_0)]}{z^2 - 3z + 1}$$

The value of i_0 can be found by substituting equation (2.10) into the equation for the end loop and solving for i_0. The current i_n can also be obtained from the power series expansion of (2.9) in powers of z^{-1}.

2.2 Solution of difference equations whose coefficients are periodic functions[28],[31]

In the solution of this type of difference equation the modified z-transform is readily applied. Consider the following type of difference equation:

$$\underset{(n+p)\,\leq\,t\,\leq\,(n+p+1)}{x(t)} = \sum_{i=0}^{p} f_i(t)x_{n+i} + \sum_{i=0}^{q} g_i(t)y_{n+i} \tag{2.13}$$

Here $f_i(t)$ and $g_i(t)$ are arbitrary periodic functions of the independent variable t with periods equal to unity.

Because of the periodicity of $f_i(t)$ and $g_i(t)$, we can replace these functions by $f_i(m)$ and $g_i(m)$, respectively, where m is a parameter which varies from zero to unity. With this change of variable equation (2.13) becomes

$$x(n + p + m) = \sum_{i=0}^{p} f_i(m)x_{n+i} + \sum_{i=0}^{q} g_i(m)y_{n+i} \tag{2.14}$$

From the definition of the modified z-transform, we have

$$\mathscr{J}_m[x(n - 1 + m)] \triangleq \mathscr{X}(z, m), \tag{2.15}$$

$$\mathscr{J}_m[x(n + k + m)] \triangleq z^{k+1}\left[\mathscr{X}(z, m) - \sum_{j=0}^{k} x(j + m - 1)z^{-j}\right],$$

$$0 \leq m \leq 1 \tag{2.16}$$

The modified z-transform of the difference equation in (2.14) gives

$$z^{p+1}\left[\mathscr{X}(z, m) - \sum_{j=0}^{p} x(j + m - 1)z^{-j}\right]$$

$$= \sum_{i=0}^{p} f_i(m)z^i\left[\mathscr{X}(z) - \sum_{j=0}^{i-1} x_j z^{-j}\right]$$

$$+ \sum_{i=0}^{q} g_i(m)z^i\left[\mathscr{Y}(z) - \sum_{j=0}^{i-1} y_j z^{-j}\right], \qquad 0 \leq m \leq 1 \tag{2.17}$$

Both $\mathscr{X}(z)$ and $\mathscr{X}(z, m)$ are unknown in this equation. However, $\mathscr{X}(z)$ can be determined by noting that $\mathscr{X}(z) = \mathscr{X}(z, m)\big|_{m=1}$. Thus, substituting $m = 1$ in equation (2.17) gives readily $\mathscr{X}(z)$. The resulting expression can be substituted in (2.17), which can then be solved for $\mathscr{X}(z, m)$. This would finally give

$$\mathscr{X}(z, m) = \frac{\mathscr{Y}(z)}{z^{p+1}} \left[\frac{\sum\limits_{i=0}^{q} g_i(1)z^i \sum\limits_{i=0}^{p} f_i(m)z^i}{z^{p+1} - \sum\limits_{i=0}^{p} f_i(1)z^i} + \sum\limits_{i=0}^{q} g_i(m)z^i \right]$$

$$+ \frac{1}{z^{p+1}} \left[\frac{z^{p+1}\sum\limits_{j=0}^{p} x_j z^{-j} - \left(\sum\limits_{i=0}^{p} f_i(1)z^i \right) \times \left(\sum\limits_{j=0}^{i-1} x_j z^{-j} \right) - \left(\sum\limits_{i=0}^{q} g_i(1)z^i \right)\left(\sum\limits_{j=0}^{i-1} y_j z^{-j} \right)}{\left(z^{p+1} - \sum\limits_{i=0}^{p} f_i(1)z^i \right)} \right]$$

$$\times \sum\limits_{i=0}^{p} f_i(m)z^i + \sum\limits_{j=0}^{p} x(j + m - 1)z^{-j} - \frac{1}{z^{p+1}}$$

$$\times \left[\sum\limits_{i=0}^{p} f_i(m)z^i \sum\limits_{j=0}^{i-1} x_j z^{-j} + \sum\limits_{i=0}^{q} g_i(m)z^i \sum\limits_{j=0}^{i-1} y_j z^{-j} \right] \quad (2.18)$$

The time function is obtained by the inverse modified z-transform

$$x(n, m) = \mathscr{Z}_m^{-1}[\mathscr{X}(z, m)], \quad t = (n - 1 + m),$$

$$0 \le m \le 1 \quad (2.19)$$

ILLUSTRATIVE EXAMPLE

Find $x(t)$ which is a solution of the following equation.

$$x(t) = x_{n+1}(2.582 - 1.582e^{-t} - t) - x_n(1 - e^{-t})$$
$$_{(n+1) \le t \le (n+2)}$$
$$+ y_{n+1}(e^{-t} + t - 1) + 0.418y_n(1 - e^{-t}) \quad (2.20)$$

We can construct the coefficients of x_k and y_k to be periodic functions with period one by replacing t in these functions by m. This gives the following equation:

$$x(n + 1 + m) = x_{n+1}(2.582 - 1.582 e^{-m} - m) + - x_n(1 - e^{-m})$$
$$+ y_{n+1}(e^{-m} + m - 1)$$
$$+ 0.418y_n(1 - e^{-m}), \quad 0 \le m \le 1 \quad (2.21)$$

where the coefficients of x_{n+1}, x_n, y_{n+1}, y_n are periodic.

The modified z-transform of equation (2.21) gives

$$z^2\{\mathscr{X}(z, m) - [x(m - 1) + x(m)z^{-1}]\}$$
$$= (2.582 - 1.532 e^{-m} - m)z.$$
$$[\mathscr{X}(z) - x_0] - (1 - e^{-m})\mathscr{X}(z)$$
$$+ (e^{-m} + m - 1)z[y(z) - y_0]$$
$$+ 0.418 (1 - e^{-m})\mathscr{Y}(z) \quad (2.22)$$

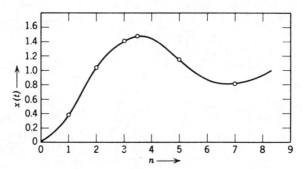

FIGURE 2.2 Particular solution for y_n = a unit step.

To obtain $\mathscr{X}(z)$, we replace $m = 1$ in equation (2.22) to obtain

$$\mathscr{X}(z) = \frac{(0.368z + 0.264)\mathscr{Y}(z)}{z^2 - z + 0.632} + \frac{z^2 x_0 + z(x_1 - x_0 - 0.368y_0)}{z^2 - z + 0.632}$$

(2.23)

If we assume y_n = unit step ($y_0 = 1$) and $x_0 = 0$, we readily obtain from equation (2.21), by letting $n = -1$, $m = 1$, the value $x_1 = 0.368$. Therefore $\mathscr{X}(z)$ becomes

$$\mathscr{X}(z) = \frac{(0.368z + 0.264)z}{(z - 1)(z^2 - z + 0.632)}$$

(2.24)

Substituting (2.24) in equation (2.22) and noting that $x(m - 1) = 0$, we obtain

$$z^2[\mathscr{X}(z, m) - x(m)z^{-1}] = (2.582 - 1.582e^{-m} - m)z\mathscr{X}(z)$$
$$- (1 - e^{-m})\mathscr{X}(z) + (1 - e^{-m})\frac{z}{z - 1}$$
$$+ (e^{-m} + m - 1)\frac{z^2}{z - 1}$$
$$- (e^{-m} + m - 1)z \qquad (2.25)$$

The initial value $x(m)$ can be obtained from equation (2.21) by letting $n = -1$ to give

$$x(m)\big|_{0 \le m \le 1} = y_0(e^{-m} + m - 1) = e^{-m} + m - 1 \qquad (2.26)$$

Substituting equation (2.24) and (2.26) in equation (2.25) and expanding in powers of z^{-1}, we obtain the particular solution $\mathscr{X}_p(z, m)$ as follows:

$$z\mathscr{X}_p(z, m) = (e^{-m} + m - 1)z^{-0} + (0.368 + 0.632m)z^{-1}$$
$$+ (1.632 - 0.632e^{-m})z^{-2} + \ldots \qquad (2.27)$$

The coefficient of z^{-k} represents $x_p(t)$ for $k \leq t < k + 1$. The final value of $x_p(t)$ which is known to exist is obtained from applying the final value theorem to $\mathcal{X}(z, m)$ to give

$$\lim_{n \to \infty} x(n - 1 + m) = \lim_{z \to 1} (z - 1)\mathcal{X}_p(z, m) = 1 \qquad (2.27a)$$

The particular solution is shown in Fig. 2.2.

2.3 Linear difference-differential equations[5,36]

In many applications of control systems a pure delay (or transportation lag) often appears in the controlled process. The mathematical description of such systems is carried through the use of mixed difference-differential equations. In the following discussion only linear constant coefficient equations involving one-time delay are considered. Extension to other cases can be performed using the same or other techniques.

The modified z-transform of the continuous functions $c(t)$ can be written in the following form:

$$z\mathscr{C}(z, m) = c_0(m) + c_1(m)z^{-1} + \ldots$$

$$+ c_n(m)z^{-n} + \ldots = \sum_{n=0}^{\infty} c_n(m)z^{-n}$$

$$t = (n + m)T, \qquad 0 \leq m \leq 1 \quad (2.28)$$

From this series expansion of $z\mathscr{C}(z, m)$, we may note that

$$c_0(1) = c_1(0), \; c_1(1) = c_2(0), \; c_n(1) = c_{n+1}(0),$$

$$\text{for } n = 0, 1, 2, \ldots$$

for continuous outputs as assumed in this case. Using the preceding form of the modified z-transform of $c(t)$, we can also write the transforms of the derivatives of $c(t)$, $c(t + n)$ with $T = 1$, from equations (1.116) and (1.117) as

$$\mathscr{Y}_m[c'(t)] = \frac{\partial}{\partial m} [\mathscr{C}(z, m)], \qquad (2.29)$$

$$\mathscr{Y}_m[c'(t + n)] = \frac{\partial}{\partial m} \mathscr{Y}_m[c(t + n)]$$

$$= \frac{\partial}{\partial m} \left\{ z^{n-1} \left[z\mathscr{C}(z, m) - \sum_{p=0}^{n-1} c_p(m)z^{-p} \right] \right\} \qquad (2.30)$$

Similar relationships could be written for higher-order derivatives.

In the solution of difference-differential equations, it is convenient to choose the sampling period as equal to the time delay itself. This will yield the response in a closed or concise form with the minimum of labor. We shall illustrate the procedure by solving the following two examples in detail.

EXAMPLE 1: FIRST-ORDER EQUATION

Consider the difference-differential equation

$$c'(t) + kc(t - 1) = 0 \tag{2.31}$$

The boundary condition is specified for a sampling interval; here let $c(t) = \beta$ for $0 \leq t \leq 1$, where both k and β are constants. We must also assume that there is no discontinuity at $t = 0$.

By taking the modified z-transform of equation (2.31),

$$\frac{\partial}{\partial m} \mathscr{C}(z, m) + kz^{-1}\mathscr{C}(z, m) = 0 \tag{2.32}$$

that is,

$$z \frac{\partial}{\partial m} \mathscr{C}(z, m) + k\mathscr{C}(z, m) = 0 \tag{2.33}$$

This can be solved as a first-order differential equation in m, treating z as constant.

The solution of equation (2.33) is

$$\mathscr{C}(z, m) = A(z)e^{-(k/z)m} \tag{2.34}$$

where $A(z)$ is to be determined. Now from the definition of the modified z-transform in equation (2.28)

$$\mathscr{C}(z, 1) + c_0(0) = z\mathscr{C}(z, 0) \tag{2.35}$$

that is,

$$A(z)e^{-k/z} + \beta = zA(z)$$

Therefore

$$zA(z) = \frac{\beta}{1 - z^{-1}e^{-k/z}} \tag{2.36}$$

Substituting in (2.34)

$$z\mathscr{C}(z, m) = \frac{\beta}{1 - z^{-1}e^{-k/z}} e^{-(k/z)m} \tag{2.37}$$

Expansion of (2.37) in powers of $z^{-1}e^{-k/z}$ gives

$$z\mathscr{C}(z, m) = \beta e^{-(k/z)m} \sum_{n=0}^{\infty} z^{-n}e^{-(k/z)n}$$

$$= \beta \sum_{n=0}^{\infty} z^{-n}e^{-(k/z)(n+m)} \tag{2.38}$$

The coefficient of z^{-n} will give the response $c_n(m)$ and if we evaluate this for all n we get the complete response.

$$z\mathscr{C}(z, m) = \beta \sum_{n=0}^{\infty} z^{-n} \sum_{q=0}^{\infty} \frac{[-(k/z)(n + m)]^q}{q!} \tag{2.39}$$

This can be simplified as

$$z\mathscr{C}(z, m) = \beta \sum_{l=0}^{\infty} z^{-l} \sum_{p=0}^{l} \frac{[-k(l + m - p)]^p}{p!} \qquad (2.40)$$

The coefficient of z^{-l} is

$$c_l(m) = \beta \sum_{p=0}^{l} \frac{(-k)^p(l + m - p)^p}{p!} \qquad (2.41)$$

Equation (2.41) is useful if one is interested in the response for large intervals of time. Generally, the process of obtaining a general time function such as (2.41) in a closed form is very difficult if not impossible. In many engineering problems, we are interested only in the transient response. This can be obtained by actually expanding equation (2.38) and identifying the coefficients of $z^{-1}, z^{-2}, \ldots$, etc. This approach is illustrated in the following example. The coefficients of $z^{-1}, z^{-2}, \ldots$ will give the responses for the 1st, 2nd, ... sampling intervals in terms of m which ranges from 0 to 1.

EXAMPLE 2: FEEDBACK CONTINUOUS SYSTEM WITH TIME DELAY[31]
Consider the feedback system shown in Fig. 2.3. The forward transfer function is $G(s)e^{-\Delta s} = [(s + 0.3)/s^2] e^{-s}$. The overall transfer function can be written as

$$\frac{C(s)}{R(s)} = \frac{(s + 0.3)e^{-s}}{s^2 + (s + 0.3)e^{-s}} \qquad (2.42)$$

Although we can obtain the modified z-transform of this equation directly, however, for sake of illustration we formulate first the difference equation.
The difference equation is, for $r(t) = tu(t)$.

$$c''(t) + c'(t - 1) + 0.3c(t - 1) = r'(t - 1) + 0.3r(t - 1)$$
$$= u(t - 1) + 0.3r(t - 1)$$
$$(2.43)$$

Equation (2.43) is also equivalent to

$$c''(t + 1) + c'(t) + 0.3c(t) = u(t) + 0.3r(t) \qquad (2.44)$$

with the initial conditions specified as

$$c(t) = 0, \, c'(t) = 0 \quad \text{for } 0 \leq t \leq 1 \qquad (2.45)$$

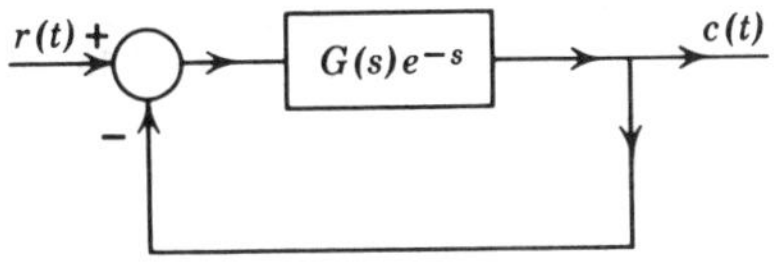

FIGURE 2.3 Continuous feedback system with pure delay.

Taking the modified z-transform of (2.44)

$$z \frac{\partial^2}{\partial m^2} \mathscr{C}(z, m) + \frac{\partial}{\partial m} \mathscr{C}(z, m) + 0.3 \mathscr{C}(z, m)$$

$$= \frac{1}{z - 1} + 0.3 \left[\frac{mT}{z - 1} + \frac{T}{(z - 1)^2} \right] \quad (2.46)$$

Treating z as constant, (2.46) is solved as a differential equation in m, and noting that T the sampling period $= 1$, we obtain

$$\mathscr{C}(z, m) = A_1 e^{s_1 m} + A_2 e^{s_2 m} + \frac{1}{(z - 1)^2} + \frac{m}{(z - 1)} \quad (2.47)$$

where A_1 and A_2 are functions of z and s_1, s_2 are roots of the characteristic equation

$$zs^2 + s + 0.3 = 0, \quad \text{that is,} \quad s_{1,2} = \frac{-1 \pm \sqrt{1 - 1.2z}}{2z} \quad (2.48)$$

Again from the definition of the modified z-transform we have

$$\mathscr{C}(z, m)\big|_{m=1} = [z\mathscr{C}(z, m) - c_0(m)]\big|_{m=0} \quad (2.49)$$

and

$$\frac{\partial}{\partial m} \mathscr{C}(z, m)\bigg|_{m=1} = \frac{\partial}{\partial m} [z\mathscr{C}(z, m) - c_0(m)]\bigg|_{m=0} \quad (2.50)$$

provided that $c'(t)$ is continuous at $t = 1, 2, \ldots$.
Substituting (2.47) in (2.49) and solving for A_1 and A_2 yields

$$zA_1 = \frac{1}{(s_1 - s_2)(z^{-1}e^{s_1} - 1)} \quad (2.51)$$

$$zA_2 = \frac{-1}{(s_1 - s_2)(z^{-1}e^{s_2} - 1)} \quad (2.52)$$

The complete solution for $z\mathscr{C}(z, m)$ is

$$z\mathscr{C}(z, m) = \frac{1}{(s_1 - s_2)(z^{-1}e^{s_1} - 1)} e^{s_1 m} - \frac{1}{(s_1 - s_2)(z^{-1}e^{s_2} - 1)}$$

$$\times e^{s_2 m} + \frac{z}{(z - 1)^2} + \frac{mz}{(z - 1)} \quad (2.53)$$

Expanding equation (2.53) in negative powers of z and identifying the coefficients of $z^{-1}, z^{-2}, \ldots$ gives the system response for all time. Although this looks formidable, considerable simplification will result if we are interested in the response only at sampling instants, so that

$$z\mathscr{C}(z, 0) = \frac{z}{(z - 1)^2} + \frac{1}{(s_1 - s_2)(z^{-1}e^{s_1} - 1)}$$

$$- \frac{1}{(s_1 - s_2)(z^{-1}e^{s_2} - 1)}$$

$$= \frac{z}{(z - 1)^2} - \frac{1}{s_1 - s_2}\left[\sum_{n=0}^{\infty}z^{-n}e^{s_1 n} - \sum_{n=0}^{\infty}z^{-n}e^{s_2 n}\right]$$

$$= \frac{z}{(z - 1)^2} - \frac{1}{s_1 - s_2}\sum_{n=1}^{\infty}(z^{-n}e^{ns_1} - z^{-n}e^{ns_2})$$

$$= \frac{z}{(z - 1)^2} - \sum_{n=1}^{\infty}z^{-n}\frac{e^{ns_1} - e^{ns_2}}{s_1 - s_2} \tag{2.54}$$

From tables[53]

$$\frac{e^{ns_1} - e^{ns_2}}{s_1 - s_2} = ne^{(1/2)(s_1+s_2)n}\prod_{k=1}^{\infty}\left[1 + \frac{(s_1 - s_2)^2 n^2}{4k^2\pi^2}\right] \tag{2.55}$$

where

$$s_{1,2} = \frac{-1 \pm \sqrt{1 - 1.2z}}{2z} \tag{2.56}$$

This reduces (2.54) to

$$z\mathscr{C}(z, 0) = \frac{z}{(z - 1)^2} - \sum_{n=1}^{\infty}z^{-n}ne^{-n/2z}\prod_{k=1}^{\infty}$$

$$\times \left[1 + \frac{(z^{-2} - 1.2z^{-1})n^2}{4k^2\pi^2}\right] \tag{2.57}$$

Although (2.57) is in a sense "closed" form, it is not useful in evaluating the response since one has to expand the infinite product to identify coefficients of z^{-1}, z^{-2}, etc. It is easier to proceed directly from (2.54) and simplify it by actual expansion.

$$\frac{e^{ns_1} - e^{ns_2}}{s_1 - s_2} = n + \frac{n^2}{2!}(s_1 + s_2) + \frac{n^3}{3!}(s_1^2 + s_1s_2 + s_2^2)$$

$$+ \frac{n^4}{4!}(s_1^3 + s_1^2s_2 + s_1s_2^2 + s_2^3)\ldots$$

$$+ \frac{n^q}{q!}(s_1^{q-1} + s_1^{q-2}s_2 + \ldots s_2^{q-1}) + \ldots \tag{2.58}$$

The polynomials in s_1s_2 can all be calculated in terms of z and it is noted that z appears only in powers of z^{-1}. $z\mathscr{C}(z, 0)$ can then be simplified as

$$z\mathscr{C}(z, 0)^* = \frac{z}{(z-1)^2} - \sum_{n=1}^{\infty} z^{-n}\left[n - \frac{n^2}{2!}z^{-1} + \frac{n^3}{3!}(z^{-2} - 0.3z^{-1})\right.$$

$$- \frac{n^4}{4!}(z^{-3} - 0.6z^{-2})$$

$$+ \frac{n^5}{5!}(z^{-4} - 0.9z^{-3} + 0.09z^{-2})$$

$$- \frac{n^6}{6!}(z^{-5} - 1.2z^{-4} + 0.27z^{-3})$$

$$+ \frac{n^7}{7!}(z^{-6} - 1.5z^{-5} + 0.54z^{-4} - 0.027z^{-3})$$

$$- \frac{n^8}{8!}(z^{-7} - 1.8z^{-6} + 0.9z^{-5} - 0.108z^{-4})$$

$$+ \frac{n^9}{9!}(z^{-8} - 2.1z^{-7} + 1.35z^{-6} - 0.27z^{-5}$$

$$\left. + 0.0081z^{-4}) + \dots\right] \tag{2.59}$$

By identifying the coefficients of z^{-k} in this expression, the response up to the fifth sampling instant can be obtained as

$$c(0) = 0 \quad c(1) = 0 \quad c(2) = 0.55$$
$$c(3) = 2.08 \quad c(4) = 4.145 \quad c(5) = 5.4135 \tag{2.60}$$

This result, as is to be expected, agrees with those obtained by other methods.[50] More terms in the expansion in (2.59) have to be taken to evaluate responses for longer times.

In this brief discussion the usefulness of modified z-transform has been demonstrated in solving linear constant coefficient difference-differential equations. It is particularly useful in calculating transient responses of continuous systems having time delays, and this method avoids having to evaluate roots of transcendental equations, but requires manipulation of series. Although in Example 2 only the response at sampling instants has been calculated, it is, however, necessary to use the modified z-transform theory to arrive at the constants A_1 and A_2. This method can be easily extended to higher-order systems having more than one but otherwise commensurable time delays.[51]

---

* It should be noted that $z\mathscr{C}(z, 0)$ is our definition of the z-transform, that is, $\mathscr{C}(z)$.

2.4 Difference equations with periodic coefficients[25,28]

Consider the following equation:

$$x_{n+1} = a_n x_n + y_n \qquad (2.61)$$

a_n is a periodic coefficient whose period is N; that is, $a_i = a_{N+i}$ for $i = 0, 1, 2, 3, \ldots, N - 1$.

To solve this equation we shall first form a constant coefficient difference equation that describes the solution for $n = kN$, $k = 0, 1, 2, \ldots$, and then use this result to find the solution for all other values of n. This procedure, in essence, removes the periodicity of the coefficients from the analysis.

Let

$$\mathscr{Y}[y_{kN}] = y_0 + y_N z^{-N} + y_{2N} z^{-2N} + y_{3N} z^{-3N} + \cdots$$
$$+ y_{kN} z^{-kN} + \cdots$$
$$\mathscr{Y}[y_{kN+1}] = y_1 + y_{N+1} z^{-N} + y_{2N+1} z^{-2N} + y_{3N+1} z^{-3N} + \cdots$$

.

.

.

$$\mathscr{Y}[y_{(k+1)N-1}] = y_{N-1} + y_{2N-1} z^{-N} + y_{3N-1} z^{-2N} + y_{4N-1} z^{-3N} + \cdots$$
$$(2.62)$$

With this pattern for x_n we solve this periodic coefficient difference equation. Let $n = kN$ so that $a_n = a_0$ (that is, $a_n = a_{kN}$ and letting at the start $k = 0$). We can then write for equation (2.61)

$$x_{kN+1} = a_0 x_{kN} + y_{kN}$$
$$x_{kN+2} = a_1 x_{kN+1} + y_{kN+1} = a_1 a_0 x_{kN} + a_1 y_{kN} + y_{kN+1}$$
$$x_{kN+3} = a_2 x_{kN+2} + y_{kN+2} = a_2 a_1 a_0 x_{kN} + a_2 a_1 y_{kN} + a_2 y_{kN+1}$$
$$+ y_{kN+2}$$

.   .

.   .

.   .

$$x_{(k+1)N} = a_{N-1} x_{(k+1)N-1} + y_{(k+1)N-1} = (a_{N-1} a_{N-2} \cdots a_0) x_{kN}$$
$$+ (a_{N-1} \cdots a_1) y_{kN} + (a_{N-1} \cdots a_2) y_{kN+1}$$
$$+ (a_{N-1} \cdots a_3) y_{kN+2} + \cdots + a_{N-1} y_{(k+1)N-2}$$
$$+ y_{(k+1)N-1} \quad (2.63)$$

The last equation is actually a constant coefficient difference equation involving x_{kN} and the various forcing terms. The z-transform method can be readily applied.

$$z^N[\mathscr{X}_{kN}(z) - x_0] = (a_{N-1} \cdots a_0)\mathscr{X}_{kN}(z) + (a_{N-1} \cdots a_1)\mathscr{Y}_{kN}(z)$$
$$+ (a_{N-1} \cdots a_2)\mathscr{Y}_{kN+1}(z) + \cdots + a_{N-1}\mathscr{Y}_{(k+1)N-2}(z) + \mathscr{Y}_{(k+1)N-1}(z)$$
$$(2.64)$$

or

$$\mathscr{X}_{kN}(z) = \frac{1}{z^N - (a_{N-1} \ldots a_0)} [z^N x_0 + (a_{N-1} \ldots)\mathscr{Y}_{kN}(z) + \ldots$$

$$+ a_{N-1}\mathscr{Y}_{(k+1)N-2}(z) + \mathscr{Y}_{(k+1)N-1}(z)]. \quad (2.65)$$

We readily obtain x_{kN} by inverse z-transformation of this equation. Knowing x_{kN} we can find x_{kN+1} from the first of the series of equation (2.63). Similarly, x_{kN+2} is obtained from the second, and so forth. We finally obtain $x_{(k+1)N}$.

Solution of simultaneous difference equations with periodic coefficients

Consider the two following difference equations where a_n, b_n, c_n, and d_n are periodic coefficients of period N, and P_n and Q_n are known for all $n(n \geq 0)$.

$$x_{n+1} = a_n x_n + b_n y_n + P_n \qquad (2.66)$$

$$y_{n+1} = c_n x_n + d_n y_n + Q_n \qquad (2.67)$$

A solution for these two equations can be obtained following the procedure for a single equation; that is, the $2N$ equations which correspond to a complete period of the coefficients are written and each equation is substituted into the following equation, as in (2.63). This results in two constant coefficient difference equations which involve x_{kN}, y_{kN} and various forcing function terms. These two equations can be simultaneously solved for the two unknowns using the indicated procedure of the z-transform method.

EXAMPLE
Find x_n which is a solution of the following equation:

$$x_{n+1} = a_n x_n + y_n \qquad (2.68)$$

with $a_i = 0.5$ for $i = 0, 1, 4, 5, 8, 9, \ldots$, and $a_i = -0.5$ for $i = 2, 3, 6, 7, 10, 11, \ldots$, and $y_n = (-1)^n$.
Here $N = 4$

$$\mathscr{Y}[y_{kN}] = 1 + z^{-4} + z^{-8} + \ldots = \frac{z^4}{z^4 - 1} \qquad (2.69)$$

$$\mathscr{Y}[y_{kN+1}] = -1 - z^{-4} - z^{-8} - \ldots = \frac{-z^4}{z^4 - 1} \qquad (2.70)$$

$$y_{kN+2} = y_{kN}, \qquad y_{kN+3} = y_{kN+1} \qquad (2.71)$$

Using this procedure, we readily obtain for $\mathscr{X}_{kN}(z)$

$$\mathscr{X}_{kN}(z) = \frac{1}{z^4 - 0.5^4}$$
$$\times \left[z^4 x_0 + \frac{0.125z^4}{z^4 - 1} + \frac{(0.25)(-z^4)}{z^4 - 1} - \frac{0.5z^4}{z^4 - 1} - \frac{z^4}{z^4 - 1} \right]$$

$$(2.72)$$

with $x_0 = 0$

$$\mathscr{X}_{kN}(z) = \frac{-1.625z^4}{(z^4 - 0.0625)(z^4 - 1)} \tag{2.73}$$

The inverse of this equation yields

$$x_{4k} = -\frac{26.0}{15} [1 - (\tfrac{1}{2})^{4k}] \tag{2.74}$$

Since we know

$$x_{4k+1} = 0.5x_{4k} + y_{1k} \tag{2.75}$$

it readily follows that

$$x_{4k+1} = -\frac{13.0}{15} [1 - (\tfrac{1}{2})^{4k}] + 1 \tag{2.76}$$

Similarly,

$$x_{4k+2} = -\frac{13.0}{30} [1 - (\tfrac{1}{2})^{4k}] - \tfrac{1}{2} \tag{2.77}$$

$$x_{4k+3} = \frac{13.0}{60} [1 - (\tfrac{1}{2})^{4k}] + \tfrac{5}{4} \tag{2.78}$$

2.5 Time-varying difference equations[7,10,23,25]

In the following section, we shall first apply the ordinary z-transform to linear difference equations with rational coefficients and then, in the next section, the time-varying z-transform will be discussed and applied. The ordinary z-transform reduces the solution of the difference equation to the solution of a differential equation in the variable z. By obtaining $\mathscr{F}(z)$, we then apply the inverse z-transform (or use of tables) to obtain the time solution. A general solution of such equations exists only for the first order case, whereas higher-order equations can be solved only for particular cases. We shall illustrate the procedure by considering the following Nth-order difference equation with rational coefficients in the variable n.

Let the difference equation be represented as

$$\sum_{k=1}^{N} (a_k n + b_k) E^k f(n) = g(n) \tag{2.79}$$

where the shift operator E denotes $Ef(n) = f(n + 1)$, and $g(n)$ is a known forcing function.

Applying the z-transform to equation (2.79), we get, using equation (1.34)

$$\sum_{k=1}^{N}\left[-a_k z \frac{d}{dz} \mathscr{F}_1(z) + b_k z^k \mathscr{F}(z) \right] = \mathscr{G}(z) + \mathscr{C}(z) \qquad (2.80)$$

where $\mathscr{C}(z)$ is a polynomial in z containing all the initial values of equation (2.79) and $\mathscr{F}_1(z) = \mathscr{z}[f(n + k)] = z^k \mathscr{F}(z) -$ (initial values).

Equation (2.80) can also be conveniently written as

$$\frac{d\mathscr{F}(z)}{dz} + \frac{B(z)}{A(z)} \mathscr{F}(z) = \frac{D(z)}{A(z)} \qquad (2.81)$$

where

$$A(z) = -\sum_{k=1}^{N} a_k z^{k+1} \qquad (2.82)$$

$$B(z) = \sum_{k=1}^{N}(ka_k + b_k)z^k \qquad (2.83)$$

and

$$D(z) = \mathscr{G}(z) + \mathscr{C}(z) \qquad (2.84)$$

It may be noted that equation (2.81) is a first-order differential equation in the variable z. The solution of this equation is generally known and is given by the following:

$$\mathscr{F}(z) = \exp\left[-\int \frac{B(z)}{A(z)}\, dz \right]\int \frac{D(z)}{A(z)} \exp\left[\int \frac{B(z)}{A(z)}\, dz \right] dz$$
$$+ K \cdot \exp\left[-\int \frac{B(z)}{A(z)}\, dz \right] \qquad (2.85)$$

where K is the integration constant.

In general, $A(z)$ can be represented as

$$A(z) = -a_N(z - \alpha_1)^{r_1}(z - \alpha_2)^{r_2} \ldots (z - \alpha_m)^{r_m}$$
$$= -a_N \prod_{i=1}^{m}(z - \alpha_i)^{r_i}, \qquad \text{with } \sum_{i=1}^{m} r_i = N + 1 \qquad (2.86)$$

Using equation (2.86), we can write

$$-\int \frac{B(z)}{A(z)}\, dz = -\int \sum_{i=1}^{m}\sum_{j=1}^{r_i}\frac{1}{(j-1)!}\left[\frac{d^{j-1}}{dz^{j-1}}\frac{B(z)(z - \alpha_i)^{r_i}}{A(z)}\right]_{z=\alpha_i}$$
$$\times \frac{dz}{(z - \alpha_i)^{r_i - j + 1}}$$
$$= -\sum_{i=1}^{m}\sum_{j=1}^{r_i}C_{ij}\int\frac{dz}{(z - \alpha_i)^{r_i - j + 1}} \qquad (2.87)$$

where

$$C_{ij} = \frac{1}{(j-1)!} \left[\frac{d^{j-1}}{dz^{j-1}} \frac{B(z)(z-\alpha_i)^{r_i}}{A(z)} \right]_{z=\alpha_i} \tag{2.88}$$

Performing the integration in equation (2.87), we have

$$-\int \frac{B(z)}{A(z)}\, dz = \sum_{i=1}^{m} \left[\sum_{j=1}^{r_i-1} \frac{C_{ij}}{r_i-j} \frac{1}{(z-\alpha_i)^{r_i-j}} - K_i \ln(z-\alpha_i) \right],$$
$$\text{where } K_i = C_{ir_i} \tag{2.89}$$

and

$$\exp\left[-\int \frac{B(z)}{A(z)}\, dz \right] = \prod_{i=1}^{m} (z-\alpha_i)^{-K_i} \prod_{i=1}^{m} \prod_{j=1}^{r_i-1} \exp \frac{C_{ij}}{(z-\alpha_i)^{r_i-j}} \tag{2.90}$$

Where all the roots of $A(z)$ are distinct, that is,

$$r_1 = r_2 = \ldots = r_m = 1, \qquad m = N + 1 \tag{2.91}$$

we obtain from equation (2.90)

$$\exp\left[-\int \frac{B(z)}{A(z)}\, dz \right] = \prod_{i=1}^{N+1} (z-\alpha_i)^{-C_i} \tag{2.92}$$

where

$$C_i = \left[\frac{B(z)(z-\alpha_i)}{A(z)} \right]_{z=\alpha_i} \tag{2.93}$$

For this case, equation (2.85) reduces to

$$\mathscr{F}(z) = \prod_{i=1}^{N+1} (z-\alpha_i)^{-C_i} \int \frac{D(z)}{A(z)} \prod_{i=1}^{N+1} (z-\alpha_i)^{C_i}\, dz$$
$$+ K \prod_{i=1}^{N+1} (z-\alpha_i)^{-C_i} \tag{2.94}$$

The inverse z-transform of equation (2.94) yields $f(n)$, the solution of the general Nth-order time-varying difference equation given in (2.79). It may be noted that if C_i is noninteger, as is often the case, $\mathscr{F}(z)$ will be an irrational function of z. In Table I of the Appendix many entries for $\mathscr{F}(z)$ of such a form are tabulated and thus can be conveniently used to obtain the final solution.

EXAMPLE

In this example we shall analyze a sampled-data feedback system with variable gain. This system is shown in Fig. 2.4.

Assuming zero initial conditions and letting $e^{-\alpha} = a$, we have for the system

$$c(n+1) - ac(n) = \frac{1-a}{\alpha} v(n) \tag{2.95}$$

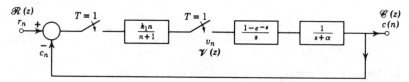

FIGURE 2.4   Time-varying sampled-data system.

and

$$v(n) = \frac{k_1 n}{n + 1} \left[r(n) - c(n) \right] \tag{2.96}$$

Eliminating $v(n)$ from these two equations and denoting $k = \dfrac{(1 - a)}{\alpha} k_1$, $b = k - a$, we have the following time-varying difference equation:

$$(n + 1)c(n + 1) + (bn - a)c(n) = knr(n) \tag{2.97}$$

Applying the z-transform to equation (2.97) we get using equation (1.34)

$$z(z + b) \frac{d\mathscr{C}(z)}{dz} + a\mathscr{C}(z) = kz \frac{d\mathscr{R}(z)}{dz} \tag{2.98}$$

Assuming a step input, that is, $\mathscr{R}(z) = z/z - 1$ and for $k = 2a$, that is, $b = a$,

$$\frac{z}{z + a} \mathscr{C}(z) = -k \int \frac{z \, dz}{(z + a)^2 (z - 1)^2} + K \tag{2.99}$$

where K is the integration constant.

We now discuss the following three cases.

1. $a \neq -1$, for this case (equation 2.99) yields

$$\mathscr{C}(z) = \frac{k}{(1 + a)^2} \left\{ \frac{z(1 - a) + 2a}{z(z - 1)} + \frac{1 - a}{1 + a} \frac{z + a}{z} \ln \frac{z - 1}{z + a} \right\}$$
$$+ K \frac{z + a}{z} \tag{2.100}$$

Since $c(n)\big|_{n=0} = \lim\limits_{z \to \infty} \mathscr{C}(z) = 0$, $K = 0$. Hence equation (2.100) becomes

$$\mathscr{C}(z) = \frac{k}{(1 + a)^2} \left\{ \frac{z(1 - a) + 2a}{z(z - 1)} + \frac{1 - a}{1 + a} \frac{z + a}{z} \ln \frac{z - 1}{z + a} \right\} \tag{2.101}$$

The inverse of this equation yields

$$c(n) = \frac{k}{(1 + a)^2} \left\{ (1 - a)u(n - 1) + 2au(n - 2) \right.$$
$$\left. + \frac{1 - a}{1 + a} [g(n) + ag(n - 1)] \right\} \tag{2.102}$$

where $g(n)$ is defined as

$$g(n) = 0, \qquad \text{for } n = 0$$

$$= \frac{1}{n}[(-a)^n - 1], \qquad \text{for } n \neq 0 \tag{2.103}$$

Equation (2.102) yields after using $g(n)$

$$c(0) = 0, \quad c(1) = 0$$

$$c(n) = \frac{k}{(1+a)^2}\left\{(1+a) - \frac{1-a}{1+a}\frac{1}{n(n-1)}\right.$$

$$\left. \times [n(a+1) - 1 + (-a)^n]\right\}, \qquad \text{for } n \geq 2 \tag{2.104}$$

2. $a = -1, k = -2$. For this case equation (2.99) becomes

$$\frac{z}{z-1}\,\mathscr{C}(z) = -k\int\frac{z\,dz}{(z-1)^4} + k_0 \tag{2.105}$$

Since $c(0) = 0 = \lim\limits_{z\to\infty}\mathscr{C}(z)$, we have $k_0 = 0$.

Equation (2.105) yields

$$\mathscr{C}(z) = k\,\frac{3z-1}{6z(z-1)^2} \tag{2.106}$$

The inverse of this equation gives

$$c(0) = 0, \quad c(1) = 0$$

$$c(n) = \frac{k(2n-1)}{6}, \qquad \text{for } n \geq 2 \tag{2.107}$$

3. $b = 0, a = 1$, or $(\alpha = 0, k = 1)$. For this case, assuming a step input, equation (2.98) becomes

$$z^2\frac{d\mathscr{C}(z)}{dz} + \mathscr{C}(z) = -\frac{z}{(z-1)^2} \tag{2.108}$$

The solution of this equation yields

$$\mathscr{C}(z) = \frac{z}{z-1} + K_0'e^{1/z} \tag{2.109}$$

To obtain the integration constant K_0', we use the following limiting case for the initial value:

$$\lim\limits_{z\to\infty}\mathscr{C}(z) = c(0) = 1 + K_0' = 0 \tag{2.110}$$

Hence

$$K_0' = -1 \tag{2.111}$$

Substituting this in equation (2.109) and finding the inverse z-transform, we finally obtain:

$$c(n) = u(n) - \frac{1}{n!} \qquad (2.112)$$

where $u(n)$ is the unit step at discrete times.

Simplification of equations before z-transform application[7,38,46]

In certain cases the rational coefficients difference equation could be reduced to a constant coefficients equation by certain function substitutions in the original equation. This reduction simplifies the application of the z-transform to obtain the time solution.

A typical unmixed difference-differential equation with rational coefficients which may be reduced to one with constant coefficients is

$$(n + k + q)(n + k - 1 + q) \ldots (n + 1 + q)y_{n+k}^{(k)}$$
$$+ \, a_{k-1}(n + k - 1 + q) \ldots (n + 1 + q)y_{n+k-1}^{(k-1)} + \ldots$$
$$+ \, a_1(n + 1 + q)y_{n+1}^{(1)} + a_0 y_n = f_n(t) \quad (2.113)$$

where

$$y_{n+1}^{(k)} = \frac{d^k}{dt^k} y_{n+1}(t) \qquad (2.114)$$

and n is a parameter.

The substitution function is

$$y_n = \frac{x_n}{\Gamma(1 + n + q)} \qquad (2.115)$$

Substituting this in equation (2.113), we obtain the following constant coefficient difference equation:

$$x_{n+k}^{(k)} + a_{k-1}x_{n+k-1}^{(k-1)} + \ldots + a_1 x_{n+1}^{(1)} + a_0 x_n$$
$$= \Gamma(1 + q + n)f_n(t) = g_n(t) \quad (2.116)$$

By applying both the Laplace and z-transform to this equation, we can obtain the solution.

1. EXAMPLE

Obtain the solution $y_n(t)$ of the following unmixed difference-differential equation:

$$y_{n+1}^{(1)} + \frac{a}{n + 1} y_n = 0, \qquad \text{with } y_n(0) = \frac{1}{n!}, \qquad a = \text{constant}$$
$$(2.117)$$

Let

$$y_n = \frac{x_n}{\Gamma(n+1)} = \frac{x_n}{n!} \tag{2.118}$$

Substituting the above in (equation 2.117), we have

$$x_{n+1}^{(1)} + ax_n = 0 \tag{2.119}$$

Applying the Laplace transform to equation (2.119), and using the initial value $x_n(0) = y_n(0)n!$, we get

$$sX_{n+1}(s) + aX_n(s) = 1 \tag{2.120}$$

Defining the z-transform of $X_n(s)$,

$$\mathscr{X}(z, s) = \mathscr{J}[X_n(s)] = \sum_{n=0}^{\infty} X_n(s)z^{-n} \tag{2.120a}$$

and applying it to this equation with s constant, we have

$$sz\mathscr{X}(z, s) - szX_0(s) + a\mathscr{X}(z, s) = \frac{z}{z-1} \tag{2.121}$$

This equation reduces to

$$\mathscr{X}(z, s) = \frac{szX_0(s)}{sz + a} + \frac{z}{(z-1)(sz+a)} \tag{2.122}$$

The inverse z-transform of this equation yields

$$X_n(s) = \left(-\frac{a}{s}\right)^n \left[X_0(s) - \frac{1}{s+a}\right] + \frac{1}{s+a} \tag{2.123}$$

We can write for $X_0(s)$ the following form:

$$X_0(s) = \frac{1}{s+a} + K_1(s) \tag{2.124}$$

where $K_1(s)$ is determined from the given initial condition.

If we let $K_1(s) = K_1 / s$, the inverse Laplace transform of equation (2.123) gives

$$x_n(t) = e^{-at} + K_1 \frac{(-a)^n}{n!} t^n \tag{2.125}$$

Using equation (2.118), we obtain for the solution

$$y_n(t) = \frac{e^{-at}}{n!} + K_1 \frac{(-a)^n t^n}{(n!)^2} \tag{2.126}$$

For the case $K_1(s) = 0$ (or $K_1 = 0$), this equation reduces to

$$y_n(t) = \frac{e^{-at}}{n!} \tag{2.127}$$

2.6 Time-varying z-transform
and the system function[10,13,25]

In this section the solution of a general linear time-varying difference equation will be indicated by using the z-transform of the system function. For the cases where closed form solution is not obtainable and the system is slowly varying, an approximate method based on the system function is used. The discussion follows closely Zadeh's work[11,12,26] as applied to time-varying differential equations and the use of the time-varying transform methods.

Assume a time-varying difference equation as follows:

$$[a_\mu(n)E^{-\mu} + a_{\mu-1}(n)E^{-(\mu-1)} + \ldots + a_1(n)E^{-1} + a_0(n)]c_n$$
$$= [b_\lambda(n)E^{-\lambda} + b_{\lambda-1}(n)E^{-(\lambda-1)} + \ldots + b_1(n)E^{-1} + b_0(n)]r_n$$

$$(2.128)$$

with $\mu \geq \lambda$ and c_n, r_n representing the output and input sequences of the system described by equation (2.128). The delay operator E^{-1} is defined as $E^{-k}f_n = f_{n-k}$.

Equation (2.128) could be expressed in a condensed form

$$A(E^{-1}, n)c_n = B(E^{-1}, n)r_n \qquad (2.129)$$

Since the system H is linear, we may define its impulse response $h(n, n - r) = h(n, k)$ by

$$A(E^{-1}, n)h(n, k) = B(E^{-1}, n)\delta_{nk} \qquad (2.130)$$

where the Kronecker delta function δ_{nk} is defined as

$$\delta_{nk} = \begin{cases} 1, & \text{if } n = k \\ 0, & \text{if } n \neq k \end{cases} \qquad (2.131)$$

Using the superposition theorem for linear systems, the output c_n is given as

$$c_n = \sum_{k=0}^{n} h(n, k)r_k \qquad (2.132)$$

It should be noted that $h(n, k)$ is sometimes written as $h(n, n - r)$ as indicated. The impulse response $h(n, k)$ is expressed from equation (2.132) as the amplitude of the pulse occurring at the output at the nth instant as a result of an input pulse of unit amplitude applied at the kth instant.

In analogy to the one-sided z-transform, we define a time-varying z-transform of $h(n, n - r)$:

$$\mathcal{H}(n, z) \triangleq \mathcal{Z}[h(n, n - r)] = \sum_{r=0}^{\infty} h(n, n - r)z^{-r} \qquad (2.133)$$

Setting $k = n - r$ in this equation, we obtain

$$\mathscr{H}(n, z) = \sum_{k=-\infty}^{n} h(n, k)z^{-n+k} = z^{-n}\sum_{k=0}^{n} h(n, k)z^k \qquad (2.134)*$$

The summation on the right-hand side of equation (2.134) represents the response of H to an input signal having the sequence of amplitude $z^0, z^1, z^2, \ldots$. Hence the system transfer function $\mathscr{H}(n, z)$ may be alternately defined by

$$\mathscr{H}(n, z) = \frac{\text{response of } H \text{ to } z^n}{z^n} \qquad (2.135)$$

Input-output relationship

The output at the nth instant may be obtained from the consideration of $\mathscr{C}_n(z)$, where

$$\mathscr{C}_n(z) = \mathscr{R}(z)\mathscr{H}(n, z) \qquad (2.136)$$

where

$$\mathscr{R}(z) \overset{\Delta}{=} \mathscr{J}[r_k] = \sum_{k=0}^{\infty} r_k z^{-k} \qquad (2.137)$$

The output sequence is given by the following inversion integral

$$c_n = \frac{1}{2\pi j} \int_{\Gamma} \mathscr{R}(z)\mathscr{H}(z, n)z^{n-1}\, dz \qquad (2.138)$$

when Γ is a counterclockwise closed contour in the z-plane which encloses the singularities of the integrand.

It should be noted that the index n in equation (2.138) is treated as a parameter; thus c_n could be obtained from the ordinary table of inverse z-transforms, that is, Table I of the Appendix. Furthermore, if $\mathscr{C}_n(z)$ is expanded in power series, the coefficient of z^{-k} is not equal to c_k except for $k = n$. Thus equation (2.136) does not represent the z-transform of the output for all sampling instants.

The z-transform of the output (sometimes referred to as the w-transform)[10] can can be obtained by using the double-difference system function in analogy to the bifrequency system function for the systems described by differential equations.[26] In addition, as noticed, the method of the preceding section yields in some cases the z-transform of the output.

---

* This equality holds because in these discussions we are assuming that no input exists preceding $k = 0$.

Determination of $\mathscr{H}(z, n)$

The system transfer function $\mathscr{H}(z, n)$ satisfies a difference equation which sometimes is easier to solve than the original difference equation (2.128). To obtain the equation for $\mathscr{H}(z, n)$, we take the z-transform of equation (2.130) with respect to the index k to get

$$\sum_{k=0}^{\infty} A(E^{-1}, n)h(n, k)z^k = \sum_{k=0}^{\infty} B(E^{-1}, n)\delta_{nk}z^k \tag{2.139}$$

and noting that $h(n, k) = 0$ for $k > n$, this yields

$$A(E^{-1}, n)\mathscr{H}(z, n)z^n = B(E^{-1}, n)z^n \tag{2.140}$$

Before rewriting equation (2.140) in a more convenient form, we utilize the following identities:

$$E^{-i}\mathscr{H}(z, n)z^n = \mathscr{H}(z, n - i)z^{n-i} = z^{n-i}E^{-i}\mathscr{H}(z, n) \tag{2.141}$$

and

$$E^{-i}z^n = z^{n-i} \tag{2.142}$$

Since $A(E^{-1}, n)$ and $B(E^{-1}, n)$ are polynomials in E^{-1}, using equations (2.141) and (2.142), the left- and right-hand sides of equation (2.140) become

$$A(E^{-1}, n)\mathscr{H}(z, n)z^n = z^n A(z^{-1}E^{-1}, n)\mathscr{H}(z, n) \tag{2.143}$$

and

$$B(E^{-1}, n)z^n = z^n B(z^{-1}, n) \tag{2.144}$$

Therefore $\mathscr{H}(z, n)$ is given from equations (2.143), (2.144), and (2.140) as

$$A(z^{-1}E^{-1}, n)\mathscr{H}(z, n) = B(z^{-1}, n) \tag{2.145}$$

Equation (2.145) is a μth order difference equation with nonconstant coefficients. By adding and subtracting $A(z^{-1}, n)\mathscr{H}(z, n)$ to equation (2.145), we may obtain

$$\mathscr{H}(z, n) = \frac{B(z^{-1}, n)}{A(z^{-1}, n)} + \frac{\left[\sum_{i=0}^{\mu} a_i(n)z^{-i} - \sum_{i=0}^{\mu} a_i(n)z^{-i}E^{-i}\right]\mathscr{H}(z, n)}{A(z^{-1}, n)} \tag{2.146}$$

or

$$\mathscr{H}(z, n) = \frac{B(z^{-1}, n)}{A(z^{-1}, n)} + \frac{\sum_{i=1}^{\mu} a_i(n)z^{-i}[\mathscr{H}(z, n) - \mathscr{H}(z, n - i)]}{A(z^{-1}, n)} \tag{2.147}$$

The second term on the right side of equation (2.147) is small compared to the first if either $\mathcal{H}(z, n)$ changes slowly with n or if the changes are small. This suggests that equation (2.147) can be solved by iterative methods. Thus if $\mathcal{H}_k(z, n)$ is the kth iterated solution we have

$$\mathcal{H}_{k+1}(z, n) = \mathcal{H}_0(z, n) + \frac{\sum_{i=1}^{\mu} a_i(n) z^{-i} [\mathcal{H}_k(z, n) - \mathcal{H}_k(z, n - i)]}{A(z^{-1}, n)}$$

(2.148)

where

$$\mathcal{H}_0(z, n) = \frac{B(z^{-1}, n)}{A(z^{-1}, n)}$$

(2.149)

is called the *frozen transfer function*.

Equation (2.148) is very useful in obtaining an approximate solution for slowly varying discrete systems. In some cases the frozen transfer function will give a good indication of the response behavior. Such situations may arise in sampled-data systems where the sampling rate changes very slowly. Another application of this technique is in the analysis of automatic gain control where the pulse-frequency modulation varies according to a sinusoidal law. Such a system will be studied as an illustrative example.

Furthermore, if $\mathcal{H}_0(z, n)$ has its poles inside the unit circle for all n, all the iterative solutions $H_1, H_2, \ldots$ will have their poles inside the unit circle and vice versa.

ILLUSTRATIVE EXAMPLE

The following example was studied by Tratakowskii[13] using a similar approach. A more detailed analysis of this system will be discussed and exact conditions on stability as well as the response approximation presented. The system under study is referred to as "pulse feedback with variable pulse repetition frequency." This system is shown in Fig. 2.5 and its equivalent feedback system in Fig. 2.6. The automatic amplification control in a receiver of pulse signals of constant amplitude when an

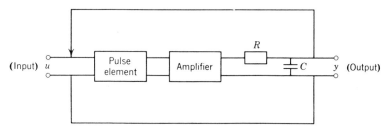

FIGURE 2.5   Example for the variable pulse feedback system.

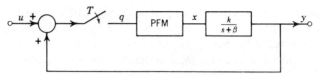

FIGURE 2.6   Block diagram of the variable pulse feedback system.

RC circuit is used for filtering in the AVC leads to the study of such a system as shown in Fig. 2.5.

The pulse-frequency modulator (PFM) yields the following equation

$$x(t) = q(t_n)[u(t - t_n) - u(t - t_n - h)], \qquad t_n < t < t_{n+1}$$

(2.150)

where t_n is the time of sampling which is determined by

$$t_n - t_{n-1} = T(1 + M \sin \Omega n)$$

(2.151)

where T is the average sampling period.

When $t_0 = 0$, h is a positive constant with the following constraint:

$$h \le T(1 - |M|)$$

(2.152)

The relation between y and x for Fig. 2.6 is given by the following differential equation:

$$\dot{y} + \beta y = kx$$

(2.153)

The solution of equation (2.153) yields

$$y(t) = y(t_0)e^{-\beta(t-t_0)} + ke^{-\beta t} \int_{t_0}^{t} x(\tau)e^{\beta \tau} \, d\tau$$

(2.154)

In particular when $t = t_n$ and $t_0 = t_{n-1}$, since $x(t) = 0$, for $t_{n-1} + h < t < t_n$, equation (2.154) yields

$$y(t_n) = y(t_{n-1})e^{-\beta(t_n-t_{n-1})} + ke^{-\beta t_n} \int_{t_{n-1}}^{t_{n-1}+h} q(t_{n-1})e^{\beta \tau} \, d\tau$$

(2.155)

Using equation (2.151) in (2.155), we obtain

$$y(t_n) = y(t_{n-1})e^{-\beta T(1+M \sin \Omega n)}$$

$$+ \frac{k}{\beta} q(t_{n-1})e^{-\beta T(1+M \sin \Omega n)}(e^{\beta h} - 1) \quad (2.156)$$

Let

$$\alpha = \beta T, \quad \gamma = \frac{h}{T}, \quad k_0 = \frac{k}{\beta}, \quad y(t_n) = y(n), \quad q(t_n) = q(n)$$

(2.157)

and assuming $\alpha \ll 1$ or $\beta h \ll 1$, we have from equation (2.156)

$$y(n) = [1 - \alpha(1 + M \sin \Omega n)]y(n - 1)$$
$$+ k_0\alpha\gamma[1 - \alpha(1 + M \sin \Omega n)]q(n - 1) \quad (2.158)$$

From Fig. 2.6, we have for the feedback equation

$$q(n) = u(n) + y(n) \quad (2.159)$$

Substituting equation (2.159) in equation (2.158), we get

$$y(n) = (1 + k_0\alpha\gamma)[1 - \alpha(1 + M \sin \Omega n)]y(n - 1)$$
$$+ k_0\alpha\gamma[1 - \alpha(1 + M \sin \Omega n)]u(n - 1) \quad (2.160)$$

The frozen transfer function is simply obtained by taking the z-transform of equation (2.160) and considering n as a parameter [this is seen from equation (2.149)]. Therefore

$$\mathscr{H}_0(z, n) = \frac{k_0\alpha\gamma[1 - \alpha(1 + M \sin \Omega n)]z^{-1}}{1 - (1 + k_0\alpha\gamma)[1 - \alpha(1 + M \sin \Omega n)]z^{-1}} \quad (2.161)$$

If we assume a slow pulse-frequency modulation, that is,

$$\alpha M \ll \frac{1}{\Omega} \quad (2.162)$$

the system function $\mathscr{H}(z, n)$ can be approximated by the frozen transfer function or by $\mathscr{H}_1(z, n)$. The response of the system for a step input has been studied for different Ω and α/β and the exact and approximate (using the frozen transfer function) responses are shown in Figs. 2.7 and 2.8. As expected, the smaller the quantity T with respect to $2\pi/\Omega$ the better is the approximation.

Equation (2.160) describes a first-order time-varying difference equation, which can be written as

$$y(n) = a(n)y(n - 1) + b(n)u(n - 1) \quad (2.163)$$

From this equation if $a(n)$ and $b(n)$ are bounded (as is usually the case) and supposing $a(n) \neq 0$,* then the system is stable if and only if

$$\lim_{N \to \infty} \frac{1}{N} \sum_{n=1}^{N} \ln |a(n)| < 0 \quad (2.164)$$

A sufficient condition for stability requires that $|a(n)| < 1$ for all n. In this example, $|a(n)| < 1$, is the same as the condition that the pole of the frozen transfer function [see equation (2.161)] should lie inside the unit circle. Hence the sufficient condition for stability (for $M > 0$) is

$$-\frac{1}{\gamma\alpha} \frac{\alpha(1 - M) - 2}{\alpha(1 - M) - 1} < k_0 < \frac{1}{\gamma} \frac{1 - M}{1 - \alpha(1 - M)} \quad (2.165)$$

---

* The same condition for stability can be proven also if $a(n) = 0$.

For the plots of Figs. 2.7 and 2.8 the preceding condition is satisfied. Thus the system is stable.

To obtain a better approximation, the first iterative solution from equation (2.148) could be used, and for this example

$$\mathcal{H}_1(z, n) = \mathcal{H}_0(z, n) + \frac{a_1(n)z^{-1}[\mathcal{H}_0(z, n) - \mathcal{H}_0(z, n - 1)]}{a_0(n) + a_1(n)z^{-1}}$$

(2.166)

where

$$a_1(n) = -(1 + k_0\alpha\gamma)[1 - \alpha(1 + M \sin \Omega n)]$$

(2.167)

$$a_0(n) = 1$$

(2.167a)

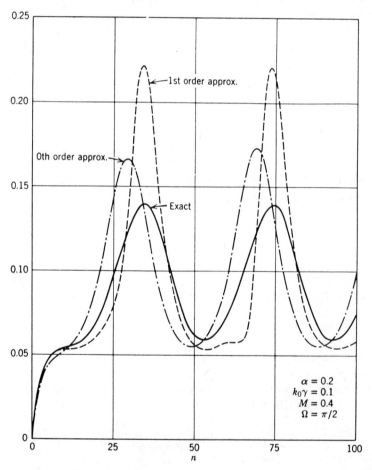

FIGURE 2.7 Exact and approximate response of system in Fig. 2.6 for a step input.

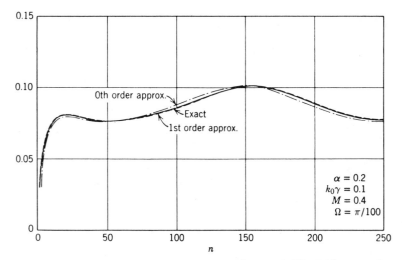

FIGURE 2.8.   Exact and approximate response of system in Fig. 2.6 for a step input.

and

$$\mathscr{H}_0(z, n) = \frac{B(z^{-1}, n)}{A(z^{-1}, n)} = \frac{k_0 \alpha \gamma[(1 - \alpha(1 + M \sin \Omega n)]}{a_0(n) + a_1(n)z^{-1}}$$

$$= \frac{b_1(n)}{a_0(n) + a_1(n)z^{-1}} \qquad (2.168)$$

It may be noticed that if the pole of $\mathscr{H}_0(z, n)$ is inside the unit circle for all n, so is the pole of $\mathscr{H}_1(z, n)$ and similarly for other higher-order iterative solutions. The response using the first-order iterative solution is also shown in Figs. 2.7 and 2.8.

2.7 Double z-transformation* and solution of partial difference equations[21,23,41,49]

Partial difference equations arise in many applications such as probability theory, boundary value problems, lattice network, and transmission lines. The systematic solution of such equations can be performed using the double z-transformation (or two-dimensional z-transform).

This transform is defined as follows:

$$U(z, w) \triangleq \mathscr{Z}_w[u(n, m)] \triangleq \sum_{n=0}^{\infty} \sum_{m=0}^{\infty} u(n, m)z^{-n}w^{-m} \qquad (2.169)$$

where $\mathscr{Z}_w$ denotes the zw-transform of $u(n, m)$.

---

* Also referred to in mathematical literature as bivariate generating function.[49]

We apply the zw-transform to the following functions to obtain

$$\mathcal{Y}_w[u(n+1, m)] = \sum_{n=0}^{\infty} \sum_{m=0}^{\infty} u(n+1, m)z^{-n}w^{-m}$$

$$= z\left[U(z, w) - \sum_{m=0}^{\infty} u(0, m)w^{-m} \right] \qquad (2.170)$$

$$\mathcal{Y}_w[u(n, m+1)] = w\left[U(z, w) - \sum_{n=0}^{\infty} u(n, 0)z^{-n} \right] \qquad (2.171)$$

$$\mathcal{Y}_w[u(n+1, m+1)] = zw\left[U(z, w) - \sum_{n=0}^{\infty} u(n, 0)z^{-n} \right.$$

$$\left. - \sum_{m=0}^{\infty} u(0, m)w^{-m} + u(0, 0) \right] \qquad (2.172)$$

Similarly, we can extend this procedure to obtain the general zw-transform of $u(n+a, m+b)$. This transform is given as follows and can be easily derived from procedure given,

$$\mathcal{Y}_w[u(n+a, m+b)] = \sum_{n=0}^{\infty} \sum_{m=0}^{\infty} u(n+a, m+b)z^{-n}w^{-m}$$

$$= z^a w^b\left[U(z, w) - \sum_{n=0}^{\infty} \sum_{m=0}^{b-1} u(n, m)z^{-n}w^{-m} \right.$$

$$- \sum_{n=0}^{a-1} \sum_{m=0}^{\infty} u(n, m)z^{-n}w^{-m}$$

$$\left. + \sum_{n=0}^{a-1} \sum_{m=0}^{b-1} u(n, m)z^{-n}w^{-m} \right]$$

$$(2.173)$$

Equation (2.173) can be readily used to obtain zw-transformation of any order linear partial difference equations. By successive inversion with respect to w and z, the discrete time function $u(n, m)$ can be obtained. This procedure is illustrated by the following example.

ILLUSTRATIVE EXAMPLE

We consider in this example a partial difference equation which arises in probability theory. Obtain $u(n, m)$ which denotes the probability of m successes in n trials and which satisfy the following partial difference equation:

$$u(n+1, m+1) - qu(n, m+1) - pu(n, m) = 0 \qquad (2.174)$$

The boundary condition on the n-axis is $u(n, 0) = q^n$ for $n \geq 0$. The number p denotes the probability for success in independent series of trials, and $q = 1 - p$ denotes the probability of failures. Applying zw-transform to equation (2.174),

$$zw\left[U(z, w) - \sum_{n=0}^{\infty} u(n, 0)z^{-n} - \sum_{m=0}^{\infty} u(0, m)w^{-m} + u(0, 0)\right]$$
$$- qw\left[U(z, w) - \sum_{n=0}^{\infty} u(n, 0)z^{-n}\right] - pU(z, w) = 0$$

$$(2.175)$$

From the formulation of the problem it is evident that $u(0, m) = \begin{cases} 0, & m > 0 \\ 1, & m = 0 \end{cases}$. Therefore equation (2.175) becomes

$$zw\left[U(z, w) - \sum_{n=0}^{\infty} \left(\frac{z}{q}\right)^{-n}\right] - qw\left[U(z, w) - \sum_{n=0}^{\infty} \left(\frac{z}{q}\right)^{-n}\right]$$
$$- pU(z, w) = 0 \quad (2.176)$$

or

$$U(z, w)(zw - qw - p) = (zw - qw)\sum_{n=0}^{\infty} \left(\frac{z}{q}\right)^{-n} \quad (2.176a)$$

Hence,

$$U(z, w) = \frac{\displaystyle\sum_{n=0}^{\infty} \left(\frac{z}{q}\right)^{-n}}{1 - \left(\dfrac{p}{zw - qw}\right)} = \frac{\displaystyle\sum_{n=0}^{\infty} \left(\frac{z}{q}\right)^{-n}}{1 - \dfrac{1}{w}\left(\dfrac{p}{z - q}\right)} \quad (2.177)$$

Taking the inverse w-transform of (2.177) we obtain

$$\mathcal{U}(z, m) = \sum_{n=0}^{\infty} \left(\frac{z}{q}\right)^{-n}\left(\frac{p}{z - q}\right)^{m} = \left(\frac{p/z}{1 - q/z}\right)^{m}\sum_{n=0}^{\infty} \left(\frac{q}{z}\right)^{n} \quad (2.178)$$
$$= \left(\frac{p}{z}\right)^{m}\left(1 - \frac{q}{z}\right)^{-m}\left(1 - \frac{q}{z}\right)^{-1} = \left(\frac{p}{z}\right)^{m}\left(1 - \frac{q}{z}\right)^{-1-m}$$

or

$$\mathcal{U}(z, m) = \left(\frac{p}{z}\right)^{m}\left[1 + \binom{-1 - m}{1}\left(\frac{q}{z}\right)(-1)\right.$$
$$\left. + \binom{-1 - m}{2}\frac{q^2}{z^2}(-1)^2 + \ldots\right] \quad (2.179)$$

The coefficient of the z^{-n} term is

$$p^m q^{n-m}\left[\binom{-1 - m}{n - m}\right](-1)^{n-m}, \quad n \geq m \quad (2.180)$$

Therefore the inverse z-transform of equation (2.179) becomes

$$u(n, m) = p^m q^{n-m}$$

$$\times \left[\frac{(-1 - m)(-2 - m)\ldots(-n + m - m)}{(n - m)!} \right](-1)^{n-m}$$

$$= p^m q^{n-m} \left[\frac{n(n - 1)\ldots(m + 1)}{(n - m)!} \right] \qquad (2.181)$$

Finally, $u(n, m)$ yields

$$u(n, m) = p^m q^{n-m} \binom{n}{m} \qquad (2.182)$$

REFERENCES

1. Boole, G., *A Treatise on the Calculus of Finite Differences*, G.E. Stechert, New York, 1926.

2. Jordan, C., *Calculus of Finite Differences*, Chelsea Publishing Co., New York, 1960.

3. Milne-Thomson, L. M., *The Calculus of Finite Difference*, Macmillan Co., London, 1951.

4. Goldberg, S., *Introduction to Difference Equations with Illustrative Examples from Economics, Psychology and Sociology*, John Wiley and Sons, New York, 1958.

5. Pinney, E., *Ordinary Difference-Differential Equations*, University of California Press, 1959.

6. Gelfund, A. O., *Differenzenrechnung*, Moscow-Leningrad, 1952 (in Russian).

7. Levy, H., and F. Lessman, *Finite Difference Equations*, Macmillan Co., New York, 1961.

8. Norlund, N. E., *Vorlesungen uber Differenzenrechnung*, Verlag Von Julius, Springer, Berlin, 1924.

9. Samuelson, P. A., *Foundation of Economic Analysis*, Harvard University Press, 1947.

10. Friedland, B., "Time-Varying Sampled-Data Systems," *Proc. Second Midwest Symposium on Circuit Theory*, Michigan State University, East Lansing, December 3–4, 1956.

11. Zadeh, L. A., "Circuit Analysis of Linear Varying-Parameter Networks," *J. Appl. Phys.*, Vol. 21, November 1950, pp. 1171–1177.

12. Zadeh, L. A., "On Stability of Linear Varying Parameter Systems," *J. Appl. Phys.*, Vol. 22, April 1951, pp. 402–405.

13. Tratakowskii, G. P., "Application of Simulation in Analyzing Linear Pulse Systems with Variable Parameters," *Avtomatica i Telemekh*, Vol. 20, May 1959, pp. 559–566.

14. Aseltine, J. A., "A Transform Method for Linear Time-Varying Systems," *J. Appl. Phys.* Vol. 25, June 1954, pp. 761–764.

15. Cooke, R. C., *Infinite Matrices and Sequence Spaces*, Macmillan Co., London, 1950.

16. Ho, E. C., and H. Davis, "Generalized Operational Calculus for Time-Varying Networks," Dept. of Engineering Report 54–71, July 1954, University of California, Los Angeles.

17. Bubb, F. W., "A New Linear Operational Calculus," U.S.A.F. Technical Report No. 6581, May 1951, Dayton, Ohio.

18. Madwed, A., "Number Series Method of Solving Linear and Nonlinear Differential Equations," Instrumentation Laboratory Report No. 6445-T-26, April 1950, M.I.T., Cambridge, Massachusetts.

19. Raymond, F. H., "Analyse du Fonctionnement des Systemes Physiques Discontinus (et son Application aux Servomechanismes)," *Ann. Telecomm.*, Vol. 4, July, August, October 1949, pp. 250–256, 367–314, 347–357.

20. Poincaré, H., "Sur les Équations Linéaires aux Différentielles Ordinaires et aux Différences Finies," *Am. J. Math.*, Vol. 7, 1885, pp. 213–217, 237–258.

21. Lawden, D. F., "On the Solution of Linear Difference Equations," *Mathematical Gazette*, Vol. 36, 1952, pp. 193–1971.

22. Bellman, R., and K. L. Cooke, *Differential-Difference Equations*, Academic Press, New York and London, 1962.

23. Meschkowski, H., *Differenzengleichungen*, Vandenhoeck and Ruprecht, Göttingen, 1959.

24. Doetsch, G., *Handbuch der Laplace Transformation*, Basel und Stuttgart, 1956.

25. Hufnegel, R. G., "Analysis of Aperiodically-Sampled-Data Feedback Control Systems," Ph.D. Thesis, Dept. of Electrical Engineering, Cornell University, Ithaca, New York, 1954.

26. Zadeh, L. A., "Frequency Analysis of Variable Networks," *Proc. IRE*, Vol. 38, 1950, pp. 291–298.

27. Kaplan, W., *Operational Methods for Linear Systems*, Addison Wesley Publishing Co., Reading, Massachusetts, 1962.

28. Jury, E. I., and F. J. Mullin, "A Note on the Operational Solution of Linear Difference Equations," *J. Franklin Inst.*, Vol. 266, No. 3, September 1958, pp. 189–205.

29. Aseltine, J., *Transform Method in Linear Systems*, McGraw-Hill Book Co., New York, 1958.

30. Montel, P., *Leçons sur les Recurrences et leurs Applications*, Gauthier-Villars, Paris, 1957.

31. Jury, E. I., *Sampled-Data Control Systems*, John Wiley and Sons, New York, 1958.

32. Monroe, J., *Digital Processes for Sampled-Data Systems*, John Wiley and Sons, New York, 1962.

33. Fort, T., "Linear Difference Equations and the Dirichlet Series Transform," *Am. Math. Monthly*, Vol. 62, No. 9, 1955, p. 641.

34. Neufeld, T., "On the Operational Solution of Linear Mixed Difference-Differential Equations," *Cambridge Phil. Soc.*, Vol. 30, 1934, p. 289.

35. Brown, B., *The Mathematical Theory of Linear Systems*, John Wiley and Sons, New York, 1961.

36. Pai, M. A., "The Operational Solution of Difference-Differential Equations Using the Modified z-Transform," *IRE, PGAC*, October 1962, pp. 124–126.

37. Tschauner, J., "Über eine Verallgemeinerung der Exponentialreihe," *Math. Zeitschr.*, Vol. 79, 1962, pp. 239–242.

38. Tschauner, J., "Erzeugende Funktionen von Zugeordneten Kugelfunktionen," *Math. Zeitschr.*, Vol. 78, 1962, pp. 131–134.

39. Erdelyi, A., *Higher Transcendental Functions*, McGraw-Hill Book Co., New York, 1955.

40. Cypkin, J. A., *Differenzengleichungen der Impuls und Regeltechnik*, Berlin, 1956.

41. Miller, K. S., *An Introduction to the Calculus of Finite Difference and Difference Equations*, Henry Holt and Co., New York, 1960.

42. Ku, Y. H., and A. A. Wolf, "Laurent-Cauchy Transforms for Analysis of Linear Systems Described by Differential-Difference and Sum Equations," *Proc. IRE*, Vol. 48, May 1960, pp. 923–931.

43. Jury, E. I., Discussion of the above reference, *Proc. IRE*, Vol. 48, No. 12, December 1960.

44. Mikusinski, Jan, *Operational Calculus*, Pergamon Press, London, 1959.

45. Jury, E. I., "Contribution to the Modified z-Transform," *J. Franklin Inst.*, Vol. 270, August 1960, pp. 118–129.

46. Tschauner, J., *Einführung in die Theorie der Abtasysteme*, Verlag R. Oldenbourg, Munich, 1960.

47. Cypkin, J., *Theory of Pulse Systems*, State Press for Physics and Mathematical Literature, Moscow, Russia, 1958 (in Russian).

48. Stone, W. M., "A List of Generalized Laplace Transforms," *Iowa State College Journal of Science*, Vol. 22, April 1948, pp. 215–225.

49. Feller, W., *An Introduction to Probability Theory and Its Applications*, John Wiley and Sons, New York (second edition), 1959, Chapter XI.

50. Wloka, J., "Über die Anwendung der Operatorenreihnung auf Lineare Differential-Differenzengleichungen mit Konstanten Koeffizienten," *J. fur die Riene und Augewandte Mathematik*, Vol. 202, October 1959, pp. 107–128.

51. Fiévet M., *On the Analysis of Feedback Systems with Transportation Lag Using the Modified z-Transform*, Master of Science Project, Dept. of E. E., University of California, Berkeley, June, 1963.

52. Alper P., *Two Dimensional z-Transforms*, Technological University Electronics Laboratory, Delft-Netherlands, August, 1963.

53. Gradstein, E. S., and E. M. Ryzik, *Tables of Integrals, Sums and Products*, State Press for Physical and Mathematical Literature, Moscow, 1962, p. 37, Formula 1.223.

3

STABILITY CONSIDERATION

FOR LINEAR DISCRETE

SYSTEMS

One of the main problems in the study of linear systems is the determination of stability. For linear continuous systems, the problem of stability reduces to the necessary and sufficient condition for the roots of $F(s)$ (system characteristic equation) to lie in the left half of the s-plane.[8] These conditions have been studied in detail and as a result the criteria of Hurwitz-Routh[8] and of Liènard-Chipart[8,36] completely solve the problem analytically. For linear discrete systems the condition of stability reduces to obtaining the necessary and sufficient condition for the roots of $F(z)$ (discrete system characteristic equation) to lie inside the unit circle in the z-plane.[9,17] Although these conditions have been studied by Schur,[28] Cohn,[2] and Marden,[4] the final stability criteria to be obtained from these papers are rather complicated and not readily applicable for system analysis and design. Therefore in this chapter a complete study of this problem is undertaken where the final solution of the stability criteria in the forms of determinant,[1] table,[12] and division[14] methods are obtained.

Stability tests within the unit unit circle are very important in many fields. For instance, the stability of difference equations with constant or periodically varying coefficients,[22] the stability of limit cycles in nonlinear discrete systems, the stability test of linear systems with randomly varying parameters, the convergence of iterative computational rule using digital computers,[21] the stability of periodic regimes in nonlinear systems with piecewise linear characteristics, and many others all reduce to stability tests within the unit circle. In view of these applications, it is felt that concerted efforts should be directed toward stability tests within the unit circle as well as the conditions on the roots distribution of $F(z)$ within the unit circle.

3.1 Definition of stability[17]

A linear discrete system is considered to be stable if to all bounded inputs there always correspond bounded outputs.*

The stability condition can be obtained if we separate the output (system response) into steady-state and transient terms. This can be easily established if we write the output z-transform $\mathscr{C}(z)$ as

$$\mathscr{C}(z) = \mathscr{E}(z)\mathscr{H}(z) \tag{3.1}$$

where $\mathscr{E}(z)$ and $\mathscr{H}(z)$ are the z-transforms of the input and the system transfer function respectively. The output related to the steady-state part (or due to the input function) can be obtained from the inverse z-transform formula as the sum of the following typical term:

$$\text{residue of } [\mathscr{E}(z) \cdot \mathscr{H}(z)]|_{z=z_m} z_m^{n-1} \tag{3.2}$$

where z_m is a typical singularity of $\mathscr{E}(z)$. Since the input is bounded, that is,

$$|z_m| \leq 1 \tag{3.3}$$

then the output part resulting from this input is also bounded.

Similarly, a typical transient term of the output can be written

$$\text{residue of } [\mathscr{H}(z) \cdot \mathscr{E}(z)]|_{z=z_k} z_k^{n-1} \tag{3.4}$$

where z_k is a typical singularity of $\mathscr{H}(z)$. From this expression, it is evident that in order for the ouptut to be bounded, the following conditions should exist.

$$|z_k| \leq 1 \tag{3.5}$$

or all the poles (singularities) of $\mathscr{H}(z)$ should lie inside or on the unit circle.

When one singularity is on the unit circle, that is, $|z_k| = 1$, then from the physical point of view such a system should be regarded as unstable, since a very small change in the physical constants may throw the critical singularity from the boundary into the exterior of the unit circle, causing actual instability. Summarizing this remark, we may state the following fundamental theorem: If all the singular points of the discrete system transfer function $\mathscr{H}(z)$ are located inside the unit circle, the system is stable. If at least one singular point lies outside or on the unit circle, the system is unstable.

---

* These outputs are considered only at discrete intervals of time (sampling instants). For a continuous output of a discrete system, the modified z-transform of the output should be used instead of equation (3.1).

This condition of stability readily applies to difference equations with constant and periodic coefficients. However, care should be exercised in defining the characteristic equation for each of these forms.

For time-varying discrete systems (or time-varying difference equations), the condition for stability depends on the transfer function $\mathcal{H}(z, n)$ for all values of n. The determination of stability for the time-varying case is rather involved and is discussed separately.

3.2 Stability condition for linear time-varying discrete systems

The definition of stability for this case is the same as that for the time invariant case discussed in the preceding section. It can be presented as:* A system is stable if and only if its impulse response $h(n, k)$ satisfies the following condition; for some N the following inequality exists:

$$\sum_{k=0}^{n} |h(n, k)| < N < \infty, \tag{3.6}$$

for all n.

Since the input r_k is bounded, there is an M such that $|r_k| \leq M$ for all k. Thus from the output relationship,

$$|c_n| \leq \sum_{k=0}^{n} |h(n, k)| \, |r_k| \leq M \sum_{k=0}^{n} |h(n, k)| \leq NM \tag{3.7}$$

This proves the sufficiency of the stability condition.

To prove the necessity of the condition, suppose it is not satisfied. Then for any fixed $P < \infty$ there is a n_0 such that

$$\sum_{k=0}^{n_0} |h(n_0, k)| > P. \tag{3.7a}$$

Choose the inputs r_k,

$$r_k = \begin{cases} +1 & \text{if } h(n_0, k) \geq 0 \\ -1 & \text{if } h(n_0, k) < 0 \end{cases} \tag{3.8}$$

We then have

$$c_{n_0} = \sum_{k=0}^{n_0} r_k h(n_0, k) = \sum_{k=0}^{n_0} |h(n_0, k)| > P \tag{3.8a}$$

Therefore for all $P < \infty$ we can find an input uniformly bounded by 1 and an n_0 such that $c_{n_0} > P$; hence the system is not stable.

---

* An alternate and more precise definition of stability is: A system is stable if for any input sequence uniformly bounded by 1, that is, $|r_k| \leq 1$, for all k, there is a $P < \infty$ such that $|c_n| \leq P$ for all n.

If every $h(n, k)$ is bounded, it is necessary only to find the limit of $\sum\limits_{k=0}^{n} |h(n, k)|$ as $n \to \infty$.

From the definition of $\mathcal{H}(z, n)$, it follows that the preceding stability requirement is equivalent to the condition that $\mathcal{H}(z, n)$ be analytic for $|z| \geq 1$, which can be shown as follows:

From the definition of $\mathcal{H}(z, n)$ we have

$$\mathcal{H}(z, n) = \sum_{k=0}^{n} h(n, k) z^{k-n} \tag{3.8b}$$

Letting $k = n - j$ this is equivalent to

$$\mathcal{H}(z, n) = \sum_{j=0}^{n} h(n, n - j) z^{-j} \tag{3.8c}$$

For $|z| \geq 1$ we have

$$\mathcal{H}(z, n) \leq \sum_{j=0}^{n} |h(n, n - j)| \, |z^{-j}| \leq \sum_{j=0}^{n} |h(n, n - j)| < N < \infty \tag{3.8d}$$

Therefore if the system is stable, $\mathcal{H}(z, n)$ is analytic on and outside the unit circle. Furthermore, if $\mathcal{H}(z, n)$ is analytic for $|z| \geq 1$, it requires that the radius of convergence of the series is strictly less than unity. From Cauchy-Hadamard[33] theorem we know that such a radius is given by

$$\limsup_{j \to \infty} |h(n, n - j)|^{1/j} \tag{3.8e}$$

It is also known that if this limit is strictly less than unity, the series $\{|h(n, n - j)|\}$ is absolutely convergent and hence for all n there exists an N such that

$$\sum_{j=0}^{n} |h(n, n - j)| \leq N < \infty \tag{3.8f}$$

Hence the necessary and sufficient condition for the stability of linear time-varying discrete system is that equation (3.8 f) be satisfied for all n. By a similar reasoning the stability requirement for the time invariant case discussed in the preceding section can be similarly established.

3.3 Tests for stability

We shall concentrate in this section only on the various analytic tests. However, we may mention that there exist several graphical tests, such as the Nyquist diagram and the root-locus method, which are discussed in detail elsewhere in the literature.

The test involved is the determination of the necessary and sufficient conditions for the roots of the following polynomial in z, which represents the system characteristic equation to lie inside the unit circle in the z-plane:

$$F(z) = a_0 + a_1 z + a_2 z^2 + \ldots + a_k z^k + \ldots + a_n z^n$$

$$\text{with } a_n > 0 \quad (3.9)$$

The various analytic tests can be summarized as follows.

Bilinear transformation:[5,9,17]

If the closed region $|z| \leq 1$ is mapped into the region Re $[w] \leq 0$ of an auxiliary w-plane, the condition for stability becomes exactly the Hurwitz condition. The bilinear transformation

$$z = \frac{w + 1}{w - 1} \quad (3.10)$$

is the simplest possible mapping of the unit circle into the left half of the w-plane. In this manner the nth-degree polynomial in z is converted to a ratio of nth-degree polynomials in w and the numerator is tested for its zeros in the left half of the w-plane.

Let the system characteristic equation in the z-plane be defined by (3.9) with $a_n > 0$. When mapped into the w-plane by (3.10), the zeros of the w-polynomial are given by

$$b_n w^n + b_{n-1} w^{n-1} + b_{n-2} w^{n-2} + \ldots + b_0 = 0, \quad b_n > 0$$

$$(3.11)$$

The relationship between the a_k and b_k is

$$b_{n-k} = \sum_{j=0}^{n} a_{n-j} \left[\binom{n-j}{k} - \binom{j}{1}\binom{n-j}{k-1} \right.$$

$$+ \binom{j}{2}\binom{n-j}{k-2} + \ldots + (-1)^{k-1}$$

$$\left. \times \binom{j}{k-1}\binom{n-j}{1} + (-1)^k \binom{j}{k} \right] \quad (3.12)$$

where

$$\binom{j}{k} = \frac{j!}{k!\,(j-k)!} \quad (3.13)$$

This procedure involves a complicated algebraic manipulation since the bilinear transformation, and the final constraints on the original polynomial coefficients are rather involved. Thus this procedure has not been used successfully for design or parameter change for systems higher than second or third order. However, it has the advantage that we can

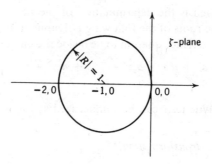

FIGURE 3.1   A shifted unit circle in the ζ-plane.

apply the Routh-Hurwitz criterion or the simpler criterion of Liènard-Chipart to the transformed polynomial in the w-plane.

In some cases the discrete system can be described in the ζ-plane[6,7] which requires a stability test for the shifted unit circle of Fig. 3.1. A criterion similar to that of Hurwitz has been developed for the shifted unit circle which offers an alternate method of testing the stability of linear discrete systems.[37,38]

3.4 Stability test directly applied in the z-plane

A logical and useful approach to the problem of stability is to be able to obtain a stability criterion directly in the z-plane, thus avoiding any transformation as in (3.10). Such a stability criterion was first established by Schur-Cohn in 1922 and further discussed by Fujiwara[3] in 1924. However, the original form of this criterion is quite complicated; Cohn's has $2n - 1$ constraints and requires the evaluation of two determinants of order n, whereas in the Hurwitz and Liènard-Chipart criteria, only n

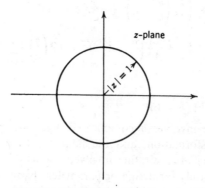

FIGURE 3.2   Unit circle in the z-plane.

constraints and one nth-order determinant are required. Thus this criterion has not proven successful and is very rarely used by engineers for higher-order systems.

The original form of the Schur-Cohn criterion for complex coefficients can be stated as follows. The polynomial

$$F(z) = a_0 + a_1 z + a_2 z^2 + \ldots + a_k z^k + \ldots + a_n z^n$$

has all its roots* inside the unit circle, as shown in Fig. 3.2, if and only if the following constraints are fulfilled.

$$|\Delta_k| < 0, \qquad k\text{-odd}$$
$$|\Delta_k| > 0, \qquad k\text{-even} \tag{3.14}$$

where the matrix Δ_k represents[4]

$$
\Delta_k =
\begin{bmatrix}
a_0 & 0 & 0 & \ldots & 0 & a_n & a_{n-1} & \ldots & a_{n-k+1} \\
a_1 & a_0 & 0 & \ldots & 0 & 0 & a_n & \ldots & a_{n-k+2} \\
\cdot & \cdot & & & & & & & \\
\cdot & \cdot & & & & & & & \\
\cdot & \cdot & & & & & & & \\
a_{k-1} & a_{k-2} & a_{k-3} & \ldots & a_0 & 0 & 0 & \ldots & a_n \\
\bar{a}_n & 0 & 0 & \ldots & 0 & \bar{a}_0 & \bar{a}_1 & \ldots & \bar{a}_{k-1} \\
\bar{a}_{n-1} & \bar{a}_n & 0 & \ldots & 0 & 0 & \bar{a}_0 & \ldots & \bar{a}_{k-2} \\
\cdot & \cdot & \cdot & & \cdot & \cdot & \cdot & & \cdot \\
\cdot & \cdot & \cdot & & & \cdot & \cdot & & \cdot \\
\cdot & \cdot & \cdot & & & & & & \cdot \\
\bar{a}_{n-k+1} & \bar{a}_{n-k+2} & \bar{a}_{n-k+3} & \ldots & \bar{a}_n & & & \ldots & \bar{a}_0
\end{bmatrix}
$$

$$k = 1, 2, \ldots, n$$
$$\bar{a}_k = \text{complex conjugate of } a_k \tag{3.15}$$

Recently, this criterion was significantly simplified, and three forms of stability criteria were derived; the analogs of the Hurwitz-Liènard-Chipart, Routh, and the continued fraction expansion methods for the continuous case. These are formulated in the following discussions.

3.5 Determinant method[1,15,30]

The determinant method developed in this section is similar to the Hurwitz or Liènard-Chipart method for the continuous case. Here the stability constraints are formulated in algebraic equations in terms of the coefficients of the polynomial $F(z)$. The derivation of this method is based on the major simplifications of the Schur-Cohn determinants which arise by assuming that the coefficients of $F(z)$ are all real, an assumption which is

---

* In the following discussions, the roots of a polynomial are also referred to as zeros.

satisfied in physical systems. The five major simplifications* which finally led to the concise formulation of the constraints are briefly discussed as follows.

1. The determinant $|\Delta_k|$ given in equation (3.15) can be presented as

$$|\Delta_k| = |X_k + Y_k| \, |X_k - Y_k| \qquad (3.16)$$

where X_k and Y_k are the following matrices:

$$X_k = \begin{bmatrix} a_0 & a_1 & a_2 & \ldots & a_{k-1} \\ 0 & a_0 & a_1 & a_2 & a_{k-2} \\ \cdot & \cdot & \cdot & \cdot & \cdot \\ \cdot & \cdot & \cdot & \cdot & \cdot \\ \cdot & \cdot & \cdot & \cdot & \cdot \\ 0 & 0 & 0 & \ldots & a_1 \\ 0 & 0 & 0 & \ldots & a_0 \end{bmatrix} \qquad (3.17)$$

and

$$Y_k = \begin{bmatrix} a_{n-k+1} & \cdots & \cdots & a_{n-1} & a_n \\ a_{n-k+2} & \cdots & \cdots & a_n & 0 \\ \cdot & \cdot & \cdot & \cdot & \cdot \\ \cdot & \cdot & \cdot & \cdot & \cdot \\ \cdot & \cdot & \cdot & \cdot & \cdot \\ a_{n-1} & \cdots & \cdots & 0 & 0 \\ a_n & 0 & \ldots & 0 & 0 \end{bmatrix} \qquad (3.18)$$

In the first simplification it is readily noticed that the Schur-Cohn determinant $|\Delta_k|$ is reduced to the product of two k-order determinants which is considerably easier to evaluate than the $2k$-order determinant $|\Delta_k|$. If the a_k's are complex, this simplification is no longer possible.

The determinants $|X_k \pm Y_k|$ can be written in terms of A_k and B_k which we designate as stability constants as follows.

$$|X_k + Y_k| = A_k + B_k \qquad (3.19)$$

$$|X_k - Y_k| = A_k - B_k \qquad (3.20)$$

In terms of the stability constants, the stability condition can be written

$$\left. \begin{array}{ll} |A_k| > |B_k|, & k\text{-even} \\ |A_k| < |B_k|, & k\text{-odd} \end{array} \right\} \quad k = 1, 2, \ldots, n \qquad (3.21)$$

---

* The proofs of these simplifications are available in the literature.[1,15,18,30] For brevity of the discussions we only state the useful results.

Based on certain properties relating the stability constants, we obtain the other simplifications.

2. The second simplification is the equivalence of the last constraint $|A_n| \gtrless |B_n|$ to a simple auxiliary constraint. This simplification is based on the following identity:

$$A_n^2 - B_n^2 = F(1)F(-1)(A_{n-1} - B_{n-1})^2 \tag{3.22}$$

Since $(A_{n-1} - B_{n-1})^2$ is a positive quantity, the last constraint can be replaced by

$$\begin{aligned} F(1)F(-1) &> 0, & n\text{-even} \\ F(1)F(-1) &< 0, & n\text{-odd} \end{aligned} \tag{3.23}$$

If we let a_n be positive and multiply if necessary, $F(z)$ by minus one, the final constraint $|A_n| \gtrless |B_n|$ can be equivalently replaced by

$$F(1) > 0, \qquad (-1)^n F(-1) > 0 \tag{3.24}$$

As an addition to this property we can also write

$$A_n + B_n = F(1)(A_{n-1} - B_{n-1}), \tag{3.25}$$

$$A_n - B_n = F(-1)(A_{n-1} - B_{n-1}) \tag{3.25a}$$

3. The third property which led to the formulation of the stability constraints for values of k of only half of equation (3.21) is given.

$$A_k^2 - B_k^2 = A_{k-1}A_{k+1} - B_{k-1}B_{k+1} = \tfrac{1}{2}[(A_{k+1} + B_{k+1})(A_{k-1} - B_{k-1})$$
$$+ (A_{k+1} - B_{k+1})(A_{k-1} + B_{k-1})],$$
$$k = 2, 3, 4, \cdots, n - 1 \tag{3.26}$$

It is noticed from this property that by forcing certain restrictions on the A's and B's before and after a certain k as required by the stability condition, we can dispense with $A_k^2 \gtrless B_k^2$.

4. The following property which can be obtained from the second and third properties is

$$A_{n-1} + B_{n-1} = \tfrac{1}{2}[F(1)(A_{n-2} - B_{n-2}) + F(-1)(A_{n-2} + B_{n-2})],$$
$$n \geq 3 \tag{3.27}$$

The importance of this equation lies in the fact that we can terminate the last constraint by $A_{n-1} - B_{n-1} \gtrless 0$ only. This is evident since the constraint on $A_{n-1} + B_{n-1}$ is necessarily satisfied when the constraints on $F(1)$, $F(-1)$, and $A_{n-2} \pm B_{n-2}$ are satisfied. The usefulness of this property will be shown in the discussion of the critical constraint as well as in the final formulation of the stability constraints for low-order systems.

5. The final property relates to the determinants $|X_k \pm Y_k| = A_k \pm B_k$, and states that by expanding the matrix $|X_{n-1} \pm Y_{n-1}|$ we can obtain all other determinants for other values of k from this expansion. This is evident if the determinant is written in detail; we can notice that it includes inside itself all the other determinants involved in the stability constraints. The matrices X_{n-1} and Y_{n-1} can be easily remembered if their form is noticed as written here in detail.

$$
X_{n-1} =
\begin{bmatrix}
a_0 & a_1 & a_2 & \cdots & a_{n-2} \\
0 & a_0 & a_1 & \cdots & a_{n-3} \\
0 & 0 & a_0 & \cdots & a_{n-4} \\
\cdot & \cdot & \cdot & \cdot & \cdot \\
\cdot & \cdot & \cdot & \cdot & \cdot \\
\cdot & \cdot & \cdot & \cdot & \cdot \\
0 & 0 & 0 & \cdots & a_0
\end{bmatrix}
\tag{3.28}
$$

and

$$
Y_{n-1} =
\begin{bmatrix}
a_2 & \cdots & a_{n-2} & a_{n-1} & a_n \\
a_3 & \cdots & a_{n-1} & a_n & 0 \\
a_4 & \cdots & a_n & 0 & 0 \\
\cdot & \cdot & \cdot & \cdot & \cdot \\
\cdot & \cdot & \cdot & \cdot & \cdot \\
\cdot & \cdot & \cdot & \cdot & \cdot \\
a_n & 0 & 0 & 0 & 0
\end{bmatrix}
\tag{3.29}
$$

It is noticed that the matrix X_{n-1} can be easily generated by starting with the first row from a_0 up to a_{n-2} and the second row the same as the first displaced by one column. This process is continued until we obtain the $n - 2$ row and column. For the matrix Y_{n-1}, we start the first row from the extreme right by a_n and continue up to a_2, and similarly, for the second row displaced by one column. Continue this process up to the first column and $(n - 2)$th row which has the entry a_n.

THE NEW STABILITY CRITERION.[1,30]   From the preceding simplifications and properties the simplified stability criterion can be written in the following form for n-odd and n-even respectively:

$$|X_{n-1} \pm Y_{n-1}| = A_{n-1} \pm B_{n-1}$$

$$
=\begin{vmatrix}
a_0\pm a_2 & a_1\pm a_3 & a_2\pm a_4 & a_3\pm a_5 & a_4\pm a_6 & a_5\pm a_7 & \cdots & a_{n-3}\pm a_{n-1} & a_{n-2}\pm a_n \\
\pm a_3 & a_0\pm a_4 & a_1\pm a_5 & a_2\pm a_6 & a_3\pm a_7 & a_4\pm a_8 & \cdots & a_{n-4}\pm a_n & a_{n-3} \\
\pm a_4 & \pm a_5 & a_0\pm a_{n-5} & a_1\pm a_{n-4} & a_2\pm a_{n-3} & a_3\pm a_{n-2} & \cdots & a_{n-4} & a_{n-4} \\
\pm a_5 & \pm a_6 & \pm a_{n-4} & a_0\pm a_{n-3} & a_1\pm a_{n-2} & a_2\pm a_{n-1} & \cdots & a_{n-5} & a_{n-5} \\
\pm a_6 & \pm a_7 & \pm a_{n-3} & \pm a_{n-2} & a_0\pm a_{n-1} & a_1\pm a_n & \cdots & a_{n-6} & a_{n-6} \\
\pm a_7 & \pm a_8 & \pm a_{n-2} & \pm a_{n-1} & \pm a_n & a_0 & \cdots & a_{n-7} & a_{n-7} \\
\vdots & & \vdots & \vdots & \vdots & & \ddots & \vdots & \vdots \\
\pm a_{n-2} & \pm a_{n-1} & \pm a_n & 0 & 0 & 0 & \cdots & a_2 & a_2 \\
\pm a_{n-1} & \pm a_n & 0 & 0 & 0 & 0 & \cdots & a_0 & a_1 \\
\pm a_n & 0 & 0 & 0 & 0 & 0 & \cdots & 0 & a_0
\end{vmatrix}
$$

(nested sub-determinants: $k=n-3$, $k=6$, $k=4$, $k=2$)

(3.30)

For n-even

$$|X_{n-1} \pm Y_{n-1}| = A_{n-1} \pm B_{n-1}$$

$$=
\begin{vmatrix}
a_0 \pm a_2 & a_1 \pm a_3 & a_2 \pm a_4 & a_3 \pm a_5 & a_4 \pm a_6 & a_5 \pm a_7 & \cdots & a_{n-3} \pm a_{n-1} & a_{n-2} \pm a_n \\[2pt]
\pm a_3 & a_0 \pm a_4 & a_1 \pm a_5 & a_2 \pm a_6 & a_3 \pm a_7 & a_4 \pm a_8 & \cdots & a_{n-4} \pm a_n & a_{n-3} \\[2pt]
\pm a_4 & \pm a_5 & a_0 \pm a_{n-4} & a_1 \pm a_{n-3} & a_2 \pm a_{n-2} & a_3 \pm a_{n-1} & \cdots & a_{n-4} \pm a_n & a_{n-4} \\[2pt]
\pm a_5 & \pm a_6 & \pm a_{n-3} & a_0 \pm a_{n-2} & a_1 \pm a_{n-1} & a_2 \pm a_n & \cdots & & a_{n-5} \\[2pt]
\pm a_6 & \pm a_7 & \pm a_{n-2} & \pm a_{n-1} & a_0 \pm a_n & a_1 & \cdots & & a_{n-6} \\[2pt]
\vdots & & \vdots & \vdots & \pm a_n & a_0 & & & \vdots \\[2pt]
& & a_3 & a_2 & a_1 & a_0 & & & \\[2pt]
\pm a_{n-1} & \pm a_{n-1} & a_2 & a_1 & a_0 & 0 & \cdots & a_1 & a_2 \\[2pt]
\pm a_n & \pm a_n & a_1 & a_0 & 0 & 0 & & a_0 & a_1 \\[2pt]
0 & 0 & a_n & 0 & 0 & 0 & \cdots & 0 & a_0
\end{vmatrix}$$

$$k = n-3, \qquad k = 5, \qquad k = 3, \qquad k = 1$$

(3.31)

The stability constraints for n-odd are

$$F(1) > 0, \qquad F(-1) < 0 \tag{3.32}$$

$$(-1)^{k(k+1)/2}(A_k \pm B_k) > 0, \qquad k = 2, 4, 6, \ldots, n - 1 \tag{3.33}$$

The stability constraints for n-even are

$$F(1) > 0, \qquad F(-1) > 0 \tag{3.34}$$

$$(-1)^{k(k+1)/2} (A_k - B_k) > 0, \qquad (-1)^{k(k+1)/2}(A_k + B_k) < 0,$$

$$k = 1, 3, 5, \ldots, n - 1 \tag{3.35}$$

From the form of these determinants it is noticed first that the matrices are symmetrical around the center. This phenomenon may be attributed to the stability conditions for the unit circle which is symmetric around the origin in the z-plane. A similar symmetry also exists if the necessary and sufficient conditions are sought for the roots of any polynomial to lie along the real axis in the complex plane. This will be discussed later in connection with the conditions that the roots of $F(z)$ lie between 0 and 1 in the z-plane. The second point to be observed is that to obtain the stability constraints both determinants $|X_k \pm Y_k|$ are to be expanded. Lastly, in the final constraints both $A_{n-1} \pm B_{n-1} \gtrless 0$ need to be satisfied. This requires the solution of two algebraic equations of degree $n - 1$. In the following discussion the last two points will be simplified.

EVALUATION OF THE STABILITY DETERMINANTS.[30] To avoid the need of expansion of two determinants of order $n - 1$, we need expand only one determinant by using the following artificial procedure. Replace the a_k's of Y_k by b_k's and then expand only $|X_{n-1} + Y_{n-1}|$. From this expansion, we can obtain all other determinants by a substitution process. For instance, $|X_{n-2} + Y_{n-2}|$ can be obtained by letting $a_0 = 0$, $a_i \to a_{i-1}$ for $i = 1, 2, \ldots, n$ in $|X_{n-1} + Y_{n-1}|$ and then dividing by $(-1)^{n-1}b_n$. Similarly, we can obtain $|X_{n-3} + Y_{n-3}|$ directly from $|X_{n-1} + Y_{n-1}|$ by letting in the latter (after expansion) $a_0 = 0$, $a_1 = 0$, $a_i \to a_{i-2}$ and dividing by $-b_n^2$. All other determinants can be obtained by a similar substitution process. To identify the A_k's and B_k's from $|X_k + Y_k|$, perform the following process. After expansion, examine every term which is a product of a_i's and b_i's; if it contains an even number (including zero) of b_i's, assign it to A_k; otherwise, assign it to B_k. After collecting the terms of A_k and B_k replace all the b_i's by the a_i's.

ILLUSTRATIVE EXAMPLE

In this example we shall obtain the stability constraints for the fifth-degree case, that is

$$F(z) = a_0 + a_1 z + a_2 z^2 + a_3 z^3 + a_4 z^4 + a_5 z^5, \qquad a_5 > 0$$
(3.36)

We form $X_4 + Y_4$ by replacing the a_i's of Y_4 by b_i's:

$$|X_4 + Y_4| = \begin{vmatrix} a_0 + b_2 & a_1 + b_3 & a_2 + b_4 & a_3 + b_5 \\ b_3 & a_0 + b_4 & a_1 + b_5 & a_2 \\ b_4 & b_5 & a_0 & a_1 \\ b_5 & 0 & 0 & a_0 \end{vmatrix}$$
(3.37)

After expansion, let $a_0 = 0$, $a_1 = 0$, $a_i \rightarrow a_{i-2}$ and divide by $-b_5^2$ to obtain $|X_2 + Y_2|$.

To identify $A_4 \pm B_4$ and $A_2 \pm B_2$ we can perform the following manipulation. The constants $A_4 + B_4$ can be readily obtained from $|X_4 + Y_4|$ by replacing all the b_i's by a_i's. Replacing the sign of all the terms which contain odd number of b_i's by negative signs and replacing all the b_i's by a_i's, we readily obtain $A_4 - B_4$. Similarly, $A_2 \pm B_2$ can be obtained from $|X_2 + Y_2|$.

The stability constraints for the fifth-degree case are

$$F(1) > 0, \qquad F(-1) < 0$$
(3.38)

$$A_2 \pm B_2 < 0, \qquad A_4 \pm B_4 > 0$$
(3.39)

ALTERNATE FORM OF THE STABILITY CRITERION.   To avoid having to satisfy for two inequality equations of degree $n - 1$, we can write the stability constraints in different forms so that only one equation of degree $n - 1$ need be satisfied. This can be readily accomplished by noting the second, third, and fourth properties among the stability constraints. The final stability constraints for any n are given as

n-odd

$$F(1) > 0, \qquad F(-1) < 0$$
(3.40)

$$(-1)^{k(k+1)/2}(A_k - B_k) > 0, \qquad (-1)^{k(k+1)/2}(A_k + B_k) < 0,$$
$$k = 1, 3, 5, \ldots, n - 2 \quad (3.41)$$

$$(-1)^{(n-1)n/2}(A_{n-1} - B_{n-1}) > 0$$
(3.42)

n-even

$$F(1) > 0, \qquad F(-1) > 0$$
(3.43)

$$(-1)^{k(k+1)/2}(A_k \pm B_k) > 0, \qquad k = 2, 4, 6, \ldots, n - 2$$
(3.44)

$$(-1)^{n(n-1)/2}(A_{n-1} - B_{n-1}) > 0.$$
(3.45)

SUMMARY OF STABILITY CONSTRAINTS FOR LOW-ORDER SYSTEMS.[1.16]   In
the following the stability constraints in terms of the coefficients of the
low-degree polynomials are presented, using the alternate form.

$n = 2$

$$F(z) = a_0 + a_1 z + a_2 z^2, \qquad a_2 > 0 \tag{3.46}$$
$$F(1) > 0, \qquad F(-1) > 0 \tag{3.47}*$$
$$a_0 - a_2 < 0 \tag{3.48}$$

$n = 3$

$$F(z) = a_0 + a_1 z + a_2 z^2 + a_3 z^3, \qquad a_3 > 0 \tag{3.49}$$
$$F(1) > 0, \qquad F(-1) < 0 \tag{3.50}$$
$$|a_0| < a_3 \tag{3.51}$$
$$a_0^2 - a_3^2 < a_0 a_2 - a_1 a_3 \tag{3.52}$$

$n = 4$

$$F(z) = a_0 + a_1 z + a_2 z^2 + a_3 z^3 + a_4 z^4, \qquad a_4 > 0 \tag{3.53}$$
$$F(1) > 0, \qquad F(-1) > 0 \tag{3.54}$$
$$a_0^2 - a_4^2 - a_0 a_3 + a_1 a_4 < 0 \tag{3.55}$$
$$a_0^2 - a_4^2 + a_0 a_3 - a_1 a_4 < 0 \tag{3.56}$$
$$a_0^3 + 2a_0 a_2 a_4 + a_1 a_3 a_4 - a_0 a_4^2 - a_2 a_4^2 - a_0 a_3^2 - a_0^2 a_4$$
$$- a_0^2 a_2 - a_1^2 a_4 + a_4^3 + a_0 a_1 a_3 > 0 \tag{3.57}$$

Using algebraic manipulations the constraints for $n = 4$ could be more
simplified so that instead of the two second-degree equations (3.55 and
3.56), we obtain the following two first-degree equations:

$$a_1 - a_3 < 2(a_4 - a_0) \tag{3.58}$$
$$a_1 - a_3 > 2(a_0 - a_4) \tag{3.59}$$

$n = 5$

$$F(z) = a_0 + a_1 z + a_2 z^2 + a_3 z^3 + a_4 z^4 + a_5 z^5, \qquad a_5 > 0 \tag{3.60}$$
$$F(1) > 0, \qquad F(-1) < 0 \tag{3.61}$$
$$|a_0| < a_5 \tag{3.62}$$
$$(a_1 a_4 a_5 - a_0 a_5^2 - a_2 a_5^2 + a_0^3 + a_0 a_3 a_5 - a_0 a_4^2) \mp$$
$$(a_1^2 a_5 - a_0 a_2 a_5 - a_5^3 + a_0^2 a_3 + a_0^2 a_5 - a_0 a_1 a_4) \begin{matrix} > 0 \\ < 0 \end{matrix} \tag{3.63}$$
$$(a_0^2 - a_5^2)^2 - (a_0 a_4 - a_1 a_5)^2 + (a_0 a_4 - a_1 a_5)(a_4^2 + a_1 a_3$$
$$- a_1^2 - a_2 a_4 - a_0^2 + a_5^2) + (a_0 a_3 - a_2 a_5)$$
$$\times (a_0 a_1 - a_4 a_5 - a_0 a_3 + a_2 a_5) - (a_0 a_2 - a_3 a_5)$$
$$\times [(a_0^2 - a_5^2) - 2(a_0 a_4 - a_1 a_5)] > 0 \tag{3.64}$$

---

* We may note that from this equation we have $a_0 + a_2 > 0$.

These constraints can also be simplified by algebraic manipulations so that instead of the two third-degree equations (3.63) we have

$$-2 < \frac{a_0(a_1 - a_3) + a_2 a_5 - a_4 a_5}{a_5^2 - a_1 a_5 - a_0^2 + a_0 a_4} < 2 \qquad (3.65)$$

In concluding this section it should be pointed out that the determinant stability method could be useful for numerical testing of polynomials for stability and with its alternate form they yield the number of roots outside the unit circle if the system is unstable. This will be illustrated later in the discussion of the number of roots outside the unit circle. If the stability constraints are further simplified as indicated for $n = 4$ and $n = 5$ (using equations (3.58), (3.59) and (3.65)) this information on the number of roots is lost at the advantage of more simplified stability constraints. For system design this simplification is only of academic value, for with higher degree polynomials the final constraint, that is,

$$A_{n-1} - B_{n-1} \genfrac{}{}{0pt}{}{< 0}{> 0}$$

is of major importance, as will be discussed in detail in the following section.

3.6 Critical stability constraints for system design[20]

In certain cases where the discrete system [whose characteristic equation is $F(z)$] is initially stable, and if one or more parameters (for example, gain) are changed so that it becomes unstable, then only certain constraints need be satisfied. These constraints are called "critical constraints" and are discussed in this section.

Assume the characteristic equation of the linear discrete system is described as follows:

$$F(z) = a_n z^n + a_{n-1} z^{n-1} + \ldots + a_1 z + a_0, \qquad \text{with } a_n > 0 \tag{3.66}$$

This equation can be also written in terms of its roots z_i as

$$F(z) = a_n \prod_i^{1,2,\ldots,n} (z - z_i) \tag{3.67}$$

We can readily ascertain that $F(1) \geq 0$ and $(-1)^n F(-1) \geq 0$ constitute two of the critical constraints, because we can write

$$F(1) = a_n \prod_i^{1,2,\ldots,n} (1 - z_i) \tag{3.68}$$

and

$$(-1)^n F(-1) = a_n \prod_i^{1,2,\ldots,n} (1 + z_i) \tag{3.69}$$

It is readily noticed from these two equations that $F(1) = 0$ and $F(-1) = 0$ constitute the critical conditions when the real roots move outside the unit circle at $z = 1$ and $z = -1$.

Furthermore, the other critical constraint which yields the condition when the complex roots move outside the unit circle is given as[20]

$$A_{n-1} - B_{n-1} = (-1)^{n(n-1)/2} a_n^{n-1} \prod_{i<k}^{1,2,\ldots,n} (1 - z_i z_k) \tag{3.70}$$

If $z_i = \bar{z}_k$ (conjugate), then $z_i z_k = |z_i|^2$ and $A_{n-1} - B_{n-1}$ changes its sign whenever a pair (or odd pairs) of complex conjugate roots move outside the unit circle.

When the complex roots are of even multiplicity, the equation

$$A_{n-1} - B_{n-1} = 0$$

is also critical although it does not change its sign. In all these cases the system becomes unstable whenever $A_{n-1} - B_{n-1} = 0$. Therefore we can summarize the preceding critical constraints discussions as follows.[20] For an initially stable linear discrete system, a certain parameter is changed so that stability ceases, the following are the critical conditions which yield the maximum variation of parameters for stability limit.

$$F(1) \geq 0, \qquad (-1)^n F(-1) \geq 0 \tag{3.71}$$

$$(-1)^{n(n-1)/2}(A_{n-1} - B_{n-1}) \geq 0 \tag{3.72}$$

This discussion shows that for analytic tests for stability when applied to the design of certain systems, it is not necessary to consider all the stability constraints but only the critical ones. There the solution of the highest-degree equation is at most of $(n - 1)$th degree; furthermore, this equation need be solved for only real roots, which can be easily done graphically. In a following section an illustrative example indicates the application and importance of this point.

3.7 Number of roots of a real polynomial inside the unit circle[1,4]

The stability criterion discussed earlier in this chapter yields the necessary and sufficient condition for all the roots of $F(z)$ to lie inside the unit circle. To obtain information on the number of roots that lie inside the unit circle if the system is unstable, we can modify the presented discussions to cover this case. Following the work of Schur-Cohn presented in equation (3.14) and using some of the properties of the stability constants A_k's and B_k's we can state the following.

The number of roots of $F(z)$ that lie inside the unit circle is equal to the number of variations of the inequalities of the following constraints:

n-even

$1 > 0$

$|A_1| \gtrless |B_1|$

$|A_2| \gtrless |B_2| \Leftrightarrow A_1A_3 \gtrless B_1B_3$

$|A_3| \gtrless |B_3|$

$|A_4| \gtrless |B_4| \Leftrightarrow A_3A_5 \gtrless B_3B_5$

$|A_5| \gtrless |B_5|$

.

.

.

$|A_{n-1}| \gtrless |B_{n-1}|$

$|A_n| \gtrless |B_n| \Leftrightarrow F(1)F(-1) \begin{smallmatrix} > 0 \\ < 0 \end{smallmatrix}$

n-odd

$1 > 0$

$|A_1| \gtrless |B_1| \Leftrightarrow A_2 \begin{smallmatrix} > 0 \\ < 0 \end{smallmatrix}$

$|A_2| \gtrless |B_2|$

$|A_3| \gtrless |B_3| \Leftrightarrow A_2A_4 \gtrless B_2B_4$

$|A_4| \gtrless |B_4|$

$|A_5| \gtrless |B_5| \Leftrightarrow A_4A_6 \gtrless B_4B_6$

$|A_6| \gtrless |B_6|$

.

.

.

$|A_{n-1}| \gtrless |B_{n-1}|$

$|A_n| \gtrless |B_n| \Leftrightarrow F(1)F(-1) \begin{smallmatrix} > 0 \\ < 0 \end{smallmatrix}$

It is noticed from the preceding that for n-even we do not have to evaluate the even determinants but can use the relationship

$$A_k^2 - B_k^2 = A_{k-1}A_{k+1} - B_{k-1}B_{k+1}$$
$$= \tfrac{1}{2}[(A_{k+1} + B_{k+1})(A_{k-1} - B_{k-1})$$
$$+ (A_{k+1} - B_{k+1})(A_{k-1} + B_{k-1})]$$

which are obtained from the calculated odd determinants. Similarly, the odd determinants are avoided for n-odd. It is assumed that in this counting of number of the inequality variations, none of the constants A_k are equal to B_k. Thus the number of roots outside the unit circle is equivalent to n minus the number inside the unit circle.

To determine the number of roots inside the unit circle when $A_{k-1} \neq B_{k-1}$ but $A_k = B_k$, a special procedure is required for this singular case.

A detailed discussion of the modifications required to determine the number of roots is discussed in Appendix 2.

3.8 Relationship between the determinant method and Hurwitz criterion[1,20]

The relationship between some of the stability constraints and Hurwitz constraints using the bilinear transformation can be established. If we write the following Hurwitz polynomial obtained from $F(z)$, with $a_n > 0$ by using the bilinear transformation

$$F_1(w) = b_0 + b_1 w + b_2 w^2 + \ldots + b_n w^n, \qquad b_n > 0 \qquad (3.73)$$

the following relationships exist:

$$b_n = F(z)\big|_{z=1}, \qquad b_0 = (-1)^n F(z)\big|_{z=-1} \qquad (3.74)$$

$$|\Delta^{II}_{n-1}| = (-2)^{n(n-1)/2}(A_{n-1} - B_{n-1}) \qquad (3.75)$$

where $|\Delta^{II}_{n-1}|$ is the next-to-last Hurwitz determinant. The relationship (3.75) has been verified by expansion for low-order systems and can be generally demonstrated through the use of Orlando's formula[8,20] and the bilinear transformation.

3.9 Table form[2,9,10,12,24,25]

In this section an alternate form of the stability test for the unit circle is discussed. This form is presented in a table form similar to the Routh table used for the stability in the left half of the s-plane. It requires evaluation of only second-order determinants and can be easily programmed on a digital computer. The table form is particularly useful for numerical testing of polynomials as well as for design purposes. The formulation of this form is based on the early work of Rouché, Cohn, and later on the work of Marden. The derivation is presented in Appendix 1 as well as the various recent modifications and their extensions.

The necessary and sufficient condition for the following polynomial

$$F(z) = a_0 + a_1 z + a_2 z^2 + \ldots + a_k z^k + \ldots + a_n z^n, \qquad a_n > 0 \qquad (3.76)$$

to have all its roots inside the unit circle can be obtained by forming the accompanying table. (It should be noted that the elements of row $2k + 2$ consist of the elements of the row $2k + 1$ written in reverse order, $k = 0, 1, 2, \ldots$)

Row	z^0	z^1	z^2	...	z^{n-k}	...	z^{n-1}	z^n
1	a_0	a_1	a_2	...	a_{n-k}	...	a_{n-1}	a_n
2	a_n	a_{n-1}	a_{n-2}	...	a_k	...	a_1	a_0
3	b_0	b_1	b_2	...	...	...	b_{n-1}	
4	b_{n-1}	b_{n-2}	b_{n-3}	...	...	...	b_0	
5	c_0	c_1	c_2	...	...	c_{n-2}		
6	c_{n-2}	c_{n-3}	c_{n-4}	...	...	c_0		
.	.	.	.	...	.			
.	.	.	.	...	.			
.	.	.	.	...	.			
$2n-5$	s_0	s_1	s_2	s_3				
$2n-4$	s_3	s_2	s_1	s_0				
$2n-3$	r_0	r_1	r_2					

$$(3.77)$$

where

$$b_k = \begin{vmatrix} a_0 & a_{n-k} \\ a_n & a_k \end{vmatrix}, \qquad d_k = \begin{vmatrix} c_0 & c_{n-2-k} \\ c_{n-2} & c_k \end{vmatrix}$$

$$c_k = \begin{vmatrix} b_0 & b_{n-1-k} \\ b_{n-1} & b_k \end{vmatrix}, \qquad r_0 = \begin{vmatrix} s_0 & s_3 \\ s_3 & s_0 \end{vmatrix}$$

$$r_2 = \begin{vmatrix} s_0 & s_1 \\ s_3 & s_2 \end{vmatrix}$$

The stability constraints are

$$F(1) > 0, \qquad (-1)^n F(-1) > 0 \tag{3.78}$$

$$\left. \begin{array}{l} |a_0| < a_n, \quad \text{or} \quad a_n > |a_0| \\[4pt] |b_0| > |b_{n-1}| \\[4pt] |c_0| > |c_{n-2}| \\[4pt] |d_0| > |d_{n-3}| \\[4pt] \\ \vdots \\ \\ |r_0| > |r_2| \end{array} \right\} (n-1) \text{ constraints}$$

It is noticed from the table that the dotted entry r_1 is not needed for calculation; hence the corresponding computation involving the dotted entries in rows $2n - 4$ and $2n - 5$ becomes redundant.

The number of roots inside the unit circle, if none of the preceding constraints becomes equal, is given by the number of the products P_k, $k = 1, 2, \ldots, n$, which are negative, where

$$P_1 = [|a_0| - a_n], \qquad P_2 = [|a_0| - a_n][|b_0| - |b_{n-1}|], \ldots$$
(3.79)

$$P_n = [|a_0| - a_n] \, |b_0| - [|b_{n-1}|] \ldots$$
$$\times \, [|r_0| - |r_2|][|r_0^2 - r_2^2| - |r_0 r_1 - r_1 r_2|] \quad (3.80)$$

The difference between n and this number yields the number of roots outside the unit circle.

EXAMPLES

(1)　　$F(z) = 3 - 2z - \frac{3}{2}z^2 + z^3, \qquad n = 3$　　　　(3.81)

By applying the constraint $F(-1)$ we notice that $F(z)|_{z=-1} > 0$; thus the system is unstable. Therefore the table need not be computed. However, to obtain information on the number of roots outside the unit circle we form the following table:

Row	z^0	z^1	z^2	z^3	
1	3	-2	$-\dfrac{3}{2}$	1	
2	1	$-\dfrac{3}{2}$	-2	3	(3.82)
3	8	$-\dfrac{9}{2}$	$\dfrac{5}{2}$		

$$P_1 = |a_0| - a_n = 3 - 1 > 0 \tag{3.83}$$

$$P_2 = 2[|b_0| - |b_{n-1}|] = 2(8 + \tfrac{5}{2}) > 0 \tag{3.84}$$

$$P_3 = \text{pos. pos.} \, \{|8^2 - (\tfrac{5}{2})^2| - |8(-\tfrac{9}{2}) - \tfrac{9}{2}(\tfrac{5}{2})|\} > 0 \tag{3.85}$$

Therefore no root exists inside the unit circle and all three roots are outside the unit circle. It may be noted in passing that the condition on $[|r_0^2 - r_0^2| - |r_0 r_1 - r_1 r_2|]$ may also be obtained from $F(1)F(-1)$ and the multiplication of the other constraints. For instance in this case the sign of this term is equivalent to the sign of $F(1)F(-1)$, that is,

$$\text{sgn} \, [|r_0^2 - r_0^2| - |r_0 r_1 - r_1 r_2|] = \text{sgn} \, F(-1)F(1) \tag{3.86}$$

In view of the preceding relationship the dotted entry in the last line need not be calculated.

(2) $\qquad F(z) = 0.0025 + 0.08z + 0.4126z^2 - 1.368z^3 + z^4, \qquad n = 4$

$$(3.87)$$

Row	z^0	z^1	z^2	z^3	z^4
1	0.0025	0.08	0.4126	−1.368	1
2	1	−1.368	0.4126	0.08	0.0025
3	$\simeq -1$	1.368	−0.4116	−0.0834	
4	−0.0834	0.4116	1.368	−1	
5	0.9936	−1.402	0.5256		

$$(3.88)$$

Stability test

$$F(1) = 0.1271 > 0, \qquad F(-1) = 2.703 > 0 \qquad (3.89)$$

$$|a_0| < a_n, \qquad 0.0025 < 1 \qquad (3.90)$$

$$|b_0| > |b_{n-1}|, \qquad 1 > 0.0834 \qquad (3.91)$$

$$|c_0| > |c_{n-2}|, \qquad 0.9936 > 0.5256 \qquad (3.92)$$

The system is stable.

Simplifications of the stability constraints[12,24]

An alternate simplified form of the stability constraints given in equation (3.78) can be obtained by noting that

$$b_0 = a_0^2 - a_n^2 < 0 \qquad (3.93)$$

and

$$b_0^2 > b_{n-1}^2, \quad \text{or} \quad |b_0| > |b_{n-1}| \qquad (3.94)$$

These two constraints can be equivalently written as

$$b_0 - b_{n-1} < 0, \qquad b_0 + b_{n-1} < 0 \qquad (3.95)$$

Similarly, for

$$d_0 = c_0^2 - c_{n-2}^2 > 0 \qquad (3.96)$$

and

$$|d_0| > |d_{n-3}| \qquad (3.97)$$

we can write

$$d_0 - d_{n-3} > 0, \qquad d_0 + d_{n-3} > 0 \qquad (3.98)$$

Similar relationships can also be obtained for the other constraints. Thus the stability constraint for $F(z)$ can be summarized as follows:

n-even

$$F(1) > 0, \qquad F(-1) > 0$$

$$
\left.
\begin{array}{ll}
a_0 - a_n < 0, & a_0 + a_n > 0 \\[4pt]
c_0 - c_{n-2} > 0, & c_0 + c_{n-2} > 0 \\[4pt]
e_0 - e_{n-4} > 0, & e_0 + e_{n-4} > 0 \\
\quad \cdot & \quad \cdot \\
\quad \cdot & \quad \cdot \\
\quad \cdot & \quad \cdot \\
s_0 - s_2 > 0, & s_0 + s_2 > 0
\end{array}
\right\} \; n \text{ constraints}
$$

n-odd

$$F(1) > 0, \qquad F(-1) < 0$$

$$
\left.
\begin{array}{ll}
b_0 - b_{n-1} < 0, & b_0 + b_{n-1} < 0 \\[4pt]
d_0 - d_{n-3} > 0, & d_0 + d_{n-3} > 0 \\[4pt]
f_0 - f_{n-5} > 0, & f_0 + f_{n-5} > 0 \\
\quad \cdot & \quad \cdot \\
\quad \cdot & \quad \cdot \\
\quad \cdot & \quad \cdot \\
r_0 - r_2 > 0, & r_0 + r_2 > 0
\end{array}
\right\}
\begin{array}{l} (n-1) \\ \text{constraints} \end{array}
\qquad (3.99)
$$

This form can be further simplified by noting that each of the above constraints is divisible by the preceding constraint with alternate signs; that is, $c_0 - c_{n-2}$ is divisible by $a_0 + a_n$, $d_0 - d_{n-3}$ by $b_0 + b_{n-1}$, etc. This property is utilized in the next section to show the equivalence between the table form and the determinant method.

*Relationship between the table form
and the determinant method*[24]

The relationship between the stability criterion introduced earlier and the table form will now be established. The importance of this relationship is that the evaluation of higher order determinants may be simplified by obtaining their value directly from the table form.

To establish the identity between the $A_k \pm B_k$ of the preceding criterion and the coefficients from the table, we may note the following by direct examination of the terms $A_1 \pm B_1$ and $A_2 \pm B_2$ and the corresponding terms of the table, that is,

$$a_0 \mp a_n = A_1 \mp B_1 \tag{3.100}$$

$$b_0 \mp b_{n-1} = A_2 \mp B_2 \tag{3.101}$$

Furthermore, by regular division, we can further identify the following relationships.

$$A_3 \mp B_3 = \frac{c_0 \mp c_{n-2}}{a_0 \pm a_n}, \qquad A_4 \mp B_4 = \frac{d_0 \mp d_{n-3}}{(a_0^2 - a_n^2)(A_2 \pm B_2)} \tag{3.102}$$

and

$$A_5 \mp B_5 = \frac{e_0 \mp e_{n-5}}{(a_0^2 - a_n^2)^2(b_0^2 - b_{n-1}^2)(A_3 \pm B_3)} \tag{3.103}$$

Using the induction method, we can show the following general relationship.

$$A_k \mp B_k = \frac{l_0 \mp l_{n-k+1}}{(a_0^2 - a_n^2)^{k-3}(b_0^2 - b_{n-1}^2)^{k-4}(c_0^2 - c_{n-2}^2)^{k-5} \cdots} \\ \times (h_0^2 - h_{n-k+3}^2)(A_{k-2} \pm B_{k-2}) \tag{3.104}$$

where the l's and h's are the appropriate entries in Table (3.77).

By imposing the stability constraints on the coefficients of the table for n-odd and n-even respectively, we readily obtain the constraints on $A_k \pm B_k$ which are noticed to coincide with the determinant method. This will be illustrated for $n = 5$ and $n = 6$, respectively.

$n = 5$:

The stability constraints for this case in terms of the constraints in equation (3.99) are

$$b_0 - b_4 < 0, \qquad b_0 + b_4 < 0 \tag{3.105}$$

$$d_0 - d_2 > 0, \qquad d_0 + d_2 > 0 \tag{3.106}$$

$$F(1) > 0, \qquad F(-1) < 0 \tag{3.107}$$

noting that $A_2 \pm B_2 = b_0 \pm b_4$, $A_4 \pm B_4 = (d_0 \pm d_2)/[(a_0^2 - a_5^2)(A_2 \mp B_2)]$ and $b_0 = a_0^2 - a_5^2$. These constraints in terms of A's and B's can be written by noting from $b_0 \mp b_4 < 0$ that $b_0 < 0$; we finally obtain for $n = 5$

$$A_2 - B_2 < 0, \qquad A_2 + B_2 < 0 \tag{3.108}$$

$$A_4 - B_4 > 0, \qquad A_4 + B_4 > 0 \tag{3.109}$$

$$F(1) > 0, \qquad F(-1) < 0 \tag{3.110}$$

$n = 6$:

In this case the constraints are

$$a_0 - a_6 < 0, \qquad a_0 + a_6 > 0 \tag{3.111}$$

$$c_0 - c_4 > 0, \qquad c_0 + c_4 > 0 \tag{3.112}$$

$$e_0 - e_2 > 0, \qquad e_0 + e_2 > 0 \tag{3.113}$$

$$F(1) > 0, \qquad F(-1) > 0 \tag{3.114}$$

Using the relationship introduced in equations (3.102) and (3.103), we obtain

$$A_1 - B_1 < 0, \qquad A_1 + B_1 > 0 \tag{3.115}$$

$$A_3 - B_3 > 0, \qquad A_3 + B_3 < 0 \tag{3.116}$$

$$A_5 - B_5 < 0, \qquad A_5 + B_5 > 0 \tag{3.117}$$

$$F(1) > 0, \qquad F(-1) > 0 \tag{3.118}$$

Following the foregoing procedure and utilizing equation (3.104), the equivalence for any n can be readily established.

The stability constraints for n-even and n-odd from the table form could be written in an alternate form that coincides with similar forms from the determinant form. This form can be obtained for n-odd by starting with constraints $a_0 - a_n < 0$, $a_0 + a_n > 0$, and thus the final constraint is $r_0 - r_2 > 0$. Similarly, for n-even starting with $b_0 - b_{n-1} < 0$ and $b_0 + b_{n-1} < 0$, the final constraint is $s_0 - s_2 > 0$.

To show that $r_0 + r_2 > 0$, or $(s_0 + s_2) > 0$ is automatically satisfied, we rewrite equation (3.104) for $k = n - 1$ to obtain

$$r_0 + r_2 = (A_{n-1} + B_{n-1})$$
$$\times \; [(a_0^2 - a_n^2)^{n-4}(b_0^2 - b_{n-1}^2)^{n-5} \ldots (A_{n-3} - B_{n-3})] \tag{3.119}$$

Since all the constraints in the bracketed terms are satisfied for stability from the constraints before $r_0 + r_2$, the constraint $r_0 + r_2$ is dependent only on $A_{n+1} + B_{n-1}$. From the property on p. 87, that is,

$$A_{n-1} + B_{n-1} = \tfrac{1}{2}[F(1)(A_{n-2} - B_{n-2}) + F(-1)(A_{n+2} + B_{n-2})],$$
$$n \geq 3 \quad (3.120)$$

we notice that $A_{n-1} + B_{n-1}$ is satisfied from $F(1)$, $F(-1)$, and $A_{n-2} \mp B_{n-2}$ constraints; thus $r_0 + r_2$ or $(s_0 + s_2)$ constraints are also satisfied from $F(1)$, $F(-1)$, and the preceding constraints.

Therefore we can state that the critical constraints for stability from the table form are

$$F(1) \geq 0, \qquad (-1)^n F(-1) \geq 0 \quad (3.120a)$$

and

$$r_0 - r_2 \geq 0 \quad (3.120b)$$

To facilitate the derivation of $A_k \pm B_k$ from Table (3.77), we can further simplify this table as follows:

Row	z^0	z^1	z^2	$\ldots$	z^{n-k}	$\ldots$	z^{n-1}	z^n
1	a_0	a_1	a_2	$\ldots$	a_{n-k}	$\ldots$	a_{n-1}	a_n
2	a_n	a_{n-1}	a_{n-2}	$\ldots$	a_k	$\ldots$	a_1	a_0
3	b_0	b_1	b_2	$\ldots$	.	.	b_{n-1}	
4	b_{n-1}	b_{n-2}	b_{n-3}	.	.	.	b_0	
5	c_0	c_1	c_2	.	.	c_{n-2}		
6	c_{n-2}	c_{n-3}	c_{n-4}	.	c_0			
7	d'_0	d'_1	d'_2	$\ldots$	d'_{n-3}			
8	d'_{n-3}	d'_{n-4}	d'_{n-5}	$\ldots$	d'_0			
9	e'_0	e'_1	$\ldots$	e'_{n-4}				
10	e'_{n-4}	e'_{n-5}	$\ldots$	e'_2				
.	.	.						
.	.	.						
.	.	.						
$2n-5$	s'_0	s'_1	s'_2	s'_3				
$2n-4$	s'_3	s'_2	s'_1	s_0				
$2n-3$	r'_0	r'_1	r'_2					

$$(3.121)$$

where b_k and c_k are the same as in Table (3.77) and the change occurs in

$$d'_k = \begin{vmatrix} c_0 & c_{n-2-k} \\ c_{n-2} & c_k \end{vmatrix} \frac{1}{b_0} \qquad e'_k = \begin{vmatrix} d'_0 & d'_{n-3-k} \\ d'_{n-3} & d_k \end{vmatrix} \frac{1}{c_0}, \ldots,$$

$$(3.122)$$

The determinants are formed by the division of the first term of two rows before. Based on this construction the stability constraints from this table are identical to Schur-Cohn determinants.

$$|\Delta_1| = b_0 < 0, \qquad |\Delta_2| = c_0 > 0, \qquad |\Delta_3| = d_0' < 0,$$

$$|\Delta_4| = e_0' > 0, \ldots, \qquad |\Delta_{n-1}| = r_0'^2 - r_2'^2 \begin{array}{ll} < 0 & n\text{-even} \\ > 0 & n\text{-odd} \end{array}$$

$$(3.123)$$

From the preceding table we can easily identify $A_k \pm B_k$ as follows:

$$A_1 \pm B_1 = a_0 \pm a_n, \qquad A_4 \pm B_4 = \frac{d_0' \pm d_{n-3}'}{b_0 \mp b_{n-1}}$$

$$A_2 \pm B_2 = b_0 \pm b_{n-1}, \qquad A_5 \pm B_5 = \frac{(e_0' \pm e_{n-4}')(a_0 \pm a_n)}{c_0 \mp c_{n-2}}$$

$$A_3 \pm B_3 = \frac{c_0 \pm c_{n-2}}{a_0 \mp a_n}, \qquad A_6 \pm B_6 = \frac{(f_0' \pm f_{n-5}')(b_0 \pm b_{n-1})}{(d_0' \mp d_{n-3}')}$$

$$(3.123a)$$

Similarly, all the others $A_k \pm B_k$ can be readily obtained from the simplified form of the Table (3.121).

Generation of the stability constraints[27,41]

In the following discussion the stability constraints which are obtained from the table form will be easily generated without the use of the table. This generation is based on a simple rule which can be easily remembered and applied.

GENERATION RULE

Given the following real polynomial (whose coefficients are given by symbols) whose roots are to be tested for stability within the unit circle.

$$F(z) = a_0 + a_1 z + a_2 z^2 + \ldots + a_{n-2} z^{n-2} + a_{n-1} z^{n-1} + a_n z^n,$$

$$a_n > 0 \quad (3.124)$$

Perform the following manipulations.

1. Form the first row from the original polynomial coefficients by replacing only a_{n-1} and a_n by b_{n-1} and b_n respectively. The second row is formed from the first by reversing the coefficients and relabeling certain of the a_k's by b_k's. Form the third row by expanding the second-order matrix formed from the first column and all the other columns (starting

first with the column at extreme right). These are summarized as follows:

Row	z^0	z^1	z^2	...	z^{n-2}	z^{n-1}	z^n
1	a_0	a_1	a_2	...	a_{n-2}	b_{n-1}	b_n
2	b_n	b_{n-1}	b_{n-2}	...	b_2	a_1	a_0
3	$a_0^2 - b_n^2$	$a_0a_1 - b_{n-1}b_n$	$a_0b_2 - b_na_{n-2}$	...	$a_0b_{n-2} - a_2b_n$	$a_0b_{n-1} - a_1b_n$	

2. Starting with $a_0^2 - b_n^2$ form a sequence of expressions, each from the preceding one, by the substitution given in row 3 with relabeling some coefficients, that is by replacing

$$
\left.
\begin{aligned}
a_0 &\rightarrow a_0^2 - b_n^2 \\
a_1 &\rightarrow a_0a_1 - b_{n-1}b_n \\
a_2 &\rightarrow a_0a_2 - b_{n-2}b_n \\
&\quad\cdot \\
&\quad\cdot \\
&\quad\cdot \\
a_{n-2} &\rightarrow a_0a_{n-2} - b_2b_n
\end{aligned}
\right\}
\qquad
\begin{aligned}
b_n &\rightarrow a_0b_{n-1} - a_1b_n \\
b_{n-1} &\rightarrow a_0b_{n-2} - a_2b_n \\
&\quad\cdot \\
&\quad\cdot \\
&\quad\cdot \\
b_2 &\rightarrow a_0b_1 - a_{n-1}b_n
\end{aligned}
\qquad (3.124a)
$$

Continue this process to generate the required $n - 1$ constraints. After performing this process, replace all the b_k's by a_k's to obtain the final constraints. These $n - 1$ constraints with $F(-1) > 0$, $(-1)^n F(-1) > 0$ constitute the necessary and sufficient conditions for the roots of $F(z)$ to lie inside the unit circle.

ILLUSTRATIVE EXAMPLE

By applying the preceding rule we shall generate the stability constraints for the following fifth-degree polynomial:

$$F(z) = a_0 + a_1z + a_2z^2 + a_3z^3 + a_4z^4 + a_5z^5, \qquad a_5 > 0$$
$$(3.125)$$

1. Form the following three rows:

Row

1	a_0	a_1	a_2	a_3	b_4	b_5
2	b_5	b_4	b_3	b_2	a_1	a_0
3	$a_0^2 - b_5^2$	$a_0a_1 - b_4b_5$	$a_0b_2 - a_3b_5$	$a_0b_3 - a_2b_5$	$a_0b_4 - a_1b_5$	

2. Form the following four constraints by replacing the various coefficients from the third row, that is,

$$
\left.
\begin{aligned}
a_0 &\rightarrow a_0^2 - b_5^2 \\
a_1 &\rightarrow a_0a_1 - b_4b_5 \\
a_2 &\rightarrow a_0a_2 - b_3b_5 \\
a_3 &\rightarrow a_0a_3 - b_2b_5
\end{aligned}
\right\}
\qquad
\begin{aligned}
b_5 &\rightarrow a_0b_4 - a_1b_5 \\
b_4 &\rightarrow a_0b_3 - a_2b_5 \\
b_3 &\rightarrow a_0b_2 - a_3b_5 \\
b_2 &\rightarrow a_0a_1 - b_4b_5
\end{aligned}
\qquad (3.125a)
$$

The constraints are

$$a_0^2 - b_5^2 = \alpha$$

$$a_0^2 - b_5^2 \rightarrow (a_0^2 - b_5^2)^2 - (a_0 b_4 - a_1 b_5)^2$$
$$= \alpha^2 - (a_0 b_4 - a_1 b_5)^2 = \beta$$

$$\beta \rightarrow \beta^2 - [(a_0^2 - b_5^2)(a_0 b_3 - a_2 b_5)$$
$$- (a_0 a_1 - b_4 b_5)(a_0 b_4 - a_1 b_5)]^2 = \gamma$$

$$\gamma \rightarrow \gamma^2 - \{[(a_0^2 - b_5^2)^2 - (a_0 b_4 - a_1 b_5)^2][(a_0^2 - b_5^2)(a_0 b_2 - a_3 b_5)$$
$$- (a_0 a_2 - b_3 b_5)(a_0 b_4 - a_1 b_5)] - [(a_0^2 - b_5^2)(a_0 a_1 - b_4 b_5)$$
$$- (a_0 b_3 - a_2 b_5)(a_0 b_4 - a_1 b_5)][(a_0^2 - b_5^2)(a_0 b_3 - a_2 b_5)$$
$$- (a_0 a_1 - b_4 b_5)(a_0 b_4 - a_1 b_5)]\}^2$$
$$= \gamma^2 - \lambda^2 = \delta \tag{3.126}$$

By replacing all the b_k's by a_k's we finally obtain the stability constraints

$$F(1) > 0, \qquad F(-1) < 0 \tag{3.127}$$

$$\alpha = a_0^2 - a_5^2 < 0 \tag{3.128}$$

$$\beta = \alpha^2 - (a_0 a_4 - a_1 a_5)^2 > 0 \tag{3.129}$$

$$\gamma = \beta^2 - [(a_0^2 - a_5^2)(a_0 a_3 - a_2 a_5)$$
$$- (a_0 a_1 - a_4 a_5)(a_0 a_4 - a_1 a_5)]^2 > 0 \tag{3.130}$$

$$\delta = \gamma^2 - \lambda^2 > 0 \tag{3.131}$$

These constraints could be simplified to obtain

$$F(1) > 0, \qquad F(-1) < 0 \tag{3.132}$$

$$(a_0^2 - a_5^2) \pm (a_0 a_4 - a_1 a_5) < 0 \tag{3.133}$$

$$\gamma \pm \lambda > 0 \tag{3.134}$$

The preceding shows that for n-odd, we can obtain these expressions directly from the polynomial coefficients by certain substitution of two steps at a time. This can be accomplished by forming rows 4 and 5 to obtain the required substitution.* Similarly, for n-even we can skip the intermediate constraints by using two steps at a time.

The relationship $\gamma \pm \lambda$ can be also written as

$$\gamma \pm \lambda = (a_0^2 - a_5^2)[(a_0^2 - a_5^2) \mp (a_0 a_4 - a_1 a_5)](A_4 \pm B_4) \tag{3.135}$$

---

* For instance, in this case $a_0 \rightarrow (a_0^2 - b_5^2)^2 - (a_0 b_4 - a_1 b_5)^2$,

$a_1 \rightarrow (a_0^2 - b_5^2)(a_0 a_1 - b_4 b_5) - (a_0 b_3 - a_2 b_5)(a_0 b_4 - a_1 b_5)$, $\qquad a_2 \rightarrow \ldots$

where A_4 and B_4 are given in an earlier discussion. Hence the constraint in equation (3.134) can be replaced [noting equation (3.135)] by $A_4 + B_4 > 0$, $A_4 - B_4 > 0$.

Furthermore, the constraint $A_4 \pm B_4$ can be also obtained from the following equivalent form of $\gamma \pm \lambda$, that is,

$$A_4 \pm B_4 + \frac{|X_2^{(2)} \pm Y_2^{(2)}|_{b_k=a_k}}{(a_0^2 - a_5^2)[(a_0^2 - a_5^2) \mp (a_0 a_4 - a_1 a_5)]} \qquad (3.136)^*$$

The terms $X_2^{(2)}$ and $Y_2^{(2)}$ are obtained from (3.17), (3.18) for $k = 2$ by replacing the elements of X_2, that is, a_0, a_1, by the two step substitution using row 3 and replacing the elements of Y_2, that is, b_4, b_5 by a similar substitution as indicated earlier. After this substitution, the b_k's are replaced by a_k's to expand the matrix.

Therefore we can replace (or obtain) any of the kth-generated constraints by a certain relationship from the expansion of the matrix $|X_{k-j}^{(j)} \pm Y_{k-j}^{(j)}|_{b_k=a_k}$, which indicates the relationship between the table form and the determinant method. The preceding equivalence could be also of advantage in numerical testing of polynomials where we are not required to expand high-order determinants.

In conclusion, we discuss how to obtain the stability constraints by a certain generating rule which can be easily applied. This rule is similar to Routh rule number 2 for the continuous case.[10] The proof of this generation process is not presented, but it can be deduced from the identity of the table form and the determinant method.

Illustrative design example

The critical stability constraints developed in an earlier section are now applied to a design problem. For the sampled data feedback system shown in Fig. 3.3, we shall obtain the maximum value of the gain k for the stability limit.

For the parameters given, the z-transform of the open-loop transfer function is given as

$$\mathcal{G}_1(z) = \mathcal{Z}\left[\frac{1 - e^{-Ts}}{s} e^{-1.25sT} \frac{k}{s(s + 1)}\right]$$

$$= 0.2223k \frac{(z + 0.03)(z + 1.755)}{z^2(z - 1)(z - 0.368)} \qquad (3.137)$$

---

* Another form of this equation can be written as

$$A_4 \pm B_4 = \frac{|X_3^{(1)} \pm Y_3^{(1)}|_{b_k=a_k}}{a_0^2 - a_5^2}$$

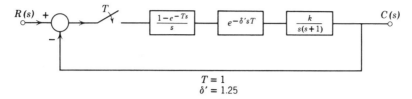

$$T = 1$$
$$\delta' = 1.25$$

FIGURE 3.3   A sampled-data system with pure delay.

The system characteristic equation for stability investigations is

$$F(z) = 1 + \mathscr{G}_1(z) = z^4 - 1.368z^3 + (0.368 + 0.2223k)z^2$$
$$+ 0.3974kz + 0.0123k = 0 \quad (3.138)$$

The preceding is a fourth-degree polynomial and we notice that if $0 < k < \varepsilon$ the system is stable. This can be readily ascertained from a sketch of the root-locus as a function of k. Hence we apply the critical constraints for $n = 4$ to obtain the maximum gain.

$$F(1) \geq 0, \quad k > 0$$
$$F(-1) \geq 0, \quad k < 16.75$$

The other critical constraint from the determinant method is

$$A_3 - B_3 \geq 0, \quad k < -247 \quad \text{or} \quad -5.5 < k < 0.72$$

From the table, form the critical constraint

$$c_0 - c_2 \geq 0$$

This constraint can be written as

$$c_0 - c_2 = (a_0 + a_4)(A_3 - B_3) \geq 0 \quad (3.139)$$

Since the critical term is $A_3 - B_3$, in both cases we obtain the maximum gain as $k_{\max} \leq 0.72$.

3.10   Division method[14],[24]

The third form of obtaining a stability test is using the simple method of division of polynomials. The derivation of this method can be obtained directly from the table form as follows.

Stability test

A necessary and sufficient condition for the real polynomial

$$F(z) = a_0 + a_1z + a_2z^2 + \ldots + a_kz^k + \ldots + a_nz^n,$$
$$\text{with } a_n > 0 \quad (3.140)$$

to have all its roots inside the unit circle in the z-plane is obtained as follows.

Form the inverse polynomial $F^*(z)$ as

$$F^*(z) = z^n F\left(\frac{1}{z}\right) = a_n + a_{n-1}z$$

$$+ a_{n-2}z^2 + \ldots + a_{n-k}z^k + \ldots + a_0 z^n \quad (3.141)$$

Obtain the stability constraints α_k by simple division as shown.

$$\frac{F(z)}{F^*(z)} \to \alpha_0 + \frac{F_1(z)}{F_1^*(z)} \to \alpha_0 + \alpha_1 \frac{F_2(z)}{F_2^*(z)} \to \alpha_0 + \alpha_1 + \alpha_2$$

$$+ \frac{F_3(z)}{F_3^*(z)} \ldots \to \alpha_0 + \alpha_1 + \alpha_2 \ldots + \alpha_{n-2} + \frac{F_{n-1}(z)}{F_{n-1}^*(z)}$$

$$(3.142)$$

where $F_1(z)$, $F_2(z)$ ... are the remainder polynomials obtained from the division and $F_1^*(z)$, $F_2^*(z)$ ... are their inverses, as defined in equation (3.141).*

We now satisfy the following constraints for the stability test.

$$F(1) > 0, F(-1) \begin{array}{ll} > 0 & n\text{-even} \\ < 0 & n\text{-odd} \end{array}$$

$$|\alpha_k| < 1, \quad k = 0, 1, 2, \ldots, n - 2 \quad (3.143)$$

The proof of the test lies in establishing the identity between the α_k's and the stability constants $a_0, b_0, c_0, \ldots$ of the table as follows:

$$\alpha_0 = \frac{a_0}{a_n}$$

$$\alpha_1 = \frac{b_{n-1}}{b_0}$$

$$\alpha_2 = \frac{c_{n-2}}{c_0} \quad (3.144)$$

$$\cdot \quad \cdot$$
$$\cdot \quad \cdot$$
$$\cdot \quad \cdot$$

$$\alpha_{n-2} = \frac{r_2}{r_0}$$

---

* To obtain the inverse of $F_1(z)$, we factor out the common factor z or its powers before we apply (3.141); also, for $F_2(z)$ and $F_3(z), \ldots$.

From the stability constraints imposed previously on the a's, b's . . . , the constraints to be imposed on the α_k's are readily established using equation (3.144).

The number of roots of $F(z)$ inside the unit circle is equal to the number of products P_k which are negative, where P_k is defined as

$$P_k = [|\alpha_0| - 1]\left[\frac{1}{|\alpha_1|} - 1\right] \ldots \left[\frac{1}{|\alpha_l|} - 1\right] \ldots \left[\frac{1}{|\alpha_{k-1}|} - 1\right]$$

$$k = 1, 2, 3, \ldots, n \quad (3.145)$$

with

$$P_1 = [|\alpha_0| - 1], \qquad P_2 = [|\alpha_0| - 1]\left[\frac{1}{|\alpha_1|} - 1\right], \ldots \quad (3.146)$$

and $|\alpha_{n-1}|$ is obtained from

$$\frac{F_{n-1}(z)}{F_{n-1}^*(z)} \to \alpha_{n-1} + \frac{F_n}{F_n^*} \quad (3.147)$$

EXAMPLE

$$F(z) = 0.0025 + 0.08z + 0.4126z^2 - 1.368z^3 + z^4 \quad (3.148)$$

$$F^*(z) = 1 - 1.368z + 0.4126z^2 + 0.08z^3 + 0.0025z^4 \quad (3.149)$$

In this case we need obtain only α_0, α_1, α_2 as follows.

$$1 - 1.368z + 0.4126z^2 + 0.08z^3$$

$$+ 0.0025z^4 \overline{)\begin{array}{l} 0.0025 + 0.08z + 0.4126z^2 - 1.368z^3 + z^4 \\ 0.0025 - 0.0034z + 0.001z^2 - 0.002z^3 \simeq 0z^4 \end{array}} \Big(0.0025$$

$$z - 1.368z^2 + 0.4116z^3$$

$$+ 0.0834z^4 \overline{)\begin{array}{l} 0.0834z + 0.4116z^2 - {\sim}1.368z^3 + z^4 \\ 0.0834z - 0.114z^2 + 0.0342z^3 + 0.007z^4 \end{array}} \Big(0.0834$$

$$0.993z^2 - 1.4022z^3$$

$$+ 0.5256z^4 \overline{)\begin{array}{l} 0.5256z^2 - 1.4022z^3 + 0.993z^4 \end{array}} \Big(0.53$$

It should be noted that in obtaining α_0, α_1, and α_2, the terms encircled in dotted lines need not be calculated.

In this case,

$$\alpha_0 = 0.0025 \qquad \alpha_1 = 0.0834 \qquad \alpha_2 = 0.53 \quad (3.150)$$

For stability constraints,

$$F(1) = 0.1271 > 0 \qquad F(-1) = 2.703 > 0$$
$$0.0025 < 1$$
$$0.0834 < 1$$
$$0.53 < 1 \tag{3.151}$$

Therefore the system described by equation (3.148) is stable.

3.11 Aperiodicity criterion for linear discrete systems[19,13]

An aperiodicity condition in discrete systems is obtained when all the roots of the characteristic equation lie on the real axis in interval $(0, 1)$ in the z-plane. Such an aperiodicity condition yields only a finite number of maxima and minima in the system response (less than n, the order of the system). This condition is important when excessive oscillations are not desirable as, for example, in instrumentation systems.

For aperiodicity criterion, we obtain the necessary and sufficient conditions (1) for the roots to be real and (2) to require that these roots be between $(0, 1)$.

The necessary and sufficient conditions for the roots to be real can be obtained by using either the Romanov conditions,[13] which require that the discriminants $D_0, D_1, \ldots, D_{n-1}$ (to be obtained from Table 3.1) be positive, or alternately, by using Fuller's conditions[34] which are based on Trudi's determinants. In the latter method, for the roots to be real it is necessary and sufficient that $A_k > 0$, $k = 2, 3, \ldots, n$, where $A_0 = 1$, $A_1 = na_n$ (always positive) and A_n is given by

$$A_n = \begin{vmatrix} a_n & a_{n-1} & \cdots & \cdots & \cdots & \cdots & 0 & . & 0 \\ 0 & A_3 & & & & & & & . \\ . & a_n & a_{n-1} & a_{n-2} & a_{n-3} & a_{n-4} & & & . \\ . & & A_2 & & & & & & . \\ 0 & 0 & a_n & a_{n-1} & a_{n-2} & & a_{n-3} & & a_0 \\ . & & & A_1 & & & & & \\ 0 & 0 & 0 & \boxed{na_n} & (n-1)a_{n-1} & (n-2)a_{n-2} & & a_1 \\ . & & & & & & & \\ 0 & na_n & (n-1)a_{n-1} & (n-2)a_{n-2} & (n-3)a_{n-3} & & 0 \\ 0 & na_n & (n-1)a_{n-1} & (n-2)a_{n-2} & (n-3)a_{n-3} & (n-4)a_{n-4} & & . \\ na_n & (n-1)a_{n-1} & \cdots & \cdots & \cdots & \cdots & & 0 \end{vmatrix} \tag{3.152}$$

In the second form we obtain $n - 1$ conditions to satisfy for the roots to be real. The D_k's of Romanov are obtained from Table 3.1.

To obtain the necessary and sufficient conditions for the roots of (3.140) to be real and to lie between zero and unity, the following additional constraints for either one of the two methods outlined can be used.

Bilinear transformation[19]

The preceding transformation involves mapping the real segment $[0, 1]$ of the z-plane onto the negative real axis of the w-plane. It is given by the following transformation:

$$z = \frac{w}{w - 1}, \quad \text{or} \quad w = \frac{z}{z - 1} \tag{3.153}$$

If equation (3.153) is substituted into (3.140), we obtain

$$F^*(w) = B_n w^n + B_{n-1} w^{n-1} + \ldots + B_{n-k} w^k + \ldots B_1 w + B_0 \tag{3.154}$$

The relationship between the a's of (3.140) and the B's of equation (3.154) is given by

$$B_{n-k} = \sum_{r=k}^{n} \binom{r}{k} a_{n-r} (-1)^k \tag{3.155}$$

where $\quad \binom{r}{k} = r!/k! \, (r - k)! \tag{3.156}$

From Romanov's or Fuller's conditions that the roots lie on the negative real axis, we require the additional constraints that

$$B_{n-k} > 0, \quad k = 0, 1, \ldots, n \tag{3.157}$$

Therefore the necessary and sufficient condition that all the roots of (3.140) lie between zero and unity in the z-plane is given as

$$D_k > 0, \quad k = 0, 1, 2, \ldots, (n - 1) \quad (\text{or } A_k > 0,$$
$$k = 2, 3, \ldots, n) \tag{3.158}$$

and

$$(-1)^k \sum_{r=k}^{n} \binom{r}{k} a_{n-r} > 0, \quad k = 0, 1, \ldots, n \tag{3.159}$$

Equations (3.158) and (3.159) yield $2n + 1$ constraints.

EXAMPLE

We obtain the aperiodicity condition for the following polynomial:

$$F(z) = a_0 + a_1 z + a_2 z^2 + a_3 z^3, \quad a_3 = 1 \tag{3.160}$$

1. Conditions for real roots
   Romanov's determinants

$$D_0 = a_1^2 - 2a_2 a_0 > 0 \tag{3.161}$$

$$D_1 = a_1^2 a_2^2 - 4a_0 a_2^3 - 2a_1^3 + 10a_0 a_1 a_2 - 9a_0^2 > 0 \tag{3.162}$$

$$D_2 = a_1^2 a_2^2 - 4a_0 a_2^3 - 4a_1^3 + 18a_0 a_1 a_2 - 27a_0^3 > 0 \tag{3.163}$$

TABLE 3.1 ROMANOV'S CONDITION TO OBTAIN D_k.

i / $k \rightarrow$	0	1	2	3	4
0	$a_1^2 - 2a_0a_2$	$a_1a_2 - 3a_0a_3$	$a_1a_3 - 4a_0a_4$	$a_1a_4 - 5a_0a_5$	$a_1a_5 - 6a_0a_6$
1		$2a_2^2 - 4a_0a_4 - 2a_1a_3$	$2a_2a_3 - 5a_0a_5 - 3a_1a_4$	$2a_2a_4 - 6a_0a_6 - 4a_1a_5$	$2a_2a_5 - 7a_0a_7 - 5a_1a_6$
2			$3a_3^2 - 6a_0a_6 - 4a_1a_5 - 2a_2a_4$	$3a_3a_4 - 7a_0a_7 - 5a_1a_6 - 3a_2a_5$	$3a_3a_5 - 8a_0a_8 - 6a_1a_7 - 4a_2a_6$
3				$4a_4^2 - 8a_0a_8 - 6a_1a_7 - 4a_2a_6 - 2a_3a_5$	$4a_4a_5 - 9a_0a_9 - 7a_1a_8 - 5a_2a_7 - 3a_3a_6$
4					$5a_5^2 - 10a_0a_{10} - 8a_1a_9 - 6a_2a_8 - 4a_3a_7 - 2a_4a_6$
5					
6					
7					
8					
9					

[1] This matrix is symmetric with respect to the main diagonal.
[2] D_k is formed by the first k rows and columns.
[3] If the system is of lower order than 10, put the higher order coefficients equal to zero.

2. For aperiodicity conditions in addition to the preceding (through transformation)

$$1 + a_2 + a_1 + a_0 > 0 \tag{3.164}$$

$$a_2 + 2a_1 + 3a_0 < 0 \tag{2.165}$$

$$a_1 + 3a_0 > 0 \tag{3.166}$$

$$a_0 < 0 \tag{3.167}$$

In this case Fuller's determinants yield

$$A_2 = a_2^3 - 3a_1 > 0 \tag{3.168}$$

$$A_3 = a_1^2a_2^2 - 4a_1^3 - 4a_0a_2^3 + 18a_0a_1a_2 - 27a_0^2 > 0 \tag{3.169}$$

5	6	7	8	9
$a_1a_6 - 7a_0a_7$	$a_1a_7 - 8a_0a_8$	$a_1a_8 - 9a_0a_9$	$a_1a_9 - 10a_0a_{10}$	a_1
$2a_2a_6 - 8a_0a_8 - 6a_1a_7$	$2a_2a_7 - 9a_0a_9 - 7a_1a_8$	$2(a_2a_8 - 4a_1a_3 - 5a_0a_{10})$	$2a_2a_9 - 9a_1a_{10}$	$2a_2$
$3a_3a_6 - 9a_0a_9 - 7a_1a_8 - 5a_2a_7$	$3a_3a_7 - 10a_0a_{10} - 8a_1a_9 - 6a_2a_8$	$3a_3a_8 - 9a_1a_{10} - 7a_2a_9$	$3a_3a_9 - 8a_2a_{10}$	$3a_3$
$4a_4a_6 - 10a_0a_9 - 8a_1a_9 - 6a_2a_8 - 4a_3a_7$	$4a_4a_7 - 9a_1a_{10} - 7a_2a_9 - 5a_3a_8$	$4a_4a_8 - 8a_2a_{10} - 6a_3a_9$	$4a_4a_9 - 7a_3a_{10}$	$4a_4$
$5a_5a_6 + 9a_1a_{10} - 7a_2a_9 - 5a_3a_8 - 3a_4a_7$	$5a_5a_7 - 8a_2a_{10} - 6a_3a_9 - 4a_4a_8$	$5a_5a_8 - 7a_3a_{10} - 5a_4a_9$	$5a_5a_9 - 6a_4a_{10}$	$5a_5$
$6a_6^2 - 8a_2a_{10} - 6a_3a_9 - 4a_4a_8 - 2a_5a_7$	$6a_6a_7 - 7a_3a_{10} - 5a_4a_9 - 3a_5a_8$	$6a_6a_8 - 6a_4a_{10} - 4a_5a_9$	$6a_6a_9 - 5a_5a_{10}$	$6a_6$
	$7a_7^2 - 6a_4a_{10} - 4a_5a_9 - 2a_6a_8$	$7a_7a_8 - 5a_5a_{10} - 3a_6a_9$	$7a_7a_9 - 4a_6a_{10}$	$7a_7$
		$8a_8^2 - 4a_6a_{10} - 2a_7a_9$	$8a_8a_9 - 3a_7a_{10}$	$8a_8$
			$9a_9^2 - 2a_8a_{10}$	$9a_9$
				10

nd factor out from the nth column (and row) a_n (finally a_n^2).

Critical constraints

Similar to critical stability constraints, we can obtain the critical aperiodicity constraints, which are given as

$$A_n \geq 0 \tag{3.170}$$

or

$$D_{n-1} \geq 0 \tag{3.171}$$

These equations indicate that when a parameter is changed for an initially aperiodic system, the determinant A_n is the first to become zero when two roots become complex.

When the roots remain real but move outside the region $(0, 1)$, the following critical constraint is satisfied:

$$F(1) \geq 0 \qquad (3.172)$$

and

$$F(-1) \geq 0 \qquad (3.173)$$

Equations (3.171) to (3.173) yield the critical constraints for aperiodicity.

3.12 Theorems related to stability and number of roots[2,25,26,32]

In this section, certain theorems are introduced which give a quick check on stability and on the number of roots within the unit circle.

Monotonic conditions

If the coefficients of $F(z)$ are such that

$$a_n > a_{n-1} > a_{n-2} > \ldots > a_1 > a_0 > 0 \qquad (3.174)$$

then all the roots are within the unit circle; thus the system is stable. This can be easily verified since the constraints given in equation (3.78) are readily satisfied, that is, $b_0 < 0$, $c_0 > 0$, $d_0 > 0, \ldots$.

As a corollary to the preceding theorem we can state the following. If

$$0 < a_n < a_{n-1} < \ldots < a_1 < a_0 \qquad (3.175)$$

then $F(z)$ has all its roots outside the unit circle. This can be easily verified from the formula of number of roots inside the unit circle. Furthermore, if the coefficients of $F(z)$ are all positive, the roots lie in the ring $m \leq |z| \leq M$. The values m and M are, respectively, the smallest and the biggest of the n-numbers[32]

$$\frac{a_{n-1}}{a_n}, \quad \frac{a_{n-2}}{a_{n-1}}, \quad \frac{a_{n-3}}{a_{n-2}}, \ldots, \frac{a_0}{a_1} \qquad (3.176)$$

Relationships between coefficients[2,25]

If the coefficients of $F(z)$ are such that

$$|a_k| > |a_n| + |a_{n-1}| + \ldots + |a_{k+1}| + |a_{k-1}| + \ldots + |a_1| + |a_0| \qquad (3.177)$$

then the polynomial is unstable.

To prove this theorem, let

$$\phi(z) = a_k z^k \qquad (3.178)$$

and

$$\psi(z) = a_n z^n + \ldots + a_{k+1} z^{k+1} + a_{k-1} z^{k-1} + \ldots + a_0. \qquad (3.178a)$$

If we consider this equation for $|z| = 1$, we have

$$|\phi(z)| = |a_k| > |a_n| + \ldots + |a_{k+1}| + |a_{k-1}| + \ldots$$
$$+ |a_0| \geq |a_n z^n + \ldots + a_{k+1} z^{k+1} + a_{k-1} z^{k-1}$$
$$+ \ldots + a_0| = |\psi(z)| \qquad (3.179)$$

Since $\phi(z) + \psi(z) = F(z)$, we can write

$$\frac{F(z)}{\phi(z)} = 1 + \frac{\psi(z)}{\phi(z)} \qquad (3.180)$$

However, $\left|\dfrac{\psi(z)}{\phi(z)}\right| < 1$; therefore in the mapping of equation (3.180) when z describes the boundary of the unit circle, the origin is not enclosed. We know that $\phi(z) = a_k z^k$ has k roots inside the unit circle (at the origin); thus, noting equation (3.180), $F(z)$ should also have the same number of roots inside the unit circle. Therefore the remaining roots of $F(z)$, that is, $n - k$, should lie outside the unit circle, and thus the system is unstable.

Minimax principle[23]

This method is useful in giving the stability conditions for certain polynomials $F(z)$ whose coefficients (with $a_n = 1$) are less than unity. It is based on giving precisely the largest root of an equation which dominates the form of $F(z)$. For stability considerations the form of the constraint is given by

$$|a_{n-k}| \leq \rho^{k-1} - \rho^k, \qquad k = 1, 2, \ldots, n - 1,$$
$$a_n = 1 \quad \text{and} \quad 0 \leq \rho < 1 \qquad (3.181)$$

and

$$|a_0| \leq \rho^{n-1} \qquad (3.182)$$

A stability chart for different values of k as a function of ρ and also for different values of n up to 7 is given in Fig. 3.4. The calculation of the chart can be extended to higher-degree polynomials of $F(z)$.

EXAMPLE

To illustrate the application of the chart we test the following polynomial for stability:

$$F(z) = z^4 + 0.2z^3 + 0.01z^2 + 0.032z - 0.024 \qquad (3.183)$$

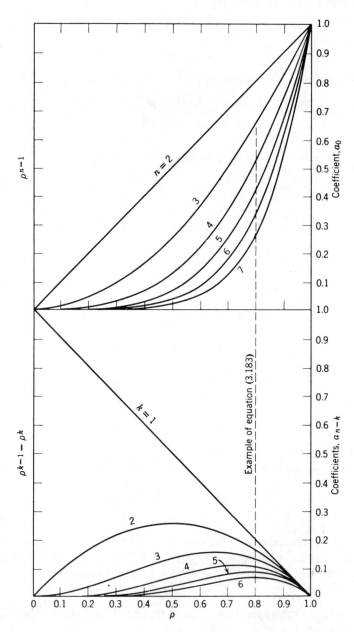

FIGURE 3.4   Stability chart for linear discrete systems.

From the chart we find that for certain ranges of values of $\rho < 0.8$ the inequalities (3.181) and (3.182) are satisfied, and hence the system has all its roots inside the unit circle.

Number of roots inside a circle of radius $\sigma < 1$[24]

To obtain information on the number of roots inside a circle of radius $\sigma < 1$, we may apply a certain transformation on $F(z)$, that is, $z' = z/\sigma$ so that the circle of radius σ becomes equivalent to the unit circle. Hence the proceeding discussion can be readily applied to this case.

This procedure is useful in testing the relative stability of the characteristic polynomial. The constraints for $F(z) = \sum_{p=0}^{n} a_p z^p = 0$ to have all its roots inside $|z| = \sigma < 1$ will be obtained by replacing in the constraints found for $\sigma = 1$ the following:

$$a_0 \to a_0, a_1 \to a_1\sigma, \ldots, a_p \to a_p\sigma^p, \ldots, a_n \to a_n\sigma^n \qquad (3.184)$$

As an extension of this theorem, we can also obtain the stability conditions or the number of roots of a shifted unit circle. This is based on the following theorem by Marden.

To obtain the number of roots in the circle $|z - s| < 1$, replace the a_p's of $F(z)$ by

$$a_p \to \sum_{k=p}^{n} \binom{k}{p} s^{k-p} a_k \qquad (3.185)$$

where the binomial $\binom{k}{p} = k!/p! \, (k - p)!$

In particular, we obtain the number of roots in the unit shifted circle as shown in Fig. 3.1 by letting $s = 1$ in the shifting transformation.

Theorem related to $F(z)$ having roots on the unit circle $|z| = 1$ and reciprocal roots[2,4,31]

In the preceding case when $F(z)$ is such that in the table constraints certain $h_0 = h_{n-k}$ or $F_{k+1} \equiv 0$, the following theorem is useful.

If for some $k < n$, $P_j \neq 0$ for all $j \leq k$, (that is, $g_0 \neq g_{n-k+1}$ in the table form), but $F_{k+1}(z) \equiv 0$, then $F(z)$ has $n - k$ zeros at the zeros of $F_k(z)$. These zeros are either on the unit circle $|z| = 1$ or occur in pairs that are inverse relative to the unit circle or are a combination of both. Furthermore $F(z)$ has p additional zeros in the circle, where p is the number of negative P_j for $j = 1, 2, \ldots, k$, and it has $q = k - p$ additional zeros outside the circle.

EXAMPLE

Let $F(z) = 1 + 2z + z^2 + 2z^3$

	z^0	z^1	z^2	z^3
$F(z)$	1	2	1	2
$F^*(z)$	2	1	2	1
$F_1(z)$	-3	0	-3	
$F_1^*(z)$	-3	0	-3	
$F_2(z)$	0	0		

$$(3.186)$$

It is noticed from the table that $|a_0| < |a_n|$, $F_2(z) \equiv 0$; thus one root is inside the unit circle and two roots are on the unit circle (since no reciprocal roots in $F_1(z)$ exist). To obtain the location of these roots we solve for

$$F_1(z) = -3 - 3z^2 = -3(1 + z^2) = 0 \qquad (3.187)$$

Therefore the roots are at $z_{2,3} = \pm j$.

When $F(z)$ has no zeros on the unit circle, but $h_0 = h_{n-k}$, the number p of zeros of $F(z)$ in the unit circle may be obtained by a limiting process as follows[4]

We replace $F_k(z)$ by the polynomial

$$f_k(z) = F_k(rz) \qquad (3.188)$$

which, because $r = 1 \pm \varepsilon$ and ε is a sufficiently small positive quantity, has as many zeros in the circle as does $F_k(z)$.

EXAMPLE

$$F(z) = -2 + 3z + 2z^2 \qquad (3.189)$$

Here it is noticed that $a_0^2 - a_n^2 = 0$ [and $F(z)$ has no zero on the unit circle]; therefore we replace z in $F(z)$ by $rz = (1 - \varepsilon)z$, with $\varepsilon = 0.1$; thus

$$f_k(z) = -2 + 2.7z + 1.62z^2 \qquad (3.190)$$

In the preceding case $a_0^2 - a_n^2 = 4 - (1.62)^2 > 0$, and

$$f_k(1) > 0, \qquad f_k(-1) < 0, \quad \text{or} \quad |b_2| < |b_{n-1}| \qquad (3.191)$$

Therefore $P_1 > 0$, $P_2 < 0$, one negative sign; hence one root exists outside the unit circle and the other root inside the circle. It should be noted that the same results are obtained if ε is considered to be negative, that is, $r = 1 + \varepsilon = 1.1$.

Several methods are available whereby existence or nonexistence of zeros on the unit circle can be determined. These methods which can be applied for testing the number of zeros on the unit circle are discussed in Appendix 2.

Appendix 1. *Derivation of the table form of stability*[4]

In this appendix we shall derive the table form of the stability test by first obtaining the conditions on the number of roots inside the unit circle. In this manner, the stability condition is obtained as a special case when all the roots of $F(z) = 0$ are within the unit circle. Before we derive the conditions for the number of roots, certain properties of $F(z)$ and its inverse $F^*(z)$ as well as other associated polynomials are introduced.

Let the considered real polynomial to be tested for the number of roots be denoted as $F(z)$ and written as follows:

$$F(z) = a_0 + a_1 z + a_2 z^2 + \ldots + a_k z^k + \ldots + a_n z^n$$

$$= a_0 \prod_{i=1}^{n} (z - z_i)$$

In addition, consider the sequence of polynomials $F_0(z) = F(z)$, $F_1(z)$, $F_2(z), \ldots F_j(z)$ whose properties will be studied in detail. If we associate to each of the polynomials $F_j(z)$ the polynomial $F_j^*(z)$ whose roots are the reciprocal with respect to the unit circle of $F_j(z)$, $F_{j+1}(z)$ can be obtained from $F_j(z)$ as follows:

$$F_{j+1}(z) = a_0^{(j)} F_j(z) - a_{n-j}^{(j)} F_j^*(z), \qquad j = 0, 1, 2, \ldots, n-1$$

(A.1)

where

$$F_j(z) = \sum_{k=0}^{n-j} a_k^{(j)} z^k, \qquad \text{with } a_k^{(0)} \text{ written as } a_k$$ (A.2)

and

$$F_j^*(z) = a_0 \prod_{i=1}^{n} \left(z - \frac{1}{z_i} \right) = z^{n-j} F_j\left(\frac{1}{z} \right), \qquad j = 0, 1, \ldots, n-1$$

(A.3)

The following properties can be deduced from (A.1) and (A.3).

1. If $F_j(z)$ is of degree $n - j$, then F_{j+1} is at most of degree $n - j - 1$ in z.
2. The coefficients of F_{j+1} can be obtained from the coefficients of F_j as follows:

$$a_k^{(j+1)} = a_0^{(j)} a_k^{(j)} - a_{n-j}^{(j)} a_{n-j-k}^{(j)}$$ (A.4)

In each polynomial $F_j(z)$, the constant real coefficient $a_0^{(j)}$ is denoted by δ_j so that

$$\delta_{j+1} = [a_0^{(j)}]^2 - [a_{n-j}^{(j)}]^2 = a_0^{(j+1)}$$ (A.5)

3. The zeros of $F_j^*(z)$ are the inverses of the zeros of $F_j(z)$, relative to the circle $|z| = 1$. In particular, if $F_j(z)$ has no zero on the unit circle and p_j zeros inside the unit circle, then $F_j^*(z)$ has $(n - j - p_j)$ zeros inside the unit circle and no zero on the unit circle.

4. The absolute value of $F_j(z)$ for $z = e^{i\theta}$ is equivalent to the absolute value $F_j^*(e^{i\theta})$, that is,

$$|F_j(e^{i\theta})| = |F_j^*(e^{i\theta})| \tag{A.6}$$

The preceding can be easily shown from the relationship

$$F_j^*(z) = z^{n-j} F_j\left(\frac{1}{z}\right) \tag{A.7}$$

When $z = e^{i\theta}$, we get

$$F_j^*(e^{i\theta}) = e^{i(n-j)\theta} F_j(e^{-i\theta}) \tag{A.8}$$

Since $|e^{i(n-j)\theta}| = 1$, then

$$|F_j^*(e^{i\theta})| = |F_j(e^{-i\theta})| = |F_j(e^{i\theta})| \tag{A.9}$$

To illustrate the mentioned properties, we shall consider the following third-degree ($n = 3$) example.

$$F(z) = z^3 - 2.5z^2 - 7z + 4 = (z - 0.5)(z + 2)(z - 4)$$

Here

$$a_3 = 1, \qquad a_2 = -2.5, \qquad a_1 = -7, \qquad a_0 = 4$$

From (A.3), we obtain the inverse polynomial $F^*(z)$.

$$F^*(z) = z^3 F\left(\frac{1}{z}\right) = z^3(z^{-3} - 2.5z^{-2} - 7z^{-1} + 4)$$

$$= 1 - 2.5z - 7z^2 + 4z^3 = 4(z - 2)(z + 0.5)(z - \tfrac{1}{4})$$

To obtain $F_1(z)$, we use (A.1) for $j = 0$

$$F_1(z) = a_0 F(z) - a_n F^*(z) = -3z^2 - 25.5z + 15$$
$$= a_2^{(1)} z^2 + a_1^{(1)} z + a_0^{(1)}$$

It is noticed that $F_1(z)$ is in this case one degree in z less than $F(z)$. By noting (A.2), we readily identify, $a_0^{(1)} = 15$, $a_1^{(1)} = -25.5$, $a_2^{(1)} = -3$. These values can also be calculated from (A.4) for $j = 0$ as follows:

$$a_0^{(1)} = a_0^2 - a_3^2 = 15$$
$$a_1^{(1)} = a_0 a_1 - a_2 a_2 = -25.5$$
$$a_2^{(1)} = a_0 a_2 - a_2 a_3 = -3$$

which are the same as those obtained from (A.1). From (A.5), we can calculate δ_1 as

$$\delta_1 = a_0^2 - a_3^2 = 15 = a_0^{(1)}$$

The zeros of $F(z)$ are $z_1 = +0.5$, $z_2 = -2$, $z_3 = 4$. The zeros of $F^*(z)$ are 2, $-\frac{1}{2}$, $\frac{1}{4}$, which are the inverses of the zeros of $F(z)$ with respect to the unit circle. Furthermore, it is noticed that $F(z)$ has one zero inside the unit circle and $F^*(z)$ has $n - 1 = 2$ zeros inside the unit circle.

Similarly, we can calculate $F_2(z)$, $F_3(z)$, δ_2, and δ_3 following the same procedure. However, a systematic method for obtaining the $F_j(z)$ and δ_{j+1} is to construct the following table for the discussed example.

Polynomial	z^0	z^1	z^2	z^3
$F(z)$	4	-7	-2.5	1
$F^*(z)$	1	-2.5	-7	4
$F_1(z)$	$\delta_1 = 15$	-25.5	-3	
$F_1^*(z)$	-3	-25.5	15	
$F_2(z)$	$\delta_2 = 216$	-459		
$F_2^*(z)$	-459	216		
$F_3(z)$	$\delta_2 \simeq -164{,}000$			

It is noticed from the table that $F_3(z)$ is a constant and thus has no roots inside the unit circle. In addition, from the table we obtain $\delta_1 = 15 > 0$, $\delta_2 = 216 > 0$, and $\delta_3 \simeq -164{,}000 < 0$. It should be noted from the following discussions that the sign of δ_{j+1} is important in determining stability or the number of roots inside and outside the unit circle.

THEOREM: If $F_j(z)$ has p_j zeros in the unit circle C and has no zeros on C and if $\delta_{j+1} \neq 0$, then $F_{j+1}(z)$ has

$$p_{j+1} = \tfrac{1}{2}\{n - j - [(n - j) - 2p_j]\,\mathrm{sgn}\,\delta_{j+1}\} \qquad (\text{A.10})$$

zeros in C and has no zeros on C.*

To prove this theorem, we assume first that $\delta_{j+1} > 0$. From equation (A.1) we can write

$$\frac{F_{j+1}(z)}{a_0^{(j)}F_j(z)} = 1 - \frac{a_{n-j}^{(j)}F_j^*(z)}{a_0^{(j)}F_j(z)} \qquad (\text{A.11})$$

Using equation (A.5) and the property of equation (A.9), we have

$$\left| \frac{a_{n-j}^{(j)}F_j^*(z)}{a_0^{(j)}F_j(z)} \right| < 1 \qquad (\text{A.12})$$

---

* The case when $F(z)$ has zeros on the unit circle will be discussed in Appendix 2.

Now if we apply the mapping theorem to equation (A.11), we notice that $F_{j+1}(z)/a_0^{(j)}F_j(z)$ does not enclose the origin when z moves on C. Therefore we deduce from Rouche's theorem (or from Cauchy's mapping theorem) that the zeros of $F_{j+1}(z)$ are of the same number p_j as the zeros of $F_j(z)$. Since sgn $\delta_{j+1} = 1$, this number is in agreement with (A.10). Furthermore, inequality (A.12) makes it impossible for $F_{j+1}(z)$ to have any zeros on the unit circle.

If we take the case $\delta_{j+1} < 0$, we have, from (A.1) and (A.19), the following:

$$\frac{F_{j+1}(z)}{a_{n-j}^{(j)}F_j^*(z)} = \frac{a_0^{(j)}F_j(z)}{a_{n-j}^{(j)}F_j^*(z)} - 1 \tag{A.13}$$

and

$$\left| \frac{a_0^{(j)}F_j(z)}{a_{n-j}^{(j)}F_j^*(z)} \right| < 1 \tag{A.14}$$

By the same reasoning as before, this case shows that the polynomial $F_{j+1}(z)$ has in C (noting property 3) the same number $(n - j - p_j)$ of zeros as $a_{n-j}^{(j)}F_j^*(z)$. Since now sgn $\delta_{j+1} = -1$, this number is also in agreement with the formula (A.10). Likewise inequality (A.14) makes it impossible for $F_{j+1}(z)$ to have any zeros on the circle C. Thus we have proved that the theorem of (A.10) is valid in both cases.

If we apply the formula (A.10) to each $F_j(z)$ in equation (A.1), we readily obtain

$$p_1 = \tfrac{1}{2}[n - (n - 2p) \text{ sgn } \delta_1] \tag{A.15}$$

where $p_0 = p =$ number of zeros of $F(z)$ inside the unit circle.

$$\begin{aligned} p_2 &= \tfrac{1}{2}[(n - 1) - (n - 1 - 2p_1) \text{ sgn } \delta_2] \\ &= \tfrac{1}{2}\{(n - 1) - [(n - 1) - n + (n - 2p) \text{ sgn } \delta_1] \text{ sgn } \delta_2\} \\ &= \tfrac{1}{2}[(n - 1) - (n - 2p) \text{ sgn } (\delta_1\delta_2) + \text{ sgn } \delta_2] \end{aligned} \tag{A.16}$$

The expression for p_2 is the special case of the formula

$$\begin{aligned} p_j = \tfrac{1}{2}[(n - j + 1) &- (n - 2p) \text{ sgn } (\delta_1\delta_2 \ldots \delta_j) \\ &+ \text{ sgn } (\delta_2\delta_3 \ldots \delta_j) + \text{ sgn } (\delta_3\delta_4 \ldots \delta_j) + \ldots + \text{ sgn } \delta_j] \end{aligned}$$

$$\tag{A.17}$$

Let us assume that the preceding formula has been verified also for $j = 3, 4, \ldots, k - 1$, and we will show by induction that it holds for all k.

Let $j = k - 1$ in equations (A.10) and (A.17) to obtain

$$
\begin{aligned}
p_k &= \tfrac{1}{2}\{n - k + 1 - [(n - k + 1) - 2p_{k-1}] \operatorname{sgn} \delta_k\} \\
&= \tfrac{1}{2}\{(n - k + 1) - [(n - k + 1) - (n - k + 2) \\
&\quad + (n - 2p) \operatorname{sgn} (\delta_1\delta_2 \ldots \delta_{k-1}) - \operatorname{sgn} (\delta_2\delta_3 \ldots \delta_{k-1}) \\
&\quad - \operatorname{sgn} (\delta_3\delta_4 \ldots \delta_{k-1}) - \ldots - \operatorname{sgn} \delta_{k-1}] \operatorname{sgn} \delta_k\} \\
&= \tfrac{1}{2}\{(n - k + 1) - (n - 2p) \operatorname{sgn} (\delta_1\delta_2 \ldots \delta_k) \\
&\quad + \operatorname{sgn} (\delta_2\delta_3 \ldots \delta_k) + \operatorname{sgn} (\delta_3\delta_4 \ldots \delta_k) + \ldots + \operatorname{sgn} \delta_k\}
\end{aligned}
$$

(A.18)

It is noticed that (A.18) is exactly equation (A.17) for $j = k$. Thus by mathematical induction we have shown that (A.17) holds for all j, $2 \leq j \leq n$.

If we let $j = n$ in (A.17) and note that $p_n = 0$ because F_n is a constant term (see F_3 for the case $n = 3$), we have

$$
0 = 1 - (n - 2p) \operatorname{sgn} (\delta_1\delta_2 \ldots \delta_n) + \operatorname{sgn} (\delta_2\delta_3 \ldots \delta_n) \\
+ \operatorname{sgn} (\delta_3\delta_4 \ldots \delta_n) + \ldots + \operatorname{sgn} \delta_n \quad \text{(A.19)}
$$

Solving this equation for p, we obtain

$$
p = \frac{1}{2}\left(n - \sum_{k=1}^{n} \operatorname{sgn} P_k\right) \tag{A.20}
$$

where

$$
P_k = \delta_1\delta_2 \ldots \delta_k, \qquad k = 1, 2, 3, \ldots, n \tag{A.21}
$$

The formula (A.20) is the key relationship which yields information on the number of roots inside the unit circle. To interpret (A.20), let us denote by v the number of negative P_k, $k = 1, 2, \ldots, n$. Then as $(n - v)$ is the number of positive P_k, we may write (A.20) as

$$
p = \tfrac{1}{2}[n + v - (n - v)] = v \tag{A.22}
$$

which leads us to express finally this important theorem.[4]

If for the polynomial

$$
F(z) = a_0 + a_1z + \ldots + a_nz^n
$$

p of the products P_k defined in (A.21) are negative and the remaining $n - p$ are positive, then $F(z)$ has p zeros in the unit circle $|z| = 1$, no zeros on this circle, and $n - p$ zeros outside the unit circle.

From this general theorem, we can deduce that the necessary and sufficient conditions for $F(z) = 0$ to have all its zeros (or roots) inside the unit circle is

$$
\delta_1 < 0, \, \delta_2 > 0, \, \delta_3 > 0, \, \ldots \delta_n > 0 \tag{A.23}
$$

which gives, in this case, $p = n$.

A convenient way to obtain δ_k and $F_j(z)$ (as noticed from the third-degree case) is to construct Table (A.24)

TABLE A.24 A STABILITY PROCEDURE FORM

Polynomial	Row	δ_k	Coefficients					
$F(z)$	1		a_0	a_1	$a_2 \ldots$	a_{n-k}	$\cdots$	a_n
$F^*(z)$	2		a_n	a_{n-1}	$\cdots$	a_k	$\cdots$	a_0
$F_1(z)$	3	$\delta_1 = a_0^{(1)}$	$a_0^{(1)}$	$a_1^{(1)}$	$\cdots$	$a_{n-1}^{(1)}$		
$F_1^*(z)$	4		$a_{n-1}^{(1)}$	$a_{n-2}^{(1)}$	$\cdots$	$a_0^{(1)}$		
.		$\delta_2 = a_0^{(2)}$						
.		.						
.		.						
.		.						
$F_{n-1}(z)$	$2n-1$	$\delta_{n-1} = a_0^{(n-1)}$	$a_0^{(n-1)}$	$a_1^{(n-1)}$				
$F_{n-1}^*(z)$	$2n$		$a_1^{(n-1)}$	$a_0^{(n-1)}$				
$F_n(z)$	$2n+1$	$\delta_n = a_0^{(n)}$	$a_0^{(n)}$					
$F_n^*(z)$	$2n+2$		$a_0^{(n)}$					

$$(A.24)$$

In Table (A.24)

$$a_0^{(1)} = \begin{vmatrix} a_0 & a_n \\ a_n & a_0 \end{vmatrix}, \quad a_k^{(1)} = \begin{vmatrix} a_0 & a_{n-k} \\ a_n & a_k \end{vmatrix},$$

$$a_0^{(2)} = \begin{vmatrix} a_0^{(1)} & a_{n-1}^{(1)} \\ a_{n-1}^{(1)} & a_0^{(1)} \end{vmatrix}, \ldots \qquad (A.25)$$

Furthermore, it should be noted that the elements of row $2k + 2$ consist of the coefficients of the row $2k + 1$ written in reverse order ($k = 0, 1, 2, \ldots, n$).

The number of roots inside the unit circle if $\delta_k \neq 0$ is equal to the negative number of the products of

$$P_k = \delta_1 \delta_2 \delta_3 \ldots \delta_k, \quad k = 1, 2, 3, 4, \ldots, n \qquad (A.26)$$

where

$$P_1 = \delta_1, \quad P_2 = \delta_1 \delta_2, \ldots \qquad (A.27)$$

The necessary and sufficient condition for all the roots to be inside the unit circle is that the negative number of the products P_k be n. This condition is satisfied if and only if the following exists:

$$\delta_1 < 0, \delta_2 > 0, \delta_3 > 0, \ldots, \delta_n > 0 \qquad (A.28)$$

In certain special cases of numerical polynomials when some of the coefficients in $F(z)$ are zero, $F_1(z)$ in Table (A.24) is of degree less than $n - 1$, which might indicate that some of the δ_k's are missing. However, in these cases we must add all the required zeros in the table for $F_1(z)$ so that all the δ_k's appear and thus the determination of stability or root distribution can proceed in the usual manner.[39] Similar procedures should be used when these cases occur for any of the intermediate polynomials in $F_k(z)$ in the entries of the table. Examples of such special cases are presented in Problem 3.9.

SIMPLIFICATION OF THE STABILITY CRITERION.[24] To simplify the criterion which will enable us to write Table (A.24) for the stability test, we relate the connection between the δ_k's and Schur-Cohn determinants Δ_k. The determinants Δ_k are discussed earlier, and they offer an alternate method for obtaining the number of roots inside the unit circle. The connection between δ_k and Δ_k was first established and proved by Marden[4] and is given by the following relation:

$$\Delta_k = \frac{\delta_k}{\delta_1^{k-2} \delta_2^{k-3} \ldots \delta_{k-2}} \tag{A.29}$$

This equation could be used to calculate the Δ_k's from the δ_k's, thus avoiding evaluation of higher-order determinants. When $k = n$, equation (A.29) yields

$$\Delta_n = \frac{\delta_n}{\delta_1^{n-2} \delta_2^{n-3} \delta_3^{n-4} \ldots \delta_{n-2}} \tag{A.30}$$

or

$$\delta_n = \delta_1^{n-2} \delta_2^{n-3} \delta_3^{n-4} \delta_4^{n-5}, \ldots, \delta_{n-3}^2 \delta_{n-2} \Delta_n \tag{A.31}$$

From the discussion of equation (3.22) it is indicated that

$$\Delta_n = A_n^2 - B_n^2 = (A_{n-1} - B_{n-1})^2 F(1) \cdot F(-1) \tag{A.32}$$

Substituting this expression in (A.31), we obtain

$$\delta_n = \delta_1^{n-2} \delta_2^{n-3} \delta_3^{n-4}, \ldots, \delta_{n-2}(A_{n-1} - B_{n-1})^2 F(1) \cdot F(-1),$$
$$n \geq 2. \tag{A.33}$$

Since $(A_{n-1} - B_{n-1})^2$ is always positive when, $\delta_1, \delta_2, \ldots, \delta_{n-1} \neq 0$, and since for the roots to be inside the unit circle $\delta_2, \delta_3, \ldots, \delta_{n-1}$ are all positive, the last condition $\delta_n > 0$ can be equivalently replaced by

$$\delta_n > 0 \Leftrightarrow (-1)^n F(1) \cdot F(-1) > 0. \tag{A.34}^*$$

---

* This equivalence can also be shown from geometric consideration of the arrangement of the zeros without the mathematical verification using equation (A.29).

If we let $a_n > 0$, $\delta_n > 0$ reduces to

$$F(1) > 0, \qquad F(-1) \begin{array}{ll} > 0, & n\text{-even} \\ < 0, & n\text{-odd} \end{array} \qquad (A.35)$$

It should be noted that the last constraint in equation (A.28) could be replaced by equation (A.35) by letting $a_n > 0$.

We may utilize the relationship (A.33) to obtain the sign of P_n without having to calculate δ_n as follows. We multiply (A.33) by $\delta_1\delta_2\ldots\delta_{n-1}$ and use (A.26) and (A.27) to obtain

$$\text{sgn } P_n = \text{sgn}(P_{n-1}P_{n-2}\ldots P_1)\,\text{sgn}[F(1)F(-1)] \qquad (A.35a)$$

If the number of negative P_k ($k = 1, 2, \ldots, n-1$) is even,

$$\text{sgn } P_n = \text{sgn}[F(1)F(-1)] \qquad (A.35b)$$

and if the number of negative P_k ($k = 1, 2, \ldots, n-1$) is odd,

$$\text{sgn } P_n = \text{sgn}[-F(1)F(-1)] \qquad (A.35c)$$

Since the connection between δ_k and $\Delta_k = A_k^2 - B_k^2$ is obtained, we can apply all the significant simplifications obtained on the A_k's and B_k's to δ_k or to the stability problem using this criterion.

Utilizing equation (A.35), we can rewrite (A.24) in the form of Table (3.77) by noting the following from (A.24) and (3.77):

$$b_k = a_k^{(1)}, \qquad c_k = a_k^{(2)}, \qquad d_k = a_k^{(3)}, \qquad e_k = a_k^{(4)}, \ldots \qquad (A.36)$$

and

$$\delta_1 = a_0^{(1)} = b_0 = a_0^2 - a_n^2, \qquad \delta_2 = a_0^{(2)} = b_0^2 - b_{n-1}^2,$$
$$\delta_3 = a_0^{(3)} = c_0^2 - c_{n-2}^2, \ldots$$
$$(A.37)$$

$$\delta_{n-1} = a_0^{(n-1)} = r_0^2 - r_0^2,$$
$$\delta_n = (r_0^2 - r_2^2)^2 - (r_0r_1 - r_1r_2)^2 = a_0^{(n)} \qquad (A.38)$$

Appendix 2.   Singular cases in
determinant and table forms[2,31,35,39,40]

Sometimes the kth determinant Δ_k or the kth entry in the table δ_k vanishes, making the method of determining the zeros of $F(z)$ inside the unit circle appear inapplicable. Such cases of vanishing Δ_k (or when $A_k = B_k$) or δ_k are called singular cases. One such case of the table form has been briefly discussed in Section 3.12, and the purpose of this appendix is to present in detail the modifications required to enable us to determine exactly the number of roots inside, on, or outside the unit circle. The results are stated without proofs, and references to this derivation will be given. To systematize the discussion the modified methods to be applied to the singular cases are divided into two main catagories, the perturbation method and the direct method.

1. PERTURBATION METHOD. This method is useful in certain cases, but its application may not be as straightforward as the direct method. The basis of this application lies in the fact that since both Δ_k and δ_k are polynomials in the coefficients of $F(z)$ of equation (3.9), a coefficient of $F(z)$ may be varied in such a way that Δ_k and δ_k become nonzero (if they vanished before the variation). To be specific, let $a_1, a_2, a_3, \ldots, a_n$ be fixed. Then Δ_k and δ_k are nonconstant polynomials in a_0. Now if we replace a_0 by a_0^* we obtain the following new polynomial

$$F^+(z) = a_0^* + a_1 z + a_2 z^2 + \ldots + a_n z^n \qquad \text{(A.39)}$$

For this polynomial Δ_k and δ_k are nonvanishing. Furthermore, assuming Δ_k and δ_k are the first vanishing elements, the signs of Δ_j and δ_j for $j < k$ will be the same for $F^+(z)$ as for $F(z)$ provided $|a_0 - a_0^*|$ is sufficiently small.

The difference between the zeros of $F(z)$ and $F^+(z)$ is also small provided that $|a_0 - a_0^*|$ is small. Therefore if $F(z)$ has no zeros on the unit circle $F^+(z)$ will have the same number of zeros inside the unit circle as $F(z)$. The foregoing method of perturbing a_0 is useful in principle for handling some singular cases. Therefore

If $F(z)$ has no zeros on the unit circle, consider $F^+(z) = a_0^* + a_1 z + \ldots + a_n z^n$. There exists an a_0^* (near a_0) such that Δ_k^* and δ_k^* do not vanish for $F^+(z)$, and the latter has the same number of zeros inside the unit circle as $F(z)$.

It should be noted that it suffices to compute Δ_j^+ and δ_j^+ for only $j \geq k$.

To determine whether $F(z)$ has any roots on the unit circle or not, which is important for this application, the following useful theorem which is stated in Section 3.12 is reintroduced.

A necessary condition for $F(z)$ to have a zero on the unit circle is for δ_m to vanish for some $1 \leq m \leq n$ and for the next (that is, $m + 1$st) row in the table to be all zeros.

Thus when δ_k vanishes, we can sometimes ascertain whether $F(z)$ has any roots on the unit circle by computing the next row of the table. The determination of the exact number of roots on the unit circle is presented in the next section in a discussion of the direct method. The criterion for determining whether $F(z)$ has a root on the unit circle when using the determinant method is given by Jury[42]: A necessary condition for $F(z)$ to have a root on the unit circle is that $\Delta_n = 0$.

For a polynomial with real coefficients, it is indicated that $\Delta_n = (A_{n-1} - B_{n-1})^2 F(1)F(-1)$ and thus the vanishing of Δ_n in some cases could be easily determined from $F(1)$ and $F(-1)$. In general, Δ_n vanishes only if $F(z)$ has roots on the unit circle or reciprocal pairs. This is evident from equation (3.70), where we notice that $A_{n-1} - B_{n-1} = 0$ when $z_i z_k = |z_i|^2$ or $z_i = \dfrac{1}{z_k}$. It should be noted that the computation of $A_{n-1} - B_{n-1}$ is rather lengthy in comparison with that for Δ_k, $k \ll n$.

If $A_{n-1} - B_{n-1} = 0$, we can factor out the polynomial that contains the roots on the unit circle or the reciprocal pairs by obtaining $D(z)$, the greatest common divisor of $F(z)$ and $F^*(z)$. Sometimes this can be easily achieved by the division process (Euclidian algorithm) by using the stability table form as shown later. The remaining polynomial $G(z) = F(z)/D(z)$ can then be studied by using the perturbation method if required.

Closely related to the perturbation method is the method used by Marden[4] to determine the number of zeros inside an r-circle, that is, $|z| \leq \dfrac{1}{r}$. Consider the following polynomial if $F(z)$ has roots on the unit circle:

$$F(rz) = a_0 + a_1(rz) + a_2(rz)^2 + \ldots + a_n(rz)^n = G(z) \qquad (A.40)$$

It is evident that $G(z)$ of equation (A.40) has as many roots in the r-circle as $F(z)$ has in the unit circle. Therefore, by examining the number of roots of $G(z)$ in a $1 + \varepsilon$ or in a $1 - \varepsilon$ circle for ε small, we can, in principle, determine the number of roots of $F(z)$ *in* and *on* the unit circle. An example has been indicated in Section 3.12.

In concluding this section, it might be mentioned that the success of the perturbation method depends on the choice of a^*. In some rare cases it might happen that one choice of a^* would not make $\Delta_k^\dagger$ and $\delta_k^\dagger$ nonzero; thus another choice is required.

Therefore this method tells us that the perturbation procedure does work and nothing further. However, the direct method, which will be discussed, seems to offer a straightforward (although lengthy) way of dealing with the singular cases and thus appears useful for application.

DIRECT METHOD. This method is only applicable to the table form and offers a convenient way for obtaining information on the roots of $F(z)$ when $\delta_k = 0$.

As indicated in Appendix 1, Table (A.24) represents a sequence of polynomials of descending degree. Any polynomial in this sequence may be replaced by another with the same number of zeros inside the unit circle (provided the rest of the sequence is computed from the new polynomial according to the same rules) without changing the validity of the table method. This fact is the basis of the direct method.

Suppose δ_{n-m+1} is the first δ_k (with $k = n - m + 1$) to vanish and that the preceding rows in the table are

$$
\begin{array}{cccccc}
b_0 & b_1 & b_2 & \cdots & b_{m-1} & b_m \\
b_m & b_{m-1} & b_{m-2} & \cdots & b_1 & b_0 \\
\hline
\end{array}
$$

$$\delta_{n-m+1} = b_0^2 - b_m^2 = 0,$$

$$b_0 b_1 - b_{m-1} b_m, \ldots, b_0 b_{m-1} - b_1 b_m \quad (A.41)$$

We notice that $\delta_{n-m+1} = 0$ iff $|b_m| = |b_0|$. The polynomial to be associated with the first row of Table (A.41) is

$$g(z) = b_0 + b_1 z + b_2 z^2 + \ldots + b_{m-1} z^{m-1} + b_m z^m \quad (A.42)$$

Our objective in the following is to try to replace $g(z)$ by a polynomial with the same number of zeros inside the unit circle and for which none of the δ_k vanishes. Two cases are distinguished.

1. Some element in the row of δ_{n-m+1} does not vanish. This is so iff $b_m = \pm b_0$ but for some $q < m/2$, $b_{m-q} \neq \pm b_q$. We shall let q denote the smallest integer such that $b_{m-q} \neq \pm b_q$ is satisfied.

For this case the following theorem due to Cohn[2,4] enables us to construct a new polynomial having the same number of zeros inside and on the unit circle as $g(z)$.

THEOREM: If the coefficients of $g(z)$ satisfy this case, $g(z)$ has as many zeros in and on the unit circle as the polynomial

$$G_1(z) = B_0 G(z) - B_{m+q} G^*(z) = \sum_{j=0}^{m+q} B_j^{(1)} z^j \quad (A.43)$$

where

$$G(z) = \left(z^q + 2 \frac{b}{|b|} \right) g(z) \quad (A.44)$$

$$b = \frac{(b_{m-q} - (b_m/b_0) b_q)}{b_m} \quad (A.45)$$

$$B_k^{(1)} = 0, \quad k > m \quad (A.46)$$

and

$$|B_0^{(1)}| < |B_m^{(1)}| \quad (A.47)$$

Equation (A.47) guarantees that for the new polynomial $G_1(z)$ [to replace $g(z)$], δ_{n-m+1} does not vanish and thus we can continue the table method to determine the exact number of zeros inside the unit circle for $g(z)$.

EXAMPLE

Let $g(z)$ be given as

$$g(z) = 1 + 2z + 3z^2 + z^3 \qquad \text{(A.48)}$$

To obtain the number of roots inside the unit circle, we form the following table:

$g(z)$	1	2	3	1
$g^*(z)$	1	3	2	1
$g_1(z)$	0	−1	1	

$$\text{(A.49)}$$

This represents the singular case discussed previously. Hence to form $G_1(z)$, we first obtain from equations (A.43) to (A.47)

$$q = 1, \quad m = 3, \quad b_0 = 1, \quad b_m = b_3 = 1 \qquad \text{(A.50)}$$

$$b = \frac{b_2 - (b_3/b_0)b_1}{b_3} \frac{3-2}{1} = 1, \, |b| = 1 \qquad \text{(A.51)}$$

$$G(z) = (z+2)g(z) = 2 + 5z + 8z^2 + 5z^3 + z^4 \qquad \text{(A.52)}$$

From equation (A.52) we have

$$B_0 = 2, \qquad B_4 = B_m = 1 \qquad \text{(A.53)}$$

and

$$G_1(z) = 2G(z) - G^*(z) = 3 + 5z + 8z^2 + 5z^3 \qquad \text{(A.54)}$$

Now we can continue the table form starting from $G_1(z)$.

$G_1(z)$	3	5	8	5
$G_1^*(z)$	5	8	5	3
$G_2(z) \, \delta_1 = $	−16	−25	−1	
$G_2^*(z)$	−1	−25	−16	
$G_3(z) \, \delta_2 = $	255	384		
$G_3^*(z)$	384	255		
	$\delta_3 < 0$			

$$\text{(A.55)}$$

The number of roots of $g(z)$ and $G_1(z)$ inside the unit circle are the same and are determined by the number of negative P_k. Here

$$P_1 = \delta_1 < 0, \qquad P_2 = \delta_1\delta_2 < 0, \qquad P_3 = \delta_1\delta_2\delta_3 > 0 \qquad \text{(A.56)}$$

Therefore the number of roots of $g(z)$ inside the unit circle is two, and the third remaining root should be outside, because if it were on the unit circle, the singular case as discussed in item 2 would have occurred.

We can readily establish for this example that no root exists on the unit circle from the fact that the multiplication of the roots is unity [from equation (A.48)] and $g(1)g(-1) \neq 0$. Hence we can apply the perturbation method for the sake of illustration as follows.

In Table A.49, replace the zero term by a small quantity (positive or negative) and then proceed with the table.

ε	-1	1
1	-1	ε
$(\varepsilon^2 - 1)$	$-(\varepsilon - 1)$	
$-(\varepsilon - 1)$	$(\varepsilon^2 - 1)$	
$(\varepsilon^2 - 1)^2 - (\varepsilon - 1)^2$		

In this case if we consider $\varepsilon > 0$, we have

$$\delta_1 = \varepsilon > 0, \, \delta_2 = (\varepsilon^2 - 1) < 0, \, \delta_3 = (\varepsilon^2 - 1)^2 - (\varepsilon - 1)^2 > 0$$

As established before, two roots are inside the unit circle and one outside the unit circle. We obtain the same distribution of the roots if we consider $\varepsilon < 0$.

In conclusion, we may mention that if the singular case occurs, we readily know that at least one root exists inside the unit circle because of the arbitrary choice of the sign of ε. Thus finding that $g(1) > 0$ and $g(-1) > 0$, we readily ascertain that two roots are inside the unit circle. This simplification can also be obtained for higher-degree polynomials by checking the sign of the constraints $g(1)$ and $g(-1)$ at the start of the test.[39]

2. The entire row of which δ_{n-m+1} is the first element vanishes. This is so iff $b_m = \pm b_0$, $b_{m-1} = \pm b_1, \ldots, b_0 = \pm b_m$ or $F_{n-m+1} \equiv 0$. For this case the following theorem due to Cohn[2,4] gives the form of a new polynomial that has the same number of zeros inside the unit circle as $F_{n-m}(z)$.

THEOREM: If the coefficients of $F_{n-m}(z)$ satisfy the preceding condition, then $F_{n-m}(z)$ has as many zeros in the unit circle as the polynomial,

$$f_{n-m+1}(z) = [F'_{(n-m)}(z)]^* = z^{m-1}F'_{n-m}\left(\frac{1}{z}\right) = \sum_{j=0}^{m-1} b_j^{(1)}z^j \qquad \text{(A.57)}$$

where

$$F'_{n-m}(z) = \frac{dF_{n-m}(z)}{dz}$$

Thus for this case, we replace the row $(b_0, b_1, b_2, \ldots, b_m)$ by $(b_0^{(1)}, b_1^{(1)} \ldots b_{m-1}^{(1)})$. If $(b_0^{(1)}, b_1^{(1)}, \ldots, b_{m-1}^{(1)})$ still satisfies the preceding case, it can be shown that $F_{n-m}(z)$ is of the form $(z + e^{j\phi})^{n-m}$. If it satisfies the first singular case, then we proceed in the method outlined earlier.

EXAMPLE

Let

$$F(z) = -0.5 + 1.65z - 0.8z^2 - 0.35z^3 - 1.8z^4 + z^5 \qquad n = 5$$

$$\text{(A.59)}$$

Form the following table:

$F(z)$		-0.5	1.65	-0.8	-0.35	-1.8	1
$F^*(z)$		1	-1.8	-0.35	-0.8	-1.65	-0.5
$F_1(z)$	$\delta_1 = -0.75$	0.975	0.75	0.975	-0.75	
$F_1^*(z)$		-0.75	0.975	0.75	0.975	-0.75	
$F_2(z)$	$\delta_2 =$	0	0	0	0	0	

$$\text{(A.60)}$$

From $\delta_2 = 0$ and $F_2(z) \equiv 0$, it is evident that the second singular case occurs; therefore we obtain $f_2(z)$ from equation (A.57)

$$f_2(z) = [F_1'(z)]^* = [0.975 + 1.5z + 2.925z^2 - 3z^3]^*$$
$$= -3 + 2.925z + 1.5z^2 + 0.975z^3 \qquad \text{(A.61)}$$

Now we continue the table for the new polynomial $f_2(z)$

$f_2(z)$		-3	2.925	1.5	0.975
$f_2^*(z)$		0.975	1.5	2.925	-3
$f_3(z)$	$\delta_2 =$	8.06	-10.24	-7.4	
$f_3^*(z)$		-7.4	-10.24	8.06	
$f_4(z)$	$\delta_3 =$	9.24	-152		
$f_4^*(z)$		-152	9.24		

$$\delta_4 < 0$$

$$\text{(A.62)}$$

The polynomial $F_1(z)$ has the same number of roots inside the unit circle as $f_2(z)$. From the preceding $f_2(z)$ has one root (zero) inside the unit circle (because $\delta_2 > 0$, $\delta_3 > 0$, $\delta_4 < 0$). Thus $F_1(z)$ has also one root inside the unit circle. As noticed from a theorem on p. 119 for this form of singular case, a root is strictly inside the unit circle if and only if there exists a reciprocal of that root outside the unit circle, and, in fact, the two roots are the reciprocals of each other. Therefore, because $F_1(z)$ is a fourth-order polynomial, the remaining two roots lie on the unit circle. Furthermore, from $F(z)$ we found that $\delta_1 < 0$; therefore the remaining root of $F(z)$ lies inside the unit circle. In summarizing, $F(z)$ has *two roots* inside the unit circle, *one root* outside the unit circle, and the remaining *two roots* are on the unit circle. The roots of equation (A.59) are $\frac{1}{2}$, 2, $\frac{1}{2}$, $0.6 \mp j0.8$.

Although the above procedure is straightforward, in some cases it becomes quite laborious to calculate all the δ_k's from the table. Therefore we can utilize the following two facts to simplify the determination of the root distribution.

1. From equation (A.35c), we can determine the sign of P_n from the signs of $F_1(1)$ and $F_1(-1)$.

2. For real polynomials complex zeros appear only in conjugate pairs.

Based on these facts we have for the example discussed

$$F_1(1) > 0, \qquad F_1(-1) < 0$$

Hence $F_1(z)$ should have only one real root between $(-1, 1)$; another real root (its reciprocal) is outside the unit circle and the remaining two should be on the unit circle. It should be noted that three real roots cannot exist between $(-1, 1)$, for this requires $F_1(z)$ to be at least a sixth-degree polynomial. Therefore, by determining only the sign of $F_1(1)$ and $F_1(-1)$ we can obtain the number of reciprocal roots with respect to the unit circle and roots on the unit circle, thus avoiding the use of the table for this example. Similar simplifications can also be obtained for other reciprocal polynomials. It should be noted that in some of these singular cases we can also obtain information on the number of roots on the unit circle or the number of reciprocal roots with certain multiplicity.[2,31,39]

In concluding the discussion of the singular cases, one may mention that, in general, cases 1 and 2 could occur in combination for the same polynomial $F(z)$. In this situation, we may count in the regular way for the sign of δ_k (or for the negative P_k) even though some of the intermediate polynomials are replaced by different ones, particularly for case 1. This becomes evident if we would consider the counting using equation (A.17).

Appendix 3. Summary of the stability criteria

In this appendix, we summarize the three forms of the stability criteria discussed in this chapter. For practical use, the summarized forms only are of importance.

DETERMINANT METHOD. This method, which is discussed in Section 3.5 and presented in equations (3.28) to (3.35), is presented here in a more convenient form so that the sign of the constraints for stability is similar to Hurwitz constraints. This can be readily achieved if the columns are interchanged in equations (3.28) and (3.29) and also a minor change of sign is made by noting that $(-1)^{k(k+1)/2} = (-1)^{k(k-1)/2}(-1)^k$.

If we denote by X'_{n-1} and Y'_{n-1} the following matrices,

$$X'_{n-1} = \begin{bmatrix} a_n & a_{n-1} & a_{n-2} & \cdots\cdots & a_2 \\ 0 & a_n & a_{n-1} & \cdots\cdots & a_3 \\ 0 & 0 & a_n & \cdots\cdots & a_4 \\ 0 & 0 & 0 & \cdots\cdots & a_5 \\ \cdot & \cdot & \cdot & \cdot & \cdot \\ \cdot & \cdot & \cdot & \cdot & \cdot \\ \cdot & \cdot & \cdot & \cdot & \cdot \\ 0 & 0 & 0 & 0 & a_n \end{bmatrix}$$

$$Y'_{n-1} = \begin{bmatrix} a_{n-2} & \cdots\cdots & a_2 & a_1 & a_0 \\ a_{n-3} & \cdots\cdots & a_1 & a_0 & 0 \\ a_{n-4} & \cdots\cdots & a_0 & 0 & 0 \\ \cdot & \cdot & \cdot & \cdot & \cdot \\ \cdot & \cdot & \cdot & \cdot & \cdot \\ \cdot & \cdot & \cdot & \cdot & \cdot \\ a_0 & 0 & 0 & 0 & 0 & 0 & 0 \end{bmatrix}$$

the stability constraints for n-even and n-odd are presented for the following polynomial:

$$F(z) = a_0 + a_1 z + a_2 z^2 + \ldots + a_k z^k + \ldots + a_n z^n, \qquad a_n > 0$$

1. n-even

$$F(1) > 0, \qquad F(-1) > 0$$

$$|X'_{k-1} \pm Y'_{k-1}| = A'_k \pm B'_k > 0, \qquad k = 1, 3, 5, 7, \ldots, n-1$$

or alternatively for this determinant

$$A'_k \pm B'_k > 0, \qquad k = 2, 4, \ldots, n - 2$$

$$A'_{n-1} - B'_{n-1} > 0$$

2. n-odd

$$F(1) > 0, \qquad F(-1) < 0$$

$$|X'_k \pm Y'_k| = A'_k \pm B'_k > 0, \qquad k = 2, 4, 6, \ldots, n - 1$$

or alternatively for this determinant

$$A'_k \pm B'_k > 0, \qquad k = 1, 3, 5, \ldots, n - 2$$

$$A'_{n-1} - B'_{n-1} > 0$$

The alternate constraints are useful for design in order not to solve for two equations of degree $n - 1$. It should be noted that all the $|X'_k \pm Y'_k|$ are obtained from $|X'_{n-1} \pm Y'_{n-1}|$ as indicated in equations (3.30) and (3.31). As an illustration, let us consider the stability constraint for the following polynomial:

$$F(z) = a_0 + a_1 z + a_2 z^2 + a_3 z^3 + a_4 z^4 + a_5 z^5 + a_6 z^6, \qquad a_6 > 0$$

Form $|X'_{n-1} \mp Y'_{n-1}|$ as follows:

$$|X'_{n-1} \mp Y'_{n-1}|_{n=6} = A_{n-1} \mp B_{n-1}$$

$a_6 \mp a_4$	$a_5 \mp a_3$	$a_4 \mp a_2$	$a_3 \mp a_1$	$a_2 \mp a_0$
$k = 3$			$A'_3 \mp B'_3$	
$\mp a_3$	$a_6 \mp a_2$	$a_5 \mp a_1$	$a_4 \mp a_0$	a_3
	$k = 1 \quad A'_1 \mp B'_1$			
$\mp a_2$	$\mp a_1$	$a_6 \mp a_0$	a_5	a_4
$\mp a_1$	$\mp a_0$	0	a_6	a_5
$\mp a_0$	0	0	0	$a_6 \quad A'_5 \mp B'_5$

The stability constraints are

$$F(1) > 0, \qquad F(-1) > 0$$

$$A'_1 \mp B'_1 > 0, \qquad A'_3 \mp B'_3 > 0, \qquad A'_5 \mp B'_5 > 0$$

TABLE FORM. The table is useful mainly for numerical test of stability or for the root distribution. It is presented in two forms in Tables (3.77) and (3.121). The latter form is particularly useful for design purposes.

We summarize mainly in this Appendix the form given in Table (3.77).

Row	z^0	z^1	z^2	z^3	...	z^{n-k}	...	z^{n-1}	z^n
1	a_0	a_1	a_2	a_3	...	a_{n-k}		a_{n-1}	a_n
2	a_n	a_{n-1}	a_{n-2}	a_{n-3}		a_k		a_1	a_0
3	b_0	b_1	b_2	b_3	.	.	.	b_{n-1}	
4	b_{n-1}	b_{n-2}	b_{n-3}	b_{n-4}	.	.	.	b_0	
5	c_0	c_1	c_2	c_3		.	.	c_{n-2}	
6	c_{n-2}	c_{n-3}	...	...			.	c_0	
.	.	.	.	.		.			
.	.	.	.	.		.			
.	.	.	.	.		.			
$2n-5$	s_0	s_1	s_2	s_3					
$2n-4$	s_3	s_2	s_1	s_0					
$2n-3$	r_0	r_1	r_2						
$2n-2$	t_0								

where

$$b_k = \begin{vmatrix} a_0 & a_{n-k} \\ a_n & a_k \end{vmatrix}, \quad c_k = \begin{vmatrix} b_0 & b_{n-1-k} \\ b_{n-1} & b_k \end{vmatrix}, \quad d_k = \begin{vmatrix} c_0 & c_{n-2-k} \\ c_{n-2} & c_k \end{vmatrix}, \ldots$$

$$r_0 = \begin{vmatrix} s_0 & s_3 \\ s_3 & s_0 \end{vmatrix}, \quad r_2 = \begin{vmatrix} s_0 & s_1 \\ s_3 & s_2 \end{vmatrix}, \quad t_0 = \begin{vmatrix} r_0 & r_2 \\ r_2 & r_0 \end{vmatrix}$$

The stability constraints are

$$F(1) > 0, (-1)^n F(-1) > 0$$
$$\underbrace{b_0 < 0, c_0 > 0, d_0 > 0, \ldots s_0 > 0, r_0 > 0, t_0 > 0}_{(n-1)\text{ constraints}}$$

It is noticed from the table that the dotted entry in row $2n - 3$ is redundant. Therefore the corresponding second-order matrix to be calculated using the dotted entries in rows $2n - 4$ and $2n - 5$ is also redundant. Finally, an easy way to remember the rule to form the table is indicated by the arrows of the first two rows.

DIVISION METHOD.   The division method is similar to the table form, but it is written in a form that can be remembered by using simple division of polynomials. It is discussed in Section 3.10 and a summary follows.

Form the inverse polynomial $F^*(z)$ as

$$F^*(z) = z^n F\left(\frac{1}{z}\right) = a_n + a_{n-1}z + a_{n-2}z^2 + \ldots + a_{n-k}z^k + \ldots$$
$$+ a_0 z^n, \qquad a_n > 0$$

Obtain the stability constraints α_k by simple division:

$$\frac{F(z)}{F^*(z)} \to \alpha_0 + \frac{F_1(z)}{F_1^*(z)} \to \alpha_0 + \alpha_1 + \frac{F_2(z)}{F_2^*(z)} \to \ldots \to$$
$$\alpha_0 + \alpha_1 + \alpha_2 + \ldots \alpha_{n-2} + \frac{F_{n-1}(z)}{F_{n-1}^*(z)}$$

where $F_1(z), F_2(z), \ldots, F_{n-2}(z)$ are the remainder polynomials obtained from the division and $F_1^*(z), F_2^*(z), \ldots, F_{n-2}^*(z)$ are their inverses.

The stability constraints are

$$F(1) > 0, \qquad (-1)^n F(-1) > 0$$
$$|\alpha_k| < 1, \qquad k = 0, 1, 2, \ldots, n - 2$$

REFERENCES

1. Jury, E. I., "A Simplified Stability Criterion for Linear Discrete Systems," University of California, Berkeley, *ERL* Report Series No. 60, Issue No. 373, June 1961. Also, *IRE Proceedings*, Vol. 50, No. 6, June 1962, pp. 1493–1500.

2. Cohn, A., "Über die Anzahl der Wurzeln einer Algebraischen Gleichung in einem Kreise," *Math. 2*, Vol. 14, August 1922, pp. 110–148.

3. Fujiwara, M., "Über die Algebraischen Gleichung deren Wurzeln in einem Kreise oder in einer Halbebeneliegen," *Math. Zeitschr.*, Vol. 24, 1926, pp. 160–169.

4. Marden, M., "The Geometry of the Zeros of a Polynomial in a Complex Variable," *Amer. Math. Soc.*, New York, 1949, pp. 152–157.

5. Samuelson, P. A., "Conditions That the Roots of a Polynomial Be Less Than Unity in Absolute Value," *Am. Math. Statis.*, Vol. 12, 1941, pp. 360–364.

6. Tschauner, J., "Die Stabilitat der Impulse Systeme," *Regelungstechnik*, Vol. 8, 1960, pp. 42–46.

7. Jury, E. I., "Discussion on the 'Stability of Sampled-Data Systems' by J. Tschauner," *Regelungstechnik*, Vol. 8, Munich, Germany, August 1961, pp. 340–342.

8. Gantmacher, F. R., *The Theory of Matrices*, Vol. II, Chelsea Publishing Co., New York, 1959.

9. Tsypkin, Y., *Theory of Pulse Systems*, State Press for Physics and Mathematical Literature, Moscow (in Russian), 1958, pp. 423–427.

10. Brown, B. M., *The Mathematical Theory of Linear Systems*, John Wiley and Sons, New York, 1961, pp. 119–152.

11. Rouche, E., "Memoire Sue la Serie de Lagrange," *J. Ecole Polytech.*, Vol. 22, 1862, pp. 217-218.

12. Jury, E. I., and J. Blanchard, "A Stability Test for Linear Discrete Systems in Table Form," *Proc. IRE*, Vol. 44, December 1961, pp. 1947-1948.

13. Romanov, M. I., "Algebraic Criteria for Aperiodicity of Linear Systems," *Soviet Physics Doklady*, Vol. 4, March-April 1960, pp. 955-961.

14. Jury, E. I., "A Stability Test for Linear Discrete Systems Using a Simple Division," *Proc. IRE*, Vol. 44, December 1961, pp. 1948-1949.

15. Jury, E. I., "Additions to Notes on the Stability Criterion for Line Linear Discrete Systems," *IRE Trans. on Automatic Control*, Vol. AC-6, September 1961, pp. 342-343.

16. Jury, E. I., and S. C. Gupta, "On the Stability of Linear Discrete Systems," *Regelungstechnik*, Munich, part 4, No. 10, April 1962, pp. 157-159.

17. Jury, E. I., *Sampled-Data Control Systems*, John Wiley and Sons, New York, 1958.

18. Jury, E. I., "Proof of a General Relationship Used in the Stability of Test of Linear Discrete Systems, Addendum to Reference 1.

19. Jury, E. I. and Pavlidis, T., "Aperiodicity Criteria for Linear Discrete Systems," *IEEE PGCT*, Vol. CT-9, No. 4, December 1962, pp. 431-434.

20. Jury, E. I., and T. Pavlidis, "Stability and Aperiodicity Constraints for System Design," *IEEE PGCT*, Vol. CT-10, No. 1, March 1963, pp. 137-141.

21. Wilf, H. S., "A Stability Criterion for Numerical Integration," *J. Assoc. Comp. Mach.*, Vol. 6, 1959, pp. 363-365.

22. Arzhanykh, I. S., "New Stability Inequalities," *Automatics and Remote Control*, Vol. 22, No. 4, April 1961, pp. 436-442.

23. Jury, E. I., "A Stability Chart for Linear Discrete Systems," *Proc. I.R.E.*, Vol. 50, No. 12, December 1962.

24. Jury, E. I., "On the Roots of a Real Polynomial Inside the Unit Circle and a Stability Criterion for Linear Discrete Systems," presented at the Second IFA Congress held August 27-September 3, 1963, Basle, Switzerland, published by the *Congress Proceedings*, 1964.

25. Thoma, V. M., "Ein einfaches Verfuhen Zur Stabilitatsprufung Von Linearen Abtastsysteme," *Regelungstechnik*, Part 7, Vol. 10, 1962, pp. 302-306.

26. Jury, E. I., "Discussion of Reference 25, *Regelungstechnik*, December 1962.

27. Jury, E. I., "On the Generation of the Stability Constraints in Linear Discrete Systems," *IEEE PGAC*, Vol. AC-8, No. 2, April 1963, p. 184.

28. Schur, I., Über Potenzreihen, die im Innern des Einheitskreises beschränkt sind, *Journal für Mathematik*, Vol. 147, 1917, pp. 205-232, and also Vol. 148, 1918, pp. 122-145.

29. Chow, T. S., and H. W. Milnes, "Numerical Solution of a Class of Hyperbolic-Parobolic Partial Differential Equations by Boundary Contraction," *S.I.A.M. Journal*, Vol. 10, No. 1, March 1962, pp. 124-148.

30. Jury, E. I., "On the Evaluation of the Stability Determinants in Linear Discrete Systems," *IRE PGAC*, Vol. AC-7, No. 4, July 1962, pp. 51-55.

31. Jury, E. I., "A Note on the Reciprocal Zeros of a Real Polynomial with Respect to the Unit Circle," *IEEE PGGT*, to be published June 1964.

32. Perron, O., *Algebra, Band II, Theorie der Algebraischen Gleichungen*, Walter de Gruyter Verlag, Berlin, 1951, pp. 32-37.

33. Knopp, K., *Theory of Function*, Dover Publications, New York, p. 68.

34. Fuller, A. T., "Conditions for Aperiodicity in Linear Systems," *British J. Appl. Phys.*, June 1955, pp. 195–198.

35. Thoma, Von M., "Über die Wurzelverteilung von Linearen Abtastsystemen," *Regelungstechnik*, Part 2, Vol. 11, 1963, pp. 70–74.

36. Liénard, and Chipart, "Sur la signe de la partie réelle des racines d'une équation algébrique," *J. Math. Pures Appl.* (6), Vol. 10, 1914, pp. 291–346.

37. Jury, E. I., and S. C. Gupta, "A General Procedure for Obtaining Tschauner's Stability Constraints," *Regelungstechnik*, November 1962.

38. Tschauner, J. "A General Formulation of the Stability Constraints, for Sampled-Data Control Systems," *IEEE Proc.* Vol. 51, No. 4, April 1963.

39. Jury, E. I. Further remarks on the paper of Reference (40), to be published by the *Regelungstechnik* No. 2, February 1964.

40. Thoma, M., "Über die Wurzelverteilung Von Linearen Abtastsystemen," *Regelungstechnik*, Vol. 11, 1963, Part 2, pp. 70–74.

41. Jury, E. I., "Proof of the Generation Rule for the Stability Constraints in Linear Discrete Systems," Technical Memorandum M-39, Electronics Res. Lab., Univ. of Calif., Berkeley, California, December 5, 1963.

42. Jury, E. I., "A Memo on Marden's Investigations of the Zero-Distribution within the Unit Circle," Technical Memorandum M-38, Electronics Res. Lab., Univ. of Calif., Berkeley, California, December 4, 1963.

4

CONVOLUTION z-TRANSFORM

The convolution z-transform is an extension of the z-transform from which a certain theorem called the complex convolution theorem is obtained. This theorem yields the z-transform of the multiplication of two (or more) discrete sequences in terms of the z-transform of the individual sequences.

This important theorem of the z-transform has many applications, such as in summation of series, in obtaining the z-transform of special functions, in extending the z-transform method to the solution of unmixed difference-differential and sum equations, and others which are discussed in detail in this chapter.

The significance of the convolution z-transform lies in the extension of the z-transform to nonlinear discrete systems. Certain types of nonlinear difference equations could be solved by this method. Thus the z-transform method which is usually considered applicable to linear discrete systems is extended to cover the nonlinear case too. This study is presented in detail in the next two chapters.

4.1 Complex convolution theorem[1-4]

Assume we have the sampled function $[f(t)h(t)]*$ with $F*(s)$ and $H*(s)$ as the Laplace transform of $f*(t)$ and $h*(t)$ respectively. To obtain the Laplace transform of the product we may use the complex convolution formula in the s-plane (see Appendix for derivation) as follows.

$$\mathscr{L}\{[f(t)h(t)]\,\delta_T(t)\} = \frac{T}{2\pi j} \int_{c-j(\pi/T)}^{c+j(\pi/T)} F*(q)H*(s-q)\,dq \qquad (4.1)$$

It should be noted that both $F^*(s)$ and $H^*(s)$ have an infinite number of poles in the s-plane because of the periodic form of these functions.

Assume as an example that $F(s)$ has a pole in the left half plane at $s = s_\alpha$, and $H(s)$ has a pole in the same plane at $s = s_\beta$ (both s_α and s_β are assumed for sake of illustration to be real), then the pole-zero pattern in both the s- and q-planes of $F^*(s)$ and $H^*(s)$ is as shown in Figs. 4.1 and 4.2.

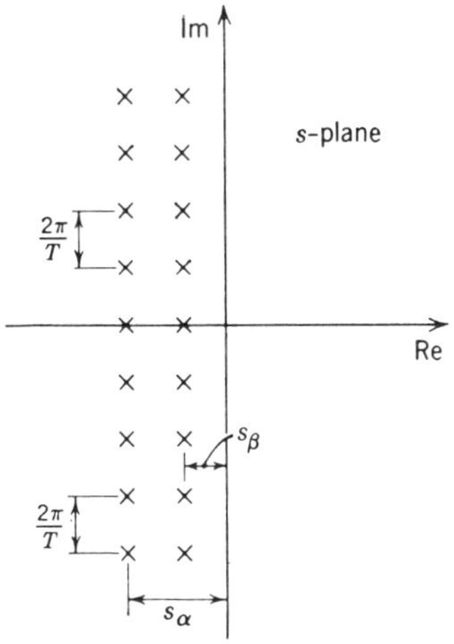

The strip of analyticity in the q-plane is shown in crosshatch and the path of integration as a dotted line. It should be noted that because of the periodicity of both $F^*(s)$ and $H^*(s)$, the path of integration is taken along one strip and the integral is divided by the period $2\pi j/T$ as required.

FIGURE 4.1   Pole-zero pattern of $F^*(s)$ and $H^*(s)$ in s-plane.

Both $F^*(s)$ and $H^*(s)$ are functions of e^{Ts} only; we can replace e^{Ts} by z and e^{Tq} by p, so that $F^*(q)$ becomes a function of p, that is, $\mathscr{F}(p)$ and $H^*(s - q)$ becomes a function of z/p, that is, $\mathscr{H}(z/p)$. As required by this mapping

$$dq = (1/Te^{Tq})\, dp = (p^{-1}/T)\, dp$$

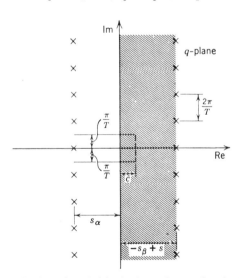

FIGURE 4.2   Region of analyticity in the q-plane and path of integration.

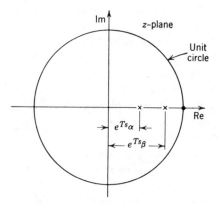

FIGURE 4.3   Poles of $\mathscr{F}(z)$ and $\mathscr{H}(z)$ in z-plane.

The mapping of the s-plane and q-plane into the z- and p-planes is shown in Figs. 4.3 and 4.4. Note that the strip of analyticity in the q-plane maps into an annulus of convergence in the p-plane. With this substitution equation (4.1) becomes

$$\mathscr{L}\{[f(t)h(t)]\,\delta_T(t)\} = \mathscr{z}[f(t)h(t)]$$

$$= \frac{1}{2\pi j}\int_\Gamma p^{-1}\mathscr{F}(p)\mathscr{H}\left(\frac{z}{p}\right)dp = \sum_{n=0}^{\infty} f_n h_n z^{-n}$$

$$(4.2)$$

where Γ is the dotted contour in the p-plane as shown in Fig. 4.4.

Equation (4.2) represents the convolution z-transform theorem which gives the z-transform of the product of two time functions, knowing the z-transform of each of these functions separately, (for $\mathscr{z}[f(t)] \triangleq \mathscr{F}(z)$,

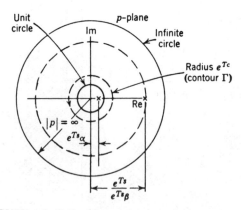

FIGURE 4.4   Path of integration in p-plane.

$\mathscr{J}[h(t)] = \mathscr{H}(z)$). Extension of this theorem to multiplication of more than two discrete time functions is evident.

Evaluation of the complex convolution integral[4,9]

By Cauchy's theorem on residues, we can evaluate residues at the singularities of $p^{-1}\mathscr{F}(p)$ (if $\mathscr{F}(p)$ has no branch points as assumed here). In addition if the value of the integral along the infinite circle tends to zero, we can evaluate residues at the singularities of $\mathscr{H}(z/p)$ (provided the path of integration is taken in a negative sense). The choice between the two methods depends on the number and complexity of poles of each of the functions $\mathscr{F}(p)$ and $\mathscr{H}(p)$. Therefore

$$\mathscr{J}[f(t)h(t)] = \frac{1}{2\pi j} \int_\Gamma p^{-1}\mathscr{F}(p)\mathscr{H}\left(\frac{z}{p}\right) dp$$

$$= \frac{1}{2\pi j} \int_\Gamma p^{-1}\mathscr{H}(p)\mathscr{F}\left(\frac{z}{p}\right) dp$$

$$= \sum \text{residues at singularities of } p^{-1}\mathscr{F}(p)$$

$$= -\sum \text{residues at singularities of } \mathscr{H}\left(\frac{z}{p}\right) \qquad (4.3)$$

If $\mathscr{F}(p)$ has simple poles only,

$$\mathscr{J}[f(t)h(t)] = \sum_{n=1}^{N} \frac{A(p_n)}{p_n B'(p_n)} \mathscr{H}\left(\frac{z}{p_n}\right) + \mathscr{F}(p_0)\mathscr{H}\left(\frac{z}{p_0}\right)\Bigg|_{p_0=0} \qquad (4.4)$$

where

$$p^{-1}\mathscr{F}(p) = \frac{A(p)}{B(p)}, \quad \text{and} \quad B(p) = 0,$$

$$\text{for } p = p_0, p_1, p_2, \ldots, p_N \quad \text{with } p_0 = 0$$

and

$$B'(p_n) = \frac{dB}{dp}\Bigg|_{p=p_n} \qquad (4.5)$$

4.2 Complex convolution theorem for the modified z-transform[4]

Similar to z-transform, we may obtain the equivalent theorem for the modified z-transform by obtaining first the Laplace transform of

$$[f(t, m)h(t, m)]\, \delta_T(t), \qquad 0 \leq m \leq 1$$

This is given by

$$\mathscr{L}\{[f(t, m)h(t, m)]\, \delta_T(t)\}$$

$$= \frac{T}{2\pi j} \int_{c-j(\pi/T)}^{c+j(\pi/T)} F^*(q, m)H^*(s - q, m)\, dq, \qquad 0 \le m \le 1$$

(4.6)†

By using the same mapping as for the z-transform case, we readily obtain

$$\mathscr{Z}_m[f(t)h(t)] = \frac{1}{2\pi j} \int_\Gamma p^{-1}\mathscr{F}(p, m)\mathscr{H}\left(\frac{z}{p}, m\right) dp$$

$$= \frac{1}{2\pi j} \int_\Gamma p^{-1}\mathscr{H}(p, m)\mathscr{F}\left(\frac{z}{p}, m\right) dp, \qquad 0 \le m \le 1 \qquad (4.7)$$

For the case $f(t) = h(t)$, we get

$$\mathscr{Z}_m[f(t)^2] = \frac{1}{2\pi j} \int_\Gamma p^{-1}\mathscr{F}(p, m)\mathscr{F}\left(\frac{z}{p}, m\right) dp \qquad (4.8)$$

When $h(t) = u(t)$, equation (4.7) readily yields $\mathscr{F}(z, m)$.

EXAMPLE

Find the modified z-transform of the following function:

$$\mathscr{Z}_m[tf(t)] \qquad (4.9)$$

In this case

$$\mathscr{Z}_m[t] = \frac{mTz - mT + T}{(z - 1)^2} \qquad (4.10)$$

and

$$\mathscr{Z}_m[f(t)] = \mathscr{F}(z, m) \qquad (4.10a)$$

From equation (4.7),

$$\mathscr{Z}_m[tf(t)] = \frac{1}{2\pi j} \int_\Gamma \frac{mTp - mT + T}{(p - 1)^2} \frac{1}{p} \mathscr{F}\left(\frac{z}{p}, m\right) dp \qquad (4.11)$$

The integrand in this integral equation has a multiple pole at $p = 1$ (and a pole at the origin; however, since its residue is zero in most cases because $\mathscr{F}(z/p, m)\big|_{p=0} = 0$, it is ignored). The residue of equation (4.11) yields

$$\mathscr{Z}_m[tf(t)] = \frac{\partial}{\partial p}\left[\frac{mTp - mT + T}{p} \mathscr{F}\left(\frac{z}{p}, m\right)\right]\Bigg|_{p=1}$$

$$= \mathscr{F}(z, m)[T(m - 1)] + T\frac{\partial}{\partial p} \mathscr{F}\left(\frac{z}{p}, m\right)\Bigg|_{p=1} \qquad (4.12)$$

---

† It may be noted that $f(t, m) = f[t - (1 - m)T]$.

We can easily verify that

$$\left.\frac{\partial}{\partial p}\mathscr{F}\left(\frac{z}{p}, m\right)\right|_{p=1} = -z\frac{\partial}{\partial z}\mathscr{F}(z, m) \tag{4.13}$$

Therefore

$$\mathscr{Z}_m[tf(t)] = T\left[(m-1)\mathscr{F}(z, m) - z\frac{\partial}{\partial z}\mathscr{F}(z, m)\right]$$

$$= \mathscr{F}_1(z, m) \text{ where } f_1(t) = tf(t) \tag{4.14}$$

Similarly,

$$\mathscr{Z}_m[t^2f(t)] = T\left[(m-1)\mathscr{F}_1(z, m) - z\frac{\partial}{\partial z}\mathscr{F}_1(z, m)\right] \tag{4.15}$$

By iterative extension of the preceding we can obtain

$$\mathscr{Z}_m[t^kf(t)], \quad \text{where } k \text{ is a positive integer}$$

4.3 Applications of the convolution modified or z-transform method[4,2]

In this section we shall introduce a few applications which are useful in discrete system analysis as well as design.

Inverse $\mathscr{Z}_m - \mathscr{L}$ transformation

In a preceding discussion* we obtained the modified z-transform from the Laplace transform without indicating the inverse process. Now we shall obtain $F(s)$, knowing $\mathscr{F}(z, m)$

$$F(s) = \mathscr{Z}_m^{-1}\mathscr{F}(z, m) \tag{4.16}$$

The Laplace transform of $f(t)$ can be written as

$$F(s) = \int_0^\infty f(t)e^{-st}\, dt = \sum_{n=0}^\infty \int_{nT}^{(n+1)T} f(t)e^{-st}\, dt \tag{4.17}$$

Now if we let $t = (n-1+m)T, 0 \le m \le 1, n = $ integer, equation (4.17) can be written

$$F(s) = T\sum_{n=0}^\infty e^{-nTs}\int_0^1 f(nT - T + mT)e^{(1-m)sT}\, dm \tag{4.18}$$

or

$$F(s) = T\int_0^1 z^{-m+1}\sum_{n=0}^\infty f(nT - T + mT)z^{-n}\, dm\big|_{z=e^{Ts}} \tag{4.19}$$

---

* See Section 1.5.

However, by definition

$$\sum_{n=0}^{\infty} f(nT - T + mT)z^{-n} = \mathscr{F}(z, m) = \mathscr{Z}_m[f(t)] \qquad (4.20)$$

Therefore

$$F(s) = Z_m^{-1} \mathscr{F}(z, m) = T \int_0^1 z^{-1+m} \mathscr{F}(z, m)\, dm \mid z = e^{Ts} \qquad (4.21)$$

It should be noted that this transformation is unique, that is, for each $\mathscr{F}(z, m)$ there exists only one form of $F(s)$.

Inverse $\mathscr{F}(z) - F(s)$ or $(z\text{-}s)$ transformation[2,4]

This transformation indicates how to obtain $F(s) = \mathscr{L}[f(t)]$ when we know $F^*(s) = \mathscr{L}[f^*(t)]$. To obtain the $z\text{-}s$ transformation, we first find $f(nT)$. This can be achieved by recognizing that $F^*(q)$ is a periodic function of q with the imaginary period $2\pi j/T$; hence the value $f(nT)$ is the coefficient of e^{-qnT} in the Fourier series representation[2] of $F^*(q)$. Hence,

$$f(nT) = \frac{T}{2\pi j} \int_{c-j(\pi/T)}^{c+j(\pi/T)} F^*(q)e^{qnT}\, dq, \qquad \text{for } f(0) = 0 \qquad (4.22)$$

where the path of integration lies to the right of the poles of $F^*(q)$.

In order to obtain a certain $f(t)$ whose sampled values coincide with $f(nT)$, we change nT into t in equation (4.22) and then apply the Laplace transform to obtain, after interchanging the order of integration,

$$F(s) = \frac{T}{2\pi j} \int_{c-j(\pi/T)}^{c+j(\pi/T)} F^*(q)\left[\int_0^{\infty} e^{-(s-q)t}\, dt\right] dq,$$

$$\text{for } f(0) = 0 \quad (4.23)$$

We note that $\int_0^{\infty} e^{-(s-q)t}\, dt = 1/(s - q)$; hence equation (4.23) reduces to

$$F(s) = \frac{T}{2\pi j} \int_{c-j(\pi/T)}^{c+j(\pi/T)} \frac{F^*(q)}{s - q}\, dq, \qquad \text{for } f(0) = 0 \qquad (4.24)$$

It should be noted that the right-hand side of equation (4.24) represents the Laplace transform of $f^*(t)u(t)$. Hence $F(s)$ can be also obtained directly from $\mathscr{L}[f^*(t)u(t)]$ using the complex convolution theorem discussed in this chapter.

If $F^*(s)$ is written in terms of $z = e^{Ts}$, the function $F^*(s)$ becomes $\mathscr{F}(z)$, the z-transform of $F(s)$. Thus equation (4.24) is considered as the inverse $z\text{-}s$ transformation, that is,

$$F(s) = \mathscr{Z}^{-1}[\mathscr{F}(z)|_{z=e^{Ts}}] = \frac{T}{2\pi j} \int_{c-j(\pi/T)}^{c+j(\pi/T)} \mathscr{F}(e^{Tq}) \frac{1}{s - q}\, dq \qquad (4.25)$$

It may be noted that this inverse transformation is not unique, that is, many forms of $F(s)$ have the same Z-transform $\mathscr{F}(z)$. This is evident since $f(t)$ is forced to coincide in values with $f*(t)$ only at sampling instants.

Skip sampling theorem[1,17,18]

This theorem signifies that, knowing the z-transform with respect to the period T/n (when n is an integer is larger than unity), we can obtain from it the z-transform with respect to the period T. This theorem is important in obtaining the limit cycle (or periodic modes of oscillation) of nonlinear discrete systems and in the study of multirate sampled-data systems.

The fundamental equation that describes this theorem is

$$f(kT) = f\left(\frac{k'T}{n}\right)u(kT), \quad \text{where } k' = nk \tag{4.26}$$

Applying the z-transform to this equation, and using the complex convolution formula, we get

$$\mathscr{F}(z) \triangleq \mathscr{Y}[f(kT)] = \frac{1}{2\pi j}\int_\Gamma \mathscr{F}(p_n)p_n^{-1}\frac{1}{1 - (z_n/p_n)^{-n}}\,dp \tag{4.27}$$

where $z_n = e^{(T/n)s} = z^{1/n}$.

We can evaluate this integral in a positive sense for the singularities of $\mathscr{F}(p_n)p_n^{-1}$, to obtain one form, or, alternatively, integrate in a negative sense with respect to the poles of $\dfrac{1}{1 - (p_n/z_n)^{-n}}$ to obtain

$$\mathscr{F}(z) = \frac{1}{n}\sum_{k=0}^{n-1}\mathscr{F}(z_n e^{j2\pi k/n}) \tag{4.28}$$

Further application of the preceding theorem is in the analysis of modulated discrete signals appearing in some systems.

Integral time function transform[4,11]

$$\mathscr{Y}_m\left[\int_0^t f(t)h(t)\,dt\right]$$

$$= \frac{T}{2\pi j(z-1)}\int_0^1\int_\Gamma p^{-1}\mathscr{F}(p, m)\mathscr{H}\left(\frac{z}{p}, m\right)dp\,dm$$

$$+ \frac{T}{2\pi j}\int_0^m\int_\Gamma p^{-1}\mathscr{F}(p, m)\mathscr{H}\left(\frac{z}{p}, m\right)dp\,dm \tag{4.29}$$

This relationship can be obtained from writing the integral in a summation form.

$$\int_0^t f(t)h(t)\,dt = T\left[\sum_{k=0}^n \int_0^1 f(k-1+m)T\,h(k-1+m)T\,dm\right.$$
$$\left. + \int_0^m f(n-1+m)T\,h(n-1+m)T\,dm\right]$$

(4.30)

The modified z-transform of the preceding, noting that when $m = 0$,
$$\mathcal{Y}\left[\sum_{k=0}^{n-1} f(k-1)T\right] = \frac{1}{z-1}\mathcal{F}(z), \text{ yields}$$

$$\mathcal{Y}_m\left[\int_0^t f(t)h(t)\,dt\right]$$
$$= \frac{T}{z-1}\int_0^1 \sum_{n=0}^\infty f(n-1+m)T\,h(n-1+m)Tz^{-n}\,dm$$
$$+ T\int_0^m \sum_{n=0}^\infty f(n-1+m)T\,h(n-1+m)Tz^{-n}\,dm \quad (4.31)$$

but the infinite summations are the modified z-transform of $f(t)h(t)$, thus

$$\mathcal{Y}_m\left[\int_0^t f(t)h(t)\,dt\right] = \frac{T}{z-1}\int_0^1 \mathcal{F}_1(z,m)\,dm + T\int_0^m \mathcal{F}_1(z,m)\,dm$$

(4.32)

where

$$\mathcal{F}_1(z,m) = \mathcal{Y}_m[f(t)h(t)] = \frac{1}{2\pi j}\int_\Gamma p^{-1}\mathcal{F}(p,m)\mathcal{H}\left(\frac{z}{p},m\right)dp$$

(4.33)

For the special case when $h(t) = u(t) = $ unit step, equation (4.33) yields

$$\mathcal{Y}_m\left[\int_0^t f(t)\,dt\right] = \frac{T}{z-1}\int_0^1 \mathcal{F}(z,m)\,dm + T\int_0^m \mathcal{F}(z,m)\,dm$$

(4.34)

where

$$\mathcal{F}(z,m) = \mathcal{Y}_m[f(t)]$$

(4.35)

Equation (4.34) also yields the modified z-transform of $F(s)/s$. Extension to obtain $\mathcal{Z}_m[F(s)/s^k]$ by iterative process is straightforward.

z-Transform of special functions[4,9,10]

One of the several applications of the convolution z-transform is to enable us to obtain the z-transform of special functions such as $\mathcal{Y}[f(t)/t^k]$, $k > 0$.

This can be achieved by obtaining first the z-transform of $(1/t)$ for $t > 0$. The z-transform of $1/t$ for $t > 0$ can be easily obtained by using the definition of the z-transform as follows:

$$\mathscr{F}(z)|_{z=p} = \sum_{n=0}^{\infty} f(nT)p^{-n} \tag{4.36}$$

Multiplying equation (4.36) by p^{-1} and integrating both sides from z to ∞, we obtain

$$\frac{1}{T} \int_z^{\infty} p^{-1}\mathscr{F}(p)\,dp + \lim_{t\to 0} \frac{f(t)}{t} = \mathscr{Z}\left[\frac{f(t)}{t}\right] \tag{4.36a}$$

If we let $f(t)$ be a unit step for $t > 0$ whose $\mathscr{F}(p) = 1/(p-1)$, we have

$$\mathscr{Z}\left[\frac{1}{t}\right] = \frac{1}{T} \int_z^{\infty} p^{-1} \frac{dp}{p-1} \qquad \text{for } t > 0 \tag{4.36b}$$

Choosing $T = 1$, we have

$$\mathscr{Z}\left[\frac{1}{t}\right] = \ln \frac{z}{z-1} \qquad t > 0. \tag{4.37}$$

For any $f(t)$ we have, applying formula (4.2),

$$\mathscr{Z}\left[\frac{f(t)}{t}\right] = \frac{1}{2\pi j} \int_\Gamma p^{-1}\mathscr{F}(p) \ln \frac{z}{z-p}\,dp + \lim_{n\to 0} \frac{f_n}{n} \tag{4.38}*$$

The function $\ln z/(z-p)$ has a branch cut in the p-plane extending from $p = z$ to $p = \infty$. Since we are free to take the branch cut anywhere in the p-plane, we shall take it along the positive real axis. This is illustrated in Fig. 4.5. As before, the crosshatched area shows annulus of convergence and we have

$$\int_{C_1} = -\int_{EA}$$

$$\int_{EA} + \int_{AB} + \int_{BCD} + \int_{DE} = 0$$

$$-\int_{EA} = \int_{AB} + \int_{DE} + \int_{BCD}$$

$$\int_{C_1} = \int_{AB} + \int_{DE} + \int_{BCD}$$

---

* In the following derivation we shall show the equivalence between this equation based on convolution z-transform and equation (4.36a) obtained directly from the z-transform.

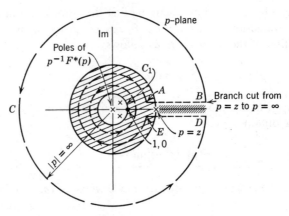

FIGURE 4.5 Branch cut in p-plane and path of integration.

Along AB, $p = |p| e^{i\phi}$, $\qquad \phi \to 0$
Along DE, $p = |p| e^{i(2\pi - \phi)}$, $\qquad \phi \to 0$

$$\ln \frac{z}{z-p} = \ln \left(-\frac{z}{p} \right) + \ln \frac{1}{1 - z/p} \tag{4.39}$$

Expansion for $\ln \dfrac{1}{1 - z/p}$ is given by the following:

$$\ln \frac{1}{1 - z/p} = \frac{z}{p} + \frac{z^2}{2p^2} + \dots \left(\left| \frac{z}{p} \right| < 1 \right) \tag{4.40}$$

Therefore

$$\ln \frac{z}{z-p} = \ln \left(-\frac{z}{p} \right) + \frac{z}{p} + \frac{z^2}{2p^2} + \dots \tag{4.41}$$

Now $\displaystyle\int_{BCD} = 0$. Hence

$$\int_{C_1} = \frac{1}{2\pi j} \int_z^\infty \left\{ p^{-1} \mathscr{F}(p) \right.$$

$$\times \left. \left[\ln \left(-\frac{z}{p} \right) + \frac{z}{p} + \frac{z^2}{2p^2} \dots \right] \right\}\Bigg|_{p=|p|e^{j\phi}, \phi \to 0} dp$$

$$- \frac{1}{2\pi j} \int_z^\infty \left\{ p^{-1} \mathscr{F}(p) \right.$$

$$\times \left. \left[\ln \left(-\frac{z}{p} \right) + \frac{z}{p} + \frac{z^2}{2p^2} + \dots \right] \right\}\Bigg|_{p=|p|e^{j(2\pi - \phi)}, \phi \to 0} dp$$

$$\tag{4.42}$$

Now ln k (where k is a complex number) $=$ ln $|k| + \arg k$. It is then easy to see that equation 4.42 reduces to

$$\int_{C_1} = \frac{1}{2\pi j} \int_z^\infty p^{-1}\mathscr{F}(p)2\pi j \, dp$$

$$= \int_z^\infty p^{-1}\mathscr{F}(p) \, dp \qquad (4.43)$$

We can generalize this result for higher powers of t in the denominator.

$$\sum_{n=1}^\infty \frac{f_n}{n} z^{-n} = \int_z^\infty p^{-1}\mathscr{F}(p) \, dp.$$

multiplying by z^{-1} and integrating from z to ∞,

$$\sum_{n=1}^\infty \frac{f_n}{n^2} z^{-n} = \int_z^\infty q^{-1} \int_q^\infty p^{-1}\mathscr{F}(p) \, dp \, dq$$

$$= \mathscr{z}\left\{\frac{f(t)}{t^2}\right\} \qquad (4.44)$$

Continuing this, we obtain

$$\mathscr{z}\left\{\frac{f(t)}{t^k}\right\} = \underbrace{\int_z^\infty w^{-1} \int_w^\infty v^{-1} \int_v^\infty u^{-1} \dots \int_q^\infty p^{-1}\mathscr{F}(p) \, dp \dots du \, dv \, dw}_{k \text{ times}} \qquad (4.45)$$

For $k > 1$ this equation is defined for $t > 0$; for $k = 1$, equation (4.38) is valid.

Although the preceding results appear to yield $\mathscr{z}[f(t)/t^k]$ for $k > 1$ in a closed form, actually it is not so because of difficulty in evaluating integrals in a closed form of the type $\int[\ln (a + bx)/x]$. Therefore it is not possible to obtain closed expressions for z-transforms of functions like $f(t)/t^k$ for $k > 1$. However, the usefulness of the result lies in evaluating infinite series since numerical evaluations of definite integrals of the preceding type are available. This is discussed in the next section.

To obtain the modified z-transform of $[f(t)/t]$ for $\lim\limits_{t\to 0} f(t) = 0$, we use another method which avoids the complex integration, based on the following derivation.

Let $\mathscr{F}(z, m)$ be presented (noting $f(nT)|_{n=0} = 0$) as follows:

$$\mathscr{F}(z, m)|_{z=p} = \sum_{n=0}^\infty f(nT - T + mT)p^{-n}$$

$$= \sum_{n=1}^\infty f(nT - T + mT)p^{-n} \qquad (4.46)$$

Where we multiply this equation by p^{-m} and integrate from z to infinity,

$$\int_z^\infty p^{-m}\mathscr{F}(p, m)\, dp = \int_z^\infty \sum_{n=1}^\infty f(nT - T + mT)p^{-(n+m)}\, dp$$

$$= \sum_{n=1}^\infty \frac{f(nT - T + mT)z^{-(n+m-1)}}{-n - m + 1}$$

$$0 < m < 1$$

or

$$\frac{1}{T} z^{m-1} \int_z^\infty p^{-m}\mathscr{F}(p, m)\, dp = \sum_{n=1}^\infty \frac{f(nT - T + mT)z^{-n}}{(nT - T + mT)} \qquad (4.47)$$

If $\dfrac{f(n - 1 + m)T}{(n - 1 + m)T} z^{-0}$ is added to both sides of equation (4.47), this term has a contribution only at $m = 1$, which is the $\lim\limits_{t \to 0} \dfrac{f(t)}{t}$; thus the right side of the above equation is $\mathscr{J}_m\!\left[\dfrac{f(t)}{t}\right]$.

$$\mathscr{J}_m\!\left[\frac{f(t)}{t}\right] = \frac{1}{T} z^{m-1} \int_z^\infty p^{-m}\mathscr{F}(p, m)\, dp + \lim_{t \to 0}\frac{f(t)}{t},$$

$$0 < m \le 1 \quad (4.48)$$

For the case of z-transform we obtain, by substituting $m = 1$ in equation (4.48)

$$\mathscr{J}\!\left[\frac{f(t)}{t}\right] = \frac{1}{T} \int_z^\infty p^{-1}\mathscr{F}(p)\, dp + \lim_{t \to 0}\frac{f(t)}{t}$$

where

$$\mathscr{F}(z) = \mathscr{F}(z, m)\big|_{m=1} \qquad (4.49)$$

Extension of equation (4.48) to obtain $\mathscr{J}_m[f(t)/t^k]$ is evident.

Special cases that stem from this theorem are indicated in the following.

$$\mathscr{J}\!\left[\frac{f(t)}{t + hT}\right] = \frac{1}{T} z^h \int_z^\infty p^{-(1+h)}\mathscr{F}(p)\, dp \qquad (4.50)$$

where h is a positive constant larger than zero. Equation (4.50) is obtained from equation (4.36) by multiplying both sides by $p^{-(1+h)}$ and integrating from z to ∞.

If we assume in equation (4.50), $T = 1, f(t) =$ unit step and if we denote h as a (integer),

$$\mathscr{J}\!\left[\frac{1}{n + a}\right] = \sum_{n=0}^\infty \frac{1}{n + a} z^{-n} = z^a \int_z^\infty p^{-(1+a)} \frac{p}{p - 1}\, dp$$

$$= z^a \int_\infty^z \left[\frac{1}{p^a} + \frac{1}{p^{a-1}} + \ldots + \frac{1}{p} - \frac{1}{p - 1}\right] dp$$

$$= z^a \left\{\ln \frac{z}{z - 1} - \left[\frac{z^{-(a-1)}}{a - 1} + \frac{z^{-(a-2)}}{a - 2} + \ldots + \frac{z^{-1}}{1}\right]\right\}$$

$$(4.51)$$

or

$$\mathscr{Y}\left[\frac{1}{n+a}\right] = z^a\left[\ln\frac{z}{z-1} - \sum_{p=1}^{a-1}\frac{1}{p}z^{-p}\right] \tag{4.52}$$

EXAMPLE

Obtain the following z-transform:

$$\mathscr{Y}\left[\frac{1}{(n+a)(n+b)}\right]$$

From equation (4.52) we can write

$$\mathscr{Y}\left[\frac{1}{(n+a)(n+b)}\right] = \mathscr{Y}\left[\frac{1}{b-a}\left(\frac{1}{n+a} - \frac{1}{n+b}\right)\right]$$

$$= \frac{1}{b-a}\left[\left(\ln\frac{z}{z-1}\right)(z^a - z^b)\right.$$

$$\left. - z^a\sum_{p=1}^{a-1}\frac{1}{p}z^{-b} + z^b\sum_{p=1}^{b-1}\frac{1}{p}z^{-p}\right] \tag{4.53}$$

If we let $a = 1$, $b = 2$,

$$\mathscr{Y}\left[\frac{1}{(n+1)(n+2)}\right] = z\left[1 + (1-z)\ln\frac{z}{z-1}\right] \tag{4.54}$$

Similarly, we can develop the z-transform of

$$\mathscr{Y}\left[\frac{1}{(n+a)(n+b)(n+c)\ldots}\right] \tag{4.55}$$

Summation of infinite and finite series[5-7,9,10]

The convolution z-transform readily yields the summation of series, where the sum exists. These summation forms are discussed as follows:

If we let $z = 1$ in equation (4.2), we readily obtain

$$\sum_{n=0}^{\infty} f_n h_n = \frac{1}{2\pi j}\int_\Gamma \frac{\mathscr{F}(p)}{p}\mathscr{H}(p^{-1})\,dp \tag{4.56}$$

where the contour Γ could be taken in a positive sense along a circle which encloses the poles of $\mathscr{F}(p)/p$. If the summation $\sum_{n=0}^{\infty} f_n h_n$ exists, then this contour could be along the unit circle in the p-plane. As a special case of equation (4.56), when $h_n = f_n$, we get

$$\sum_{n=0}^{\infty} f_n^2 = \frac{1}{2\pi j}\int_\Gamma \frac{\mathscr{F}(p)}{p}\mathscr{F}(p^{-1})\,dp \tag{4.57}$$

where the contour Γ in this case is along the unit circle where the poles of $\mathscr{F}(p)/p$ are enclosed. A method for obtaining equation (4.57) without having to obtain the poles of $\mathscr{F}(p)/p$ is given in Table III of the Appendix by letting $m = 1$ in I_n. The proof is presented in Appendix 2 of this chapter.

Another important summation could be obtained by letting $z = 1$ in equation (4.45), which gives

$$\sum_{n=0}^{\infty} \frac{f_n}{n^k} = \lim_{z \to 1} \underbrace{\int_z^{\infty} w^{-1} \int_w^{\infty} v^{-1} \ldots \int_q^{\infty} p^{-1} \mathscr{F}(p)\, dp \ldots dv\, dw}_{k\text{-times}} \quad (4.58)$$

To obtain the summation $\sum\limits_{n=0}^{\infty} n^r x^n$, $x < 1$, which often appears in the analysis of discrete filters, we can also apply the convolution z-transform as follows:

$$\sum_{n=0}^{\infty} n^r x^n = \frac{1}{2\pi j} \int_{\Gamma} \frac{p}{(p - x)p} \mathscr{H}(p^{-1})\, dp \quad (4.59)$$

where Γ encloses the poles of $1/(p - x)$ in a positive sense, and

$$\mathscr{H}(p^{-1}) = \mathscr{Z}[n^r]\big|_{z=p^{-1}} \quad (4.60)$$

The list of Table IV in the Appendix presents this summation for values of r up to 10. As a special case of equation (4.59), we can also obtain the finite sum of the following series[5,10]

$$S_r = \sum_{i=0}^{n-1} i^r x^i, \qquad r = 0, 1, 2, \ldots \quad (4.61)$$

for which

$$S_r = x \frac{dS_{r-1}}{dx}, \qquad \text{with } S_0 = \frac{x^n - 1}{x - 1} \quad (4.62)$$

Finite summation of the form $\sum\limits_{n=0}^{k} f_n$ can also be obtained from equation (4.56) by letting

$$h(t)\big|_{t=n} = u(t)\big|_{t=n} - u[t - (k + 1)]\big|_{t=n} \quad (4.63)$$

Therefore equation (4.56) reduces for this case to

$$\sum_{n=0}^{k} f_n = \frac{1}{2\pi j} \int_{\Gamma} \frac{\mathscr{F}(p)}{p} \frac{p^{-1}}{p^{-1} - 1} [1 - p^{k+1}]\, dp$$

$$= \frac{1}{2\pi j} \int_{\Gamma} \frac{\mathscr{F}(p)}{p} \frac{(p^{k+1} - 1)}{p - 1}\, dp \quad (4.64)$$

where the contour Γ encloses the poles of the integrand.

Obtain the following summation:

(1) $\displaystyle\sum_{n=1}^{\infty} \frac{1}{n^2}$

Using equation (4.58) for this particular case, we have

$$\sum_{n=1}^{\infty} \frac{1}{n^2} = \int_1^{\infty} p^{-1} \ln \frac{p}{p-1}\, dp$$

With the change of the variables of integration from $p^{-1} = x$ and using tables of integral, we finally obtain

$$\sum_{n=1}^{\infty} \frac{1}{n^2} = \int_0^1 x^{-1} \ln \left(\frac{1}{1-x} \right) dx = \frac{\pi^2}{6}$$

Summation of the form $\displaystyle\sum_{n=1}^{\infty} \left(\frac{1}{n^k} \right)$ for even values of $k > 2$ can be similarly obtained.

(2) $\displaystyle\sum_{n=0}^{\infty} n x^n, \quad x < 1$

This summation can be obtained from equation (4.59) as follows:

$$\sum_{n=0}^{\infty} n x^n = \frac{1}{2\pi j} \int_{\Gamma} \frac{p}{(p-x)p} \frac{p^{-1}}{(p^{-1}-1)^2}\, dp$$

where Γ is the contour in the p-plane which encloses the pole of $1/(p-x)$. Evaluating this integral, we get

$$\sum_{n=0}^{\infty} n x^n = \frac{x}{(1-x)^2}, \quad x < 1$$

(3) $\displaystyle\sum_{n=0}^{k} n$

From equation (4.64), we have

$$\sum_{n=0}^{k} n = \frac{1}{2\pi j} \int_{\Gamma} \frac{p^{k+1}-1}{(p-1)^2(p-1)}\, dp$$

This contour integral yields

$$\sum_{n=0}^{k} n = \frac{1}{2!} \frac{d^2}{dp^2} [p^{k+1}-1]\big|_{p=1} = \frac{k(k+1)}{2}$$

(4) $\displaystyle\sum_{n=0}^{\infty} \frac{(-1)^n}{(n+1)(n+2)}$

This summation can be obtained from equation (4.54) by letting $z = -1$, which gives

$$\sum_{n=0}^{\infty} \frac{(-1)^n}{(n+1)(n+2)} = 2 \ln 2 - 1$$

Finally, summations of the form $\sum_{n=0}^{\infty} f_n h_{n+m}$, $0 \le m \le 1$ can be similarly obtained from the convolution modified z-transform. Furthermore, from the integrand form we can ascertain the conditions on convergence of the series or the possibility of obtaining a closed form.

Unmixed difference-differential and sum equations[7,8]

The convolution z-transform is readily applicable to the solution of equations of the following form:

$$\sum_{m=0}^{M} \sum_{k=0}^{K} \alpha_{km} y_{n+m}^{(k)}(t) + \sum_{k=0}^{n} \beta_k y_k(t) = x_n(t) \tag{4.65}$$

Assuming zero initial conditions, we proceed to solve this equation by applying first the Laplace transform and then the z-transform to obtain

$$\sum_{m=0}^{M} \sum_{k=0}^{K} \alpha_{km} s^k \mathscr{Z}[Y_{n+m}(s)] + \mathscr{Z}\left[\sum_{k=0}^{n} \beta_k Y_k(s)\right] = \mathscr{Z}[X_n(s)] \tag{4.66}$$

where $\mathscr{L}[y_{n+m}^{(k)}(t)] = s^k Y_{n+m}(s)$.

Using the convolution z-transform and noting that

$$\mathscr{Z}\left[\sum_{k=0}^{n} f_k\right] = \frac{z}{z-1} \mathscr{F}(z),$$

we obtain for

$$\mathscr{Z}\left[\sum_{k=0}^{n} \beta_k Y_k(s)\right] = \left(\frac{z}{z-1}\right)\frac{1}{2\pi j} \int_{\Gamma} \frac{B(p)}{p} \mathscr{Y}\left(\frac{z}{p}, s\right) dp \tag{4.67}$$

where $B(z) = \mathscr{Z}[B_n]$ and $\mathscr{Y}(z, s) = \mathscr{Z}[Y_n(s)]$ as defined in equation (2.120a). Using equation (4.67) in obtaining the z-transform of equation (4.66) we get

$$\mathscr{Y}(z, s) \sum_{m=0}^{M} \sum_{k=0}^{K} \alpha_{km} s^k z^m + \frac{z}{z-1} \frac{1}{2\pi j} \int_{\Gamma} \frac{B(p)}{p} \mathscr{Y}\left(\frac{z}{p}, s\right) dp$$

$$= \mathscr{X}(z, s) \tag{4.68}$$

This linear integral equation cannot be solved in terms of elementary functions, but it can be solved by a convergent iterative process.

If we examine the special case where $\beta_k = \beta$, when β is a constant, equation (4.68) reduces to

$$\mathscr{Y}(z, s) \sum_{m=0}^{M} \sum_{k=0}^{K} \alpha_{km} s^k z^m + \frac{z\beta}{z - 1} \mathscr{Y}(z, s) = \mathscr{X}(z, s) \qquad (4.69)$$

This can be written

$$\mathscr{Y}(z, s) = \frac{\mathscr{X}(z, s)}{\displaystyle\sum_{m=0}^{M} \sum_{k=0}^{K} \alpha_{km} s^k z^m + \frac{z\beta}{z - 1}} = \frac{\mathscr{X}(z, s)}{\mathscr{H}(z, s)} \qquad (4.70)$$

To obtain $y_n(t)$, it is necessary to know the zeros of the denominator. Knowing these zeros, we can apply the inverse Laplace transform and then the inverse z-transform as follows:

$$y_n(t) = \mathscr{Z}^{-1}\mathscr{L}^{-1}[\mathscr{Y}(z, s)] = \mathscr{Z}^{-1}\mathscr{Y}(z, t) \qquad (4.71)$$

or

$$y_n(t) = \mathscr{L}^{-1}\mathscr{Z}^{-1}[\mathscr{Y}(z, s)] = \mathscr{L}^{-1}[Y_n(s)] \qquad (4.72)$$

Evaluation of integrals of time functions[2,4,11,22]

We shall use the convolution modified z-transform to evaluate the following integral:

$$\int_0^\infty f(t)h(t)\, dt \qquad (4.73)$$

We obtain this integral from equation (4.29) by using the final value theorem for the modified z-transform

$$\int_0^\infty f(t)h(t)\, dt = \frac{T}{2\pi j} \int_0^1 \int_\Gamma \frac{\mathscr{F}(p, m)}{p} \mathscr{H}(p^{-1}, m)\, dp\, dm \qquad (4.74)$$

The contour Γ can be taken in a positive sense which encloses the poles of $\mathscr{F}(p, m)/p$ or in a negative sense that encloses the poles of $\mathscr{H}(p^{-1}, m)$ in the p-plane.

As special cases of the preceding, let $h(t) = f(t)$; then

$$\int_0^\infty [f(t)]^2\, dt = \frac{T}{2\pi j} \int_0^1 \int_\Gamma p^{-1}\mathscr{F}(p, m)\mathscr{F}(p^{-1}, m)\, dp\, dm \qquad (4.75)$$

where the contour Γ is taken along the unit circle since all the poles of $\mathscr{F}(p, m)/p$ are inside the unit circle if the integral is finite. It should be noted that in the evaluation of the integral

$$I_n = \frac{1}{2\pi j} \int_\Gamma p^{-1}\mathscr{F}(p, m)\mathscr{F}(p^{-1}, m)\, dp \qquad (4.76)$$

we do not need to find the poles of $\mathscr{F}(p, m)$ for the integral can be calculated as the ratio of two determinants in the coefficients of the numerator and denominator of $\mathscr{F}(p, m)$. The evaluation of this integral is presented in Table III and calculated up to values $n = 4$.

It should be noted that the evaluation of the integral in equation (4.75) is simplified if the order of integration in p and m is interchanged. This is possible since the integrand is continuous along Γ and in the interval $0 \leq m \leq 1$.

Furthermore, if we let $h(t) = tf(t)$

$$\int_0^\infty t[f(t)]^2 \, dt = \frac{T^2}{2\pi j} \int_0^1 \int_\Gamma p^{-1} \Big[(m - 1)\mathscr{F}(p, m) $$
$$ - p \frac{\partial}{\partial p} \mathscr{F}(p, m) \Big] [\mathscr{F}(p^{-1}, m)] \, dp \, dm \quad (4.77)$$

Similar relations can be obtained for higher-order moments.

In conclusion, by utilizing equation (1.178) of the modified z-transform which states

$$T \int_0^1 \mathscr{F}(z, m) \mathscr{H}(z^{-1}, m) \, dm = \mathscr{Z}[F(s)H(-s)], \qquad 0 \leq m \leq 1$$

we can rewrite equation (4.74) in the following simplified form:

$$\int_0^\infty f(t)h(t) \, dt = \frac{1}{2\pi j} \int_\Gamma \mathscr{Z}[F(s), H(-s)]\big|_{z=p} \, p^{-1} \, dp \quad (4.78)$$

Similar relationship could be obtained for evaluating finite integrals of the following form:

$$\int_0^{t_1} f_1(t) \, dt = \int_0^{t_1} f(t)h(t) \, dt \quad (4.79)$$

where t_1 is finite integer.

The evaluation of the integral of the square of the time function is very important in the design of sampled-data feedback system that is based on the minimization of the total square value of the error function. It is also important in the statistical design of a system that is based on the minimization of the mean square error function. The entries of Table III are important in obtaining the noise power gain in a discrete filter.

Two-sided z-transform[12,15,16,17,18]

In the preceding chapters, the z-transform of $f(n)$ is defined for positive values of n, that is, $n \geq 0$, which we may refer to as the one-sided z-transform. In some applications such as in the statistical study of discrete

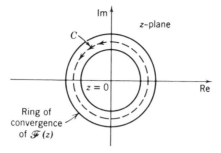

FIGURE 4.6   The contour C and the ring of convergence of $\mathscr{F}(z)$.

systems, the statistical functions may also be described for negative n, thus the z-transform definition should be modified to cover such cases. The two-sided z-transform is defined as follows:

$$\mathscr{F}(z) = \mathscr{Z}[f(n)] = \sum_{n=-\infty}^{n=\infty} f(n)z^{-n} \tag{4.80}$$

where $\mathscr{F}(z)$ is analytic in the ring shown in Fig. 4.6.
The inverse of $\mathscr{F}(z)$ is unique and is given by

$$f(n) = \mathscr{Z}^{-1}[\mathscr{F}(z)] = \frac{1}{2\pi j} \int_C \mathscr{F}(z)z^{n-1} \, dz \tag{4.81}$$

where the closed contour C lies in the ring of convergence of $\mathscr{F}(z)$ with the point $z = 0$ in its interior. The definition of the two-sided z-transform requires that $\mathscr{F}(z)$ converge in some ring (of nonzero area) about $z = 0$ in the complex plane. The contour C is shown in Fig. 4.6.
If the function $f(n)$ is bounded, the contour Γ of Fig 4.7 enclosing the unit circle will belong to the ring of convergence. Here we write

$$f(n) = \mathscr{Z}^{-1}[\mathscr{F}(z)] = \frac{1}{2\pi j} \int_\Gamma \mathscr{F}(z)z^{n-1} \, dz, \qquad (-\infty < n < \infty) \tag{4.82}$$

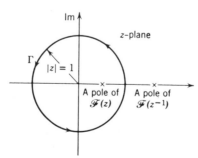

FIGURE 4.7   The contour Γ in the z-plane.

If the only singularities of $\mathscr{F}(z)$ are poles of finite order, the inverse can be evaluated as usual by the residue method, that is,

$$f(n) = \sum_{\substack{\text{all poles} \\ \text{inside unit} \\ \text{circle}}} \text{residue } \mathscr{F}(z)z^{n-1}, \qquad (-\infty < n < \infty) \qquad (4.83)$$

We may note that we could also evaluate $f(n)$ by considering the poles *outside* the unit circle; then we will have

$$f(n) = - \sum_{\substack{\text{all poles} \\ \text{outside the} \\ \text{unit circle}}} \text{residue } \mathscr{F}(z)z^{n-1}, \qquad (-\infty < n < \infty)$$

$$(4.84)$$

Although both equations (4.83) and (4.84) are valid for all n for computational purposes, equation (4.83) is preferable for $n \geq 0$, and equation (4.84) is preferable for $n \leq 0$.

Since, in statistical study of signals in discrete systems, both boundedness and symmetry around the time origin are assumed, we could then write

$$\mathscr{F}(z) = \sum_{n=-\infty}^{0} f(n)z^{-n} + \sum_{n=0}^{\infty} f(n)z^{-n} - f(0) \qquad (4.85)$$

If we let $m = -n$ in the first term of the right side and impose the condition $f(n) = f(-n)$, we will have

$$\mathscr{F}(z) = \mathscr{F}_1(z^{-1}) + \mathscr{F}_1(z) - f(0) \qquad (4.86)$$

where $\mathscr{F}_1(z)$ has all its poles inside the unit circle and it is defined for positive n, and $\mathscr{F}_1(z^{-1})$ has all its poles outside the unit circle and is defined for negative n.

The inverse of equation (4.86) gives

$$f(n) = \mathscr{J}^{-1}[\mathscr{F}_1(z^{-1})] + \mathscr{J}^{-1}[\mathscr{F}_1(z)] - f(0)\delta_{n_0} \qquad (4.87)$$

where $\delta_{n_0} = 1$ for $n = 0$
      $\quad\quad = 0$ otherwise

We may note that here we might use equation (4.83) for $n \geq 0$, substituting only $\mathscr{F}_1(z)$ for $\mathscr{F}(z)$. Similarly, we may use equation (4.84) for $n \leq 0$, substituting only $\mathscr{F}_1(z^{-1})$ for $\mathscr{F}(z)$.

The general case where $f(n)$ is not symmetrical and boundedness condition does not exist can also be treated. However, in this situation care should be exercised in defining the ring of convergence of $\mathscr{F}(z)$. If such a ring is nonexistent the z-transform does not exist.

For instance, if a pole exists inside the unit circle, then this indicates a decreasing exponential for positive n, or a nonzero value for the time function for negative n. The decision as to which time function is represented by the z-transform depends on the ring of convergence in the

z-plane in which $\mathscr{F}(z)$ is defined and on the manner in which the ring divides the poles of $\mathscr{F}(z)$ within or outside this contour.

ILLUSTRATIVE EXAMPLE

Let $\mathscr{F}(z)$ be given as follows:

$$\mathscr{F}(z) = \frac{-z(1 - q^2)}{q(z - q^{-1})(z - q)}, \qquad \text{with } q < 1$$

To obtain $f(n)$ for $n \geq 0$, we use equation (4.83) for roots inside the unit circle. In this case, we obtain

$$f(n) = \text{residue of } [\mathscr{F}(z)z^{n-1}] \big|_{z=q} = q^n, \qquad n \geq 0$$

For $n \leq 0$, we obtain from equation (4.84) the following:

$$f(n) = q^{-n}, \qquad n \leq 0$$

The total function $f(n)$ is represented by

$$f(n) = q^n, \qquad n \geq 1; \qquad f(n) = q^{-n}, \qquad n \leq -1$$

and

$$f(0) = 1$$

Applications to correlation functions and spectral analysis[16,17]

One of the applications of the two-sided z-transform is in obtaining the power spectrum density of the discrete random signal. This discrete power spectrum is defined as the two-sided z-transform of the auto-correlation function of the signal. For instance, if the signal is represented as $f(k)$, its correlation function is defined as

$$\phi(n) = \lim_{N \to \infty} \frac{1}{2N + 1} \sum_{k=-N}^{N} f(k)f(k - n), \qquad (4.88)$$

where n is an integer.

The power-spectrum density of the random signal is defined as

$$\Phi(z) \overset{\Delta}{=} \sum_{n=-\infty}^{n=\infty} \phi(n)z^{-n} \overset{\Delta}{=} \mathscr{J}[\phi(n)] \qquad (4.89)$$

Since $\phi(n)$ is an even function of time and bounded, it can be obtained from equation (4.89) as

$$\phi(n) = \mathscr{J}^{-1}[\Phi(z)] = \frac{1}{2\pi j} \int_{\Gamma} \Phi(z)z^{n-1} \, dz \qquad (4.90)$$

where Γ is the boundary of the unit circle in the z-plane.

It is seen from equation (4.88) that when $n = 0$, we get

$$\phi(0) = \lim_{N \to \infty} \frac{1}{2N+1} \sum_{k=-N}^{k=N} \{f(k)\}^2 = \bar{f}^2$$

$\triangleq$ mean square value of the signal   (4.91)

Substituting for $n = 0$ in (4.90) and using (4.91), we obtain:

$$\bar{f}^2 = \frac{1}{2\pi j} \int_\Gamma \Phi(z) z^{-1}\, dz \tag{4.92}$$

Since $\Phi(z)$ is a symmetric function with respect to z, it can be written as

$$\Phi(z) = \mathcal{F}(z)\mathcal{F}(z^{-1}) \tag{4.93}$$

If we substitute (4.93) in (4.92), we can evaluate $\bar{f}^2$ readily by using the tables of total square integrals which we discussed earlier.

$$\bar{f}^2 = I_n = \frac{1}{2\pi j} \int_\Gamma \mathcal{F}(z)\mathcal{F}(z^{-1}) z^{-1}\, dz. \tag{4.94}$$

Furthermore, if the stationary signal f_k having the power spectrum $\Phi(z)$ is sent through a linear, time-invariant system with discrete stable transfer function $\mathcal{G}(z)$, the output mean square value of the signal is given as

$$\bar{f_{ok}^2} = \frac{1}{2\pi j} \int_\Gamma \Phi_o(z) z^{-1}\, dz \tag{4.95}$$

where

$$\Phi_o(z) = \mathcal{G}(z)\mathcal{G}(z^{-1})\Phi(z)$$

EXAMPLE

1. We shall calculate the mean square value of the output of a discrete system shown in Fig. 4.8.

Given the power spectrum density of the input

$$\Phi_i(z) = N^2$$

where N is a constant (this represents white noise). To obtain the system transfer function $\mathcal{G}(z)$ from Fig. 4.8, we use

$$\mathcal{G}(z) = \frac{\mathcal{F}_0(z)}{\mathcal{F}_i(z)} = \frac{\dfrac{c}{z-1}\left[1 + \dfrac{(b/c)z}{z-1}\right]}{1 + \dfrac{c}{z-1}\left[1 + \dfrac{(b/c)z}{z-1}\right]}$$

$$= \frac{z(b+c) - c}{z^2 + (b+c-2)z + (1-c)} \tag{4.96}$$

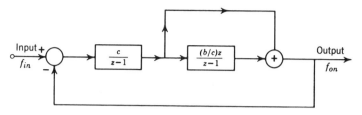

FIGURE 4.8 A feedback discrete system.

The mean square value of the output is given as

$$\overline{f_{on}^2} = \frac{1}{2\pi j} \int_\Gamma \mathcal{G}(z)\mathcal{G}(z^{-1})\Phi_i(z)\, z^{-1}\, dz$$

$$= \frac{N^2}{2\pi j} \int_\Gamma \frac{z(b+c) - c}{z^2 + (b+c-2)z + (1-c)}$$

$$\times \frac{z^{-1}(b+c) - c}{z^{-2} + (b+c-2)z^{-1} + (1-c)}\, z^{-1}\, dz \qquad (4.97)$$

This integral can be easily evaluated by using Table III for the second-order case and noting the following constants:

$$b_0 = 0, \quad b_1 = b + c, \quad b_2 = -c$$
$$a_0 = 1, \quad a_1 = (b + c - 2), \quad a_2 = 1 - c \qquad (4.98)$$

Substituting these values in the I_2 formula of the second-order case to obtain finally

$$\overline{f_{on}^2} = \frac{N^2[c(1 + b/c^2) + b/2]}{2 - c - (b/2)} \qquad (4.99)$$

When $b = 0$, this reduces to

$$\overline{f_{on}^2} = \frac{cN^2}{2 - c} \qquad (4.100)$$

Extension of two-sided z-transform to continuous output[12,16,23]

In this application the two-sided z-transform is applied to the continuous correlation function as follows:

$$\Phi_o(z, m) \triangleq \sum_{n=-\infty}^{n=\infty} z^{-n} \lim_{N \to \infty} \frac{1}{2N + 1} \sum_{k=-N}^{N}$$

$$\times f_o(k + m - 1)f_o(k - n + m - 1), \quad 0 \le m \le 1 \quad (4.101)$$

If we denote the coefficient of z^{-n} as $\phi_0(n, m)$, the continuous spectral density is

$$\Phi_o(z, m) = \sum_{n=-\infty}^{n=\infty} z^{-n}\phi_o(n, m) \tag{4.102}$$

To obtain the mean square value of the output $\overline{f_o^2(t)}$, we use the following form:

$$\overline{f_o^2} = \lim_{N \to \infty} \frac{1}{2N + 1} \sum_{k=-N}^{N} \int_0^1 f_o^2(k + m - 1)\, dm, \qquad 0 \le m \le 1 \tag{4.103}$$

This equation can be obtained from $\phi_0(n, m)$ by letting $n = 0$ as follows:

$$\overline{f_o^2} = \int_0^1 \phi_o(0, m)\, dm \tag{4.104}$$

On the other hand, $\phi_0(n, m)$ is obtained from $\Phi_0(z, m)$ as inverse z-transform relationship, that is,

$$\phi_o(n, m) = \frac{1}{2\pi j} \int_\Gamma \Phi_o(z, m) z^{n-1}\, dz \tag{4.105}$$

where Γ is taken along the unit circle for stable $\phi_0(n, m)$ as is usually the case.

Therefore

$$\phi_o(0, m) = \frac{1}{2\pi j} \int_\Gamma \Phi_o(z, m) z^{-1}\, dz \tag{4.106}$$

Inserting equation (4.106) in (4.104), we finally obtain

$$\overline{f_o^2} = \frac{1}{2\pi j} \int_\Gamma \int_0^1 \Phi_o(z, m) z^{-1}\, dm\, dz = \frac{1}{2\pi j} \int_\Gamma \overline{\Phi_o(z, m)} z^{-1}\, dz \tag{4.107}$$

Evaluation of equation (4.107) can be readily obtained by using the tables of integrals which were derived in Table III. It should be noted that $\overline{\Phi_0(z, m)}$ can be always written in the form

$$\overline{\Phi_0(z, m)} = \mathscr{F}(z)\mathscr{F}(z^{-1}) \tag{4.108}$$

which is readily amenable to table form.

Finally, we may note that the mean square value of the ouput for a discrete system could also be obtained from the Laplace transform theory. An illustrative example of optimization and filtering using Laplace and z-transform methods is discussed in detail in Section 8.3.

Appendix 1: Proof of complex convolution formula†[11,14,20]

Suppose $F^*(s)$ and $H^*(s)$ are the Laplace transforms of sampled function $f^*(t)$ and $h^*(t)$, respectively, defined by

$$F^*(s) = \mathcal{L}[f^*(t)] = \frac{1}{2\pi j} \int_{q_0-j\infty}^{q_0+j\infty} F(q) \frac{1}{1 - e^{-T(s-q)}} dq + \tfrac{1}{2}f(0)$$

(A.1)

with Re $[s] > q_0 > $ max [real part of poles of $F(s)$], and $F(s) = \mathcal{L}[f(t)]$. To find $\mathcal{L}\{[f(t)h(t)] \cdot \delta_T(t)\}$, we use the following definition from (A.1):

$$\mathcal{L}\{[f(t)h(t)] \cdot \delta_T(t)\} = \frac{1}{2\pi j} \int_{w_0-j\infty}^{w_0+j\infty} \mathcal{L}[f(t)h(t)] \frac{1}{1 - e^{-T(s-w)}} dw$$

(A.2)‡

From the convolution theorem of Laplace transform,[3] equation (A.2) can be written as

$$\mathcal{L}\{[f(t)h(t)] \cdot \delta_T(t)\} = \frac{1}{2\pi j} \int_{w_0-j\infty}^{w_0+j\infty}$$
$$\times \left[\frac{1}{2\pi j} \int_{c-j\infty}^{c+j\infty} F(q)H(w - q) dq \right] \frac{1}{1 - e^{-T(s-w)}} dw \quad \text{(A.3)}$$

In equation (A.3) we interchange the integration with respect to w and q. Therefore

$$\mathcal{L}\{[f(t)h(t)] \cdot \delta_T(t)\}$$
$$= \frac{1}{2\pi j} \int_{c-j\infty}^{c+j\infty} F(q) \, dq \, \frac{1}{2\pi j} \int_{w_0-j\infty}^{w_0+j\infty} H(w - q) \frac{1}{1 - e^{-T(s-w)}} dw$$

(A.4)

Noting equation (A.1), we obtain for the right side of equation (A.4)

$$\frac{1}{2\pi j} \int_{c-j\infty}^{c+j\infty} F(q)H^*(s - q) \, dq$$

(A.5)

It should be noted that $H^*(s - q)$ is a function of $e^{T(s-q)}$ only. In equation (A.5) we divide the range of integration into intervals of length $\omega_0 = 2\pi/T$ so that equation (A.5) becomes

$$\mathcal{L}\{[f(t)h(t)] \cdot \delta_T(t)\} = \frac{1}{2\pi j} \sum_{k=-\infty}^{k=\infty} \left[\int_{c+(k-\frac{1}{2})j\omega_0}^{c+(k+\frac{1}{2})j\omega_0} F(q)H^*(s - q) \, dq \right]$$

(A.6)

---

† Another derivation of the convolution formula can be directly obtained from the z-transform definition.[13,21] (See also Problem 4.1.)
‡ For simplicity we assume that $f(0)h(0) = 0$. However, the same result is obtained if $f(0)h(0) \neq 0$. The exact derivation is left as an exercise for the reader.

Changing q to $q + jk\omega_0$, and since $H^*(s - q)$ is a function of $e^{T(s-q)}$ only, we get

$$\mathscr{L}\{[f(t)h(t)] \cdot \delta_T(t)\}$$

$$= \frac{1}{2\pi j} \sum_{k=-\infty}^{k=\infty} \int_{c-j\omega_0/2}^{c+j\omega_0/2} F(q + jk\omega_0)H^*(s - q)\, dq, \qquad \omega_0 = \frac{2\pi}{T}$$

(A.7)

Equation (A.7) is further simplified as follows:

$$\mathscr{L}\{[f(t)h(t)] \cdot \delta_T(t)\}$$

$$= \frac{T}{2\pi j} \int_{c-j(\pi/T)}^{c+j(\pi/T)} H^*(s - q)\, dq \left[\frac{1}{T} \sum_{k=-\infty}^{k=\infty} F\left(q + j\frac{2k\pi}{T}\right) \right] \quad (A.8)$$

Noting that the bracketed term is $F^*(q)$,

$$\mathscr{L}\{[f(t)h(t)] \cdot \delta_T(t)\} = \frac{T}{2\pi j} \int_{c-j(\pi/T)}^{c+j(\pi/T)} H^*(s - q)F^*(q)\, dq \quad (A.9)$$

Similar derivations could be used to prove the formula for the modified z-transform convolutions.

Appendix 2: Derivation of total square integrals formula[11,22]

The solution of the integral I_n given as

$$I_n = \sum_{k=0}^{\infty} h(k)^2 = \frac{1}{2\pi j} \oint_{\substack{\text{unit} \\ \text{circle}}} \mathscr{H}(z)\mathscr{H}(z^{-1}) \frac{dz}{z} \quad (A.10)$$

is presented in this Appendix. The derivation is based on obtaining the right side of equation (A.10) as a sum of residues. However, instead of using the explicit expressions for the residues, we obtain a set of $2n + 1$ linear equations, with the sum of the residues as one variable. Because of symmetry this set reduces to $n + 1$ equations.

Assuming $\mathscr{H}(z)$ is given,

$$\mathscr{H}(z) = \frac{B(z)}{A(z)} = \frac{\displaystyle\sum_{i=0}^{n} b_i z^{n-i}}{\displaystyle\sum_{i=0}^{n} a_i z^{n-i}} = K^2 \frac{\displaystyle\prod_{i=1}^{n} (z - q_i)}{\displaystyle\prod_{i=1}^{n} (z - p_i)} \quad (A.11)$$

The integral of equation (A.10) is solved by the method of the residues; thus we are interested in

$$\frac{zA(z)}{z - p_k} = \sum_{i=0}^{n} c_{i,k} z^i, \qquad k = 0, 1, 2, \ldots, n \quad (A.12)$$

Since we assume p_0 to be the location of the pole at the origin of the z-plane, we have

$$c_{0,k} = 0 \quad \text{when } k \neq 0$$
$$c_{0,0} = a_n \tag{A.13}$$

We also have

$$\frac{zA(z^{-1})}{z - p_k^{-1}} = \frac{zA(z^{-1})p_k}{z(p_k - z^{-1})} = -zp_k \frac{z^{-1}A(z^{-1})}{z^{-1} - p_k} = -zp_k \sum_{i=0}^{n} c_{i,k} z^{-i} \tag{A.14}$$

and

$$\frac{zA(z)A(z^{-1})}{(z - p_k)} = \sum_{j=0}^{n} z^j \sum_{i=0}^{n} c_{j+i,k} a_{n-i} + \sum_{j=1}^{n} z^{-j} \sum_{i=0}^{n} c_{i,k} a_{n-i-j} \tag{A.15}$$

$$\frac{zA(z)A(z^{-1})}{z - p_k^{-1}} = -zp_k \left[\sum_{j=0}^{n} z^j \sum_{i=0}^{n} c_{i,k} a_{n-i-j} + \sum_{j=1}^{n} z^{-j} \sum_{i=0}^{n} c_{i+j,k} a_{n-i} \right] \tag{A.16}$$

By partial fraction expansion,

$$\frac{B(z)B(z^{-1})}{zA(z)A(z^{-1})} = \sum_{k=0}^{n} \frac{R_{p_k}}{z - p_k} + \sum_{k=1}^{n} \frac{R_{p_k}^{-1}}{z - p_k^{-1}} \tag{A.17}$$

where R_{p_k} equals residue at p_k; $R_{p_k}^{-1}$ equals residue at p_k^{-1}.

In the preceding we have assumed only simple poles. Later we shall indicate that the results are also valid for multiple poles.

For $k \neq 0$, we have

$$zA(z)A(z^{-1}) = z(z - p_k)(z^{-1} - p_k)[A'(p_k)A'(p_k^{-1})]_{p_k=z}$$
$$= -p_k(z - p_k)(z - p_k^{-1})[A'(p_k)A'(p_k^{-1})]_{p_k=z} \tag{A.18}$$

and

$$R_{p_k} = \frac{B(p_k)B(p_k^{-1})}{-p_k(p_k - p_k^{-1})A'(p_k)A'(p_k^{-1})} = -R_{p_k}^{-1} \tag{A.19}$$

Combining equations (A.15), (A.16), (A.17), and (A.19), we obtain

$$B(z)B(z^{-1}) = \sum_{k=0}^{n} \sum_{j=0}^{n} \sum_{i=0}^{n} z^j R_{p_k} c_{j+i,k} a_{n-i}$$

$$+ \sum_{k=0}^{n} \sum_{j=1}^{n} \sum_{i=0}^{n} z^{-j} R_{p_k} c_{i,k} a_{n-i-j}$$

$$+ z \sum_{k=1}^{n} \sum_{j=0}^{n} \sum_{i=0}^{n} z^j R_{p_k} p_k c_{i,k} a_{n-i-j}$$

$$+ z \sum_{k=1}^{n} \sum_{j=1}^{n} \sum_{i=0}^{n} z^{-j} R_{p_k} p_k c_{i+j,k} a_{n-i} \tag{A.20}$$

We can also write

$$B(z)B(z^{-1}) = \sum_{j=0}^{n} z^j \sum_{i=0}^{n} b_{n-i+j}b_{n-i} + \sum_{j=1}^{n} z^{-j} \sum_{i=0}^{n} b_{n-i-j}b_{n-i} \tag{A.21}$$

Let

$$M_i = \sum_{k=0}^{n} c_{i,k} R_{p_k} \tag{A.22}$$

and

$$Q_i = \sum_{k=1}^{n} c_{i,k} R_{p_k} p_k \tag{A.23}$$

From equation (A.12), we have

$$c_{nk} = a_0, \quad k = 0, 1, \ldots, n \quad \text{and} \quad c_{1k} = -\frac{a_n}{p_k},$$
$$k = 1, 2, \ldots, n \tag{A.24}$$

Then

$$M_n = a_0 \sum_{k=0}^{n} R_{p_k} = I_n a_0 \tag{A.25}$$

In addition,

$$Q_1 = -a_n \sum_{k=1}^{n} R_{p_k} = -a_n I_n + a_n R_0 \tag{A.26}$$

Since

$$c_{0k} = 0, \quad \text{when } k \neq 0$$

then

$$Q_0 = 0 \tag{A.27}$$

Combining equations (A.20) and (A.21) and using the preceding relation-ships, we have

$$\sum_{j=0}^{n} z^j \sum_{i=0}^{n} b_{n-i+j}b_{n-i} + \sum_{j=1}^{n} z^{-j} \sum_{i=0}^{n} b_{n-i-j}b_{n-i}$$
$$= \sum_{j=0}^{n} z^j \sum_{i=0}^{n} M_{j+i} a_{n-i} + \sum_{j=1}^{n} z^{-j} \sum_{i=0}^{n} M_i a_{n-i-j}$$
$$+ \sum_{j=0}^{n} z^{j+1} \sum_{i=1}^{n} Q_i a_{n-i-j} + \sum_{j=1}^{n} z^{-j+1} \sum_{i=0}^{n} Q_{i+j} a_{n-i} \tag{A.28}$$

Equating the coefficients of z^0 in equation (A.28), we get

$$\sum_{i=0}^{n} b_i^2 = \sum_{i=0}^{n} M_{n-i} a_i + \sum_{i=0}^{n} a_i Q_{n-i+1} \tag{A.29}$$

We notice from equation (A.28) the coefficients of z^j is equal to the*

---

* Note that $\displaystyle\sum_{i=0}^{n} b_i b_{i+j} = \sum_{i=0}^{n} b_i b_{i-j}.$

coefficient of z^{-j}. Thus, by summing the equations for j and $-j$,

$$2 \sum_{i=0}^{n} b_i b_{i+j} = \sum_{i=0}^{n} M_{j+n-i} a_i + \sum_{i=0}^{n} M_{n-i} a_{i-j}$$
$$+ \sum_{i=0}^{n-1} Q_{n-i} a_{i-j+1} + \sum_{i=0}^{n} Q_{n-i+j+1} a_i$$
$$= \sum_{i=0}^{n} a_i (M_{j+n-i} + Q_{n-i+j+1}) + \sum_{i=0}^{n} a_{i-j} (M_{n-i} + Q_{n-i+1}),$$

$$\text{for } j = 1, 2, 3, \ldots, n \quad \text{(A.30)}^*$$

where $a_i = 0$ when $n < i$ and $0 > i$.
Equation (A.30) can also be written as

$$2 \sum_{i=0}^{n} b_i b_{i+j} = \sum_{i=0}^{n} a_{i-j} (M_{n+i} + Q_{n-i+1}) + \sum_{i=0}^{n} a_{i-j} (M_{n-i} + Q_{n-i+1})$$
$$= \sum_{i=0}^{n} (a_{i-j} + a_{i+j})(M_{n-i} + Q_{n-i+1}),$$

$$\text{for } j = 1, 2, \ldots, n \quad \text{(A.31)}$$

The $n + 1$ simultaneous linear equations (A.29) and (A.31) can be written as the vector equation

$$\Omega \mathbf{m} = \mathbf{d} \tag{A.32}$$

where $\mathbf{m}$ and $\mathbf{d}$ are the vectors

$$\begin{bmatrix} M_n \\ M_{n-1} + Q_n \\ M_{n-2} + Q_{n-1} \\ \cdot \\ \cdot \\ \cdot \\ M_0 + Q_1 \end{bmatrix} \quad \text{and} \quad \begin{bmatrix} \sum b_i^2 \\ 2 \sum b_i b_{i+1} \\ 2 \sum b_i b_{i+2} \\ \cdot \\ \cdot \\ \cdot \\ 2 b_0 b_n \end{bmatrix} \tag{A.33}$$

and Ω is the matrix

$$\Omega = \begin{bmatrix} a_0 & a_1 & a_2 & a_3 & \cdots & a_n \\ a_1 & a_0 + a_2 & a_1 + a_3 & a_2 + a_4 & \cdots & a_{n-1} \\ a_2 & a_3 & a_0 + a_4 & a_1 + a_5 & \cdots & a_{n-2} \\ \cdot \\ \cdot \\ \cdot \\ a_n & 0 & 0 & \cdots & \cdots & a_0 \end{bmatrix} \tag{A.34}$$

---

* It should be noted that this equation also yields equation (A.29) when $j = 0$.

Since, from equation (A.25)

$$I_n = \frac{M_n}{a_0} \tag{A.35}$$

Hence

$$I_n = \frac{|\Omega_1|}{a_0 |\Omega|} \tag{A.36}$$

where Ω_1 is the matrix formed from Ω by replacing the first column by the vector d. Since $I_n = I_n(a_0, a_1, \ldots, a_n, b_0, b_1, \ldots, b_n)$ is an analytic function of the coefficients a_i and b_i, $0 \leq i \leq n$, the result is also valid for multiple poles.

Table III presents the values of I_n for $n = 1, 2, 3, 4$.

REFERENCES

1. Jury, E. I., *Sampled-Data Control Systems*, John Wiley and Sons, New York, 1958.

2. Tsypkin, Y. Z., *Theory of Pulse Systems* (in Russian), State Press for Physics and Mathematical Literature, Moscow, 1958.

3. Gardner, M. F., and J. L. Barnes, *Transients in Linear Systems*, Vol. 1, John Wiley and Sons, New York, 1942.

4. Jury, E. I., "A Contribution to Modified z-Transform Theory," *J. Franklin Inst.*, Vol. 270, 1960, pp. 114–129.

5. Lawden, D. F., "The Functions $\sum\limits_{n=1}^{\infty} n^r z^n$ and Associated Polynomials," *Proceedings of the Cambridge Philosophical Society*, Vol. 47, Part 2, 1954, pp. 309–314.

6. Wheelon, A. D., "On the Summation of Infinite Series in Closed Form," *J. Appl. Phys.*, Vol. 25, 1954, pp. 113–118.

7. Ku, Y. H., and A. Wolf, "Laurent-Cauchy Transforms for Analysis of Linear Systems Described by Differential Difference and Sum Equations," *Proc. IRE.* Vol. 48, 1960, pp. 923–431.

8. Discussion of Reference 7 by E. I. Jury in *Proc. IRE*, Vol. 48, 1960, pp. 2026–27.

9. Jury, E. I., and M. A. Pai, "On the Summation of $\sum\limits_{n=0}^{\infty} \frac{f_n}{n^k}$ and Its Associated Integrals," *J. Franklin Inst.*, Vol. 271, No. 2, February 1961.

10. Stone, W. M., "A List of Generalized Laplace Transforms," *Iowa State College Journal of Science*, Vol. 22, April 1948, pp. 215–225.

11. Whalen, B. A., "Noise Power Gain of Discrete Filters," Master of Science Thesis, University of California, Berkeley, June 1959.

12. Mori, M., "Statistical Treatment of Sampled-Data Control Systems for Actual Random Inputs," *Trans. ASME*, Vol. 80, No. 2, February 1958.

13. Kaplan, Wilfred, *Operational Methods for Linear Systems*, Addison Wesley Publishing Co., Reading, Massachusetts, 1962.

14. Pai, M. A., "The Analysis of Non-linear Feedback Sampled-Data Systems," Ph.D. Thesis, Dept. of Electrical Engineering, University of California, Berkeley, 1961.

15. Thellier, P. L., Doctor of Science Thesis, University of Grenoble, France, 1962.

16. Nishimura, T., and E. I. Jury, "Contribution to Statistical Designing of Sampled-Data Control Systems," Electronics Research Laboratory Report Series 60, Issue No. 210, August 5, 1958, University of California, Berkeley.

17. Ragazzini, J. R., and G. F. Franklin, *Sampled-Data Control Systems*, McGraw-Hill Book Co., New York, 1958.

18. Tou, J. T., *Digital and Sampled-Data Control Systems*, McGraw-Hill Book Co, New York, 1959.

19. Monroe, A. J., *Digital Processes for Sampled-Data Systems*, John Wiley and Sons, New York, 1962.

20. Montel, Paul, *Leçons sur les Recurrences et Leurs Applications*, Gauthier-Villars, Paris, 1957.

21. Friedland, B., "Sampled-Data Control Systems Containing Periodically Varying Members," *Automatic and Remote Control, Proceedings of the First I.F.A.C. Congress*, Moscow, 1960, Butterworths, London, 1961, p. 369.

22. Bharucha, B. A., "Analysis of Integral-Square Error in Sampled-Data Control Systems," Electronics Research Laboratory Report Series 60, Issue No. 206, June 1958, University of California, Berkeley.

23. Nishimura, T., "On the Modified z-Transform of Power Spectral Densities," *Trans. IRE, PGAC*, Vol. AC-7, No. 4, July 1962, pp. 55–56.

24. Sawaragi, Y., and A. Fukaw, "On the Sum of Squares Values of Sampled-Data," *Trans. of Japanese S.M.E.*, Part I, No. 155, Vol. 25, July 1959.

5

CONVOLUTION z-TRANSFORM

APPLIED TO NONLINEAR

DISCRETE SYSTEMS[1,3,5]

In the preceding discussions, the z-transform method has been mainly applied to linear discrete systems. For time-invariant systems, the z-transform offers some advantages as has been explained in detail. However, for time-varying systems this advantage is no longer apparent except in a few particular cases. Nevertheless, the method is still applicable as shown earlier.

In this discussion, the convolution z-transform will be applied for the solution of certain nonlinear discrete systems described by nonlinear difference equations. It will be shown that the method proposed is general in solving such difference equations. The form is

$$\sum_{p=0}^{r} h_p x(n + p) + F[x(n), x(n + 1) \ldots x(n + r - 1)] = 0 \quad (5.1)$$

where n is the discrete time variable and $F[x(n), x(n + 1) \ldots]$ is the nonlinear term containing terms in $x(n + p)$ of degree two and higher. This form of the difference equation is fairly general in the sense that it describes many nonlinear discrete systems with saturation-type nonlinearities. This type is quite common in feedback sampled-data systems.

The objective of this chapter is to obtain an approximate closed-form solution of equation (5.1) in a systematic manner using the convolution z-transform; a few examples are also discussed to explain in detail the method of solution and to compare it with the exact method using the difference equation as a recurrence relationship.

In order for the method of solution to be applicable, certain assumptions are to be imposed on the difference equation. These assumptions are not restrictive, for in practical situations they are usually satisfied. It should be noted that there is no general method of solution for any nonlinear difference equation,[4,6–10] but certain techniques are applicable to certain types of difference equations or nonlinear discrete systems. In this chapter the application of only one such method is discussed in detail. This method is analogous to the application of the convolution Laplace transform[2] to certain nonlinear differential equations. Rigorous mathematical justification of this method was proposed by Wasow.[11] Similar justification for the method has been indicated[5] and by applying Wasow's techniques a rigorous mathematical validity has been obtained.[12]

5.1 Assumptions

1. The nonlinear difference equation in (5.1) has a steady-state or equilibrium value A_0 given by

$$\sum_{p=0}^{r} h_p A_0 + F(A_0, \ldots, A_0) = 0 \tag{5.2}$$

2. The nonlinear function $F[x(n) \ldots x(n + r - 1)]$ is analytic in its variables $x(n)$, $x(n + 1) \ldots x(n + r - 1)$ around the equilibrium point. Only nonlinear functions involving polynomials are to be considered.

3. The equilibrium point is asymptotically stable in the sense that $x(n)$ converges to the equilibrium point A_0 as $n \to \infty$. The initial values of the dependent variable must lie "close" to the equilibrium point in order that a convergent solution may be obtained. However, in some cases, as will be explained later, by shifting the time axis (using the difference equation as a recurrence relationship) by one or two sampling periods, quicker convergence can be expected.

The basis of the solution of the difference equation is to assume $\mathscr{F}(z) = \mathfrak{z}[x_n]$ to be a meromorphic function of the form

$$\mathscr{F}(z) = \sum_{\alpha=0}^{\infty} \frac{A_\alpha}{1 - a_\alpha z^{-1}} \tag{5.3}$$

where a_α's are distinct with modulus less than unity, and $a_0 = 1$.

Because of this assumed basic form of the solution, we have to obtain the z-transform of functions of the form

$$\mathfrak{z}[f(n + k)^l] \text{ or } \mathfrak{z}[f(n + r)^k f(n + q)^l],$$

and so on. Therefore we shall proceed first to derive this z-transform by the convolution z-transform method as discussed in Chapter 4.

5.2 Convolution z-transforms of certain functions

Assume $f(n)$ is a time function defined for discrete values of $n = 0, 1, 2,$ $\ldots$, and its z-transform is of the form

$$\mathcal{J}[f(n)] = \mathcal{F}(z) = \sum_{\alpha=0}^{\infty} \frac{A_\alpha}{1 - a_\alpha z^{-1}} \tag{5.4}$$

where $a_0 = 1$ and the other a_α's are distinct with absolute values less than unity. Using the convolution integral,

$$\mathcal{J}[f(n)^2] = \frac{1}{2\pi j} \int_\Gamma p^{-1} \mathcal{F}(p) \mathcal{F}\left(\frac{z}{p}\right) dp \tag{5.5}$$

where Γ encloses all the singularities of $p^{-1}\mathcal{F}(p)$ in a positive direction in the p-plane. Therefore

$$\begin{aligned}
\mathcal{J}[f(n)^2] &= \frac{1}{2\pi j} \int_\Gamma p^{-1} \sum_{\alpha=0}^{\infty} \frac{A_\alpha}{1 - a_\alpha p^{-1}} \sum_{\beta=0}^{\infty} \frac{A_\beta}{1 - a_\beta z^{-1} p} \, dp \\
&= \sum_{\alpha=0}^{\infty} \sum_{\beta=0}^{\infty} \frac{A_\alpha A_\beta}{1 - a_\alpha a_\beta z^{-1}}
\end{aligned} \tag{5.6}$$

Similarly,

$$\mathcal{J}[f(n)^3] = \sum_{\alpha=0}^{\infty} \sum_{\beta=0}^{\infty} \sum_{\gamma=0}^{\infty} \frac{A_\alpha A_\beta A_\gamma}{1 - a_\alpha a_\beta a_\gamma z^{-1}} \tag{5.7}$$

The extension to $\mathcal{J}[f(n)^l]$ is evident.

It is also easy to obtain the following transforms in a similar manner.

$$\mathcal{J}[f(n + k)^l] = z^k \left[\mathcal{J}[f(n)^l] - \sum_{q=0}^{k-1} [f(q)^l] z^{-q} \right] \tag{5.8}$$

For the nonlinear terms of the form $f(n)f(n + k)$, we use the following:

$$\begin{aligned}
\mathcal{J}[f(n)f(n + k)] &= \frac{1}{2\pi j} \int_\Gamma p^{-1} p^k \\
&\quad \times \left[\mathcal{F}(p) - \sum_{q=0}^{k-1} f(q) p^{-q} \right] \mathcal{F}\left(\frac{z}{p}\right) dp
\end{aligned} \tag{5.9}$$

where Γ encloses the singularities of $p^{-1} p^k \left[\mathcal{F}(p) - \sum_{q=0}^{k-1} f(q) p^{-q} \right]$
Equation (5.9) is evaluated as

$$\mathcal{J}[f(n)f(n + k)] = \sum_{\alpha=0}^{\infty} \sum_{\beta=0}^{\infty} \frac{a_\alpha^k A_\alpha A_\beta}{1 - a_\alpha a_\beta z^{-1}} \tag{5.10}$$

Following the procedure outlined, we can, in general, find the z-transform of nonlinear terms of the type $f(n + r)^k f(n + q)^l$, where r, k, q, l are integers > 0, providing $\mathcal{J}[f(n)]$ is given by equation (5.4).

5.3 Method of solution for second- and higher-order equations

Consider a second-order nonlinear difference equation

$$x(n + 2) + bx(n + 1) + cx(n) + kx(n)^3 = \beta u(n) \qquad (5.11)$$

where $u(n)$ is a sampled unit step function and the coefficients b, c, k are constants. The constant β is the magnitude of the step forcing function.

1. Assume the z-transform $\mathscr{X}(z)$ of $x(n)$ to be a meromorphic function of the form

$$
\begin{aligned}
\mathscr{X}(z) &= \sum_{\alpha=0}^{\infty} \frac{A_\alpha}{1 - a_\alpha z^{-1}} \\
&= \frac{A_0}{1 - z^{-1}} + \frac{A_1}{1 - a_1 z^{-1}} + \frac{A_2}{1 - a_2 z^{-1}} \\
&\quad + \frac{A_3}{1 - a_3 z^{-1}} + \frac{A_4}{1 - a_4 z^{-1}} + \dots
\end{aligned}
\qquad (5.12)
$$

The term a_α for $\alpha \geq 3$ is of the form $a_1^\gamma a_2^\delta$ (γ and δ are positive integers, $\gamma + \delta \geq 2$) arranged in decreasing order of magnitude so that

$$1 > |a_1| > |a_2| > |a_3| > |a_4| > \dots \qquad (5.13)$$

2. Take z-transforms of all the terms in equation (5.11) to yield

$$\mathscr{X}(z)(z^2 + bz + c) + k\mathscr{Y}[x(n)^3] = \frac{\beta z}{z - 1} + (z^2 + bz)x(0) + zx(1).$$
$$(5.14)$$

Dividing by $z^2 + bz + c = (z - a_1')(z - a_2')$ gives

$$
\begin{aligned}
&\mathscr{X}(z) + \frac{k}{(z - a_1')(z - a_2')}\mathscr{Y}[x(n)^3] \\
&= \frac{1}{(z - a_1')(z - a_2')}\left[\frac{\beta z}{z - 1} + (z^2 + bz)x(0) + zx(1)\right]
\end{aligned}
\qquad (5.15)
$$

Now if $\mathscr{X}(z)$ is written in the form

$$
\begin{aligned}
\mathscr{X}(z) &= \frac{A_0}{1 - z^{-1}} + \frac{A_1}{1 - a_1 z^{-1}} + \frac{A_2}{1 - a_2 z^{-1}} + \frac{A_{20}}{1 - a_1^2 z^{-1}} \\
&\quad + \frac{A_{30}}{1 - a_1^3 z^{-1}} + \dots + \frac{A_{02}}{1 - a_2^2 z^{-1}} \\
&\quad + \frac{A_{03}}{1 - a_2^3 z^{-1}} + \dots + \frac{A_{11}}{1 - a_1 a_2 z^{-1}} \\
&\quad + \frac{A_{21}}{1 - a_1^2 a_2 z^{-1}} + \frac{A_{12}}{1 - a_1 a_2^2 z^{-1}} + \dots
\end{aligned}
\qquad (5.16)
$$

the z-transform of $x(n)^3$ can be written as

$$\mathcal{J}[x(n)^3] = \frac{A_0^3}{1 - z^{-1}} + \frac{3A_0^2 A_1}{1 - a_1 z^{-1}} + \frac{3A_0^2 A_2}{1 - a_2 z^{-1}}$$

$$+ \frac{3A_0^2 A_{20} + 3A_0 A_1^2}{1 - a_1^2 z^{-1}}$$

$$+ \frac{3A_0^2 A_{30} + A_1^3 + 6A_0 A_1 A_{20}}{1 - a_1^3 z^{-1}}$$

$$+ \frac{3A_0^2 A_{40} + 3A_{20}^2 A_0 + 6A_0 A_1 A_{30} + 3A_1^2 A_{20}}{1 - a_1^4 z^{-1}}$$

$$+ \ldots + \frac{3A_0^2 A_{02} + 3A_0 A_2^2}{1 - a_2^2 z^{-1}} + \ldots$$

$$+ \frac{3A_0^2 A_{21} + 3A_1^2 A_2 + 6A_0 A_{20} A_2}{1 - a_1^2 a_2 z^{-1}}$$

$$+ \frac{3A_0^2 A_{11} + 6A_0 A_1 A_2}{1 - a_1 a_2 z^{-1}} + \ldots \tag{5.17}$$

It is assumed that a_1', a_2' in equation (5.15) are distinct from the a's in equation (5.12). Comparison of coefficients is now possible in equation (5.15).

3. By multiplying both sides of equation (5.15) by $z - 1$ and letting $z \to 1$, the steady-state relation involving A_0 is obtained. A_0 can also be obtained by letting $x(n) = x(n + 1) = x(n + 2) = A_0$ in equation (5.11).

4. By multiplying equation (5.15) by $z - a_\alpha$, $\alpha = 1, 2$ and by letting in each case $z \to a_\alpha$, we obtain

$$A_{1,2}(a_{1,2}^2 + ba_{1,2} + c + k3A_0^2) = 0 \tag{5.18}$$

For nontrivial solutions of A_1, A_2 in equation (5.18),

$$a_{1,2}^2 + ba_{1,2} + c + k3A_0^2 = 0 \tag{5.19}$$

which determines a_1 and a_2 in terms of steady-state amplitude A_0. All the a_α's ($\alpha \geq 3$) can then be evaluated as explained earlier in equation (5.12).

5. By multiplying equation (5.15) by $z - a_\alpha$, $\alpha \geq 3$ and by letting in each case $z \to a_\alpha$, the following relations are obtained:

$$A_3 = f_1(A_0, A_1, A_2)$$

$$A_4 = f_2(A_0, A_1, A_2, A_3)$$

$$\begin{matrix} \cdot & & \cdot \\ \cdot & & \cdot \\ \cdot & & \cdot \\ \cdot & & \cdot \end{matrix}$$

$$\tag{5.20}$$

where $f_1, f_2, \ldots$, etc., denote functional relationships. The process by which any $A_\alpha (\alpha \geq 3)$ in equation (5.20) is found in terms of previous A_α's is possible because of the manner in which the a_α's were ordered in equation (5.12). Thus all A_α's ($\alpha \geq 3$) can be expressed ultimately in terms of A_0, A_1, and A_2.

6. Finally, by multiplying equation (5.15) by $z - a_\alpha'$, $\alpha = 1, 2$ and letting in each case $z \rightarrow a_\alpha'$, two nonlinear relations are obtained.

$$k\left(\frac{A_0^3}{a_\alpha' - 1} + \frac{3A_0^2 A_1}{a_0' - a_1} + \frac{3A_0^2 A_2}{a_\alpha' - a_2} + \ldots\right) = \frac{\beta}{a_\alpha' - 1}$$
$$+ (a_\alpha' + b)x(0) + x(1) \qquad \alpha = 1, 2 \quad (5.21)$$

The convergence of these nonlinear relations depends on the initial values of $x(n)$ and the magnitude of the nonlinearity. If the nonlinearity is "small," then for a fairly large range of initial values convergence could be expected. On the other hand, when the nonlinear terms are comparable to the linear terms, then the range of initial values is necessarily restricted. At any rate, convergence is best judged from the particular problem on hand. With first-order difference equations, this does not pose a serious problem. However, for higher-order systems the numerical computations become too involved and it is also sometimes difficult to determine the convergence. The procedure just detailed can be easily extended to higher-order equations.

5.4 Illustrative examples

To illustrate the method discussed in the preceding section, two examples are introduced. The first example represents the solution of a certain nonlinear first-order difference equation. This equation can be solved by other methods which are limited only to first-order case.[4] The second example represents the analysis of a first-order saturating sampled-data feedback system.[1] We limited these examples to first-order for ease of computation. However, as outlined in Section 5.3, the method is general and can be applied to second- and higher-order nonlinear difference equations or discrete systems. A study of a second-order system is included in Chapter 8.

EXAMPLE 1

Consider the solution of the following difference equation.

$$8y(n + 1) = \frac{8y(n)^2 + 3}{y(n)^2 + 1} \qquad (5.22)$$

Equation (5.22) can be rewritten as

$$8y(n + 1) + 8y(n + 1)y(n)^2 - 8y(n)^2 = 3 \qquad (5.23)$$

Assume

$$\mathcal{Y}(z) = \sum_{\alpha=0}^{\infty} \frac{A_\alpha}{1 - a_\alpha z^{-1}}$$

$$= \frac{A_0}{1 - z^{-1}} + \frac{A_1}{1 - a_1 z^{-1}} + \frac{A_2}{1 - a_1^2 z^{-1}} + \cdots \quad (5.24)$$

By taking the z-transform of equation (5.23),

$$8z[\mathcal{Y}(z) - y(0)] + 8\mathcal{J}[y(n+1)y(n)^2] - 8\mathcal{J}[y(n)^2] = \frac{3z}{z-1}$$

$$(5.25)$$

But, as shown in Section 5.2,

$$\mathcal{J}[y(n)^2] = \sum_{\alpha=0}^{\infty} \sum_{\beta=0}^{\infty} \frac{A_\alpha A_\beta}{1 - a_\alpha a_\beta z^{-1}} \quad (5.26)$$

and

$$\mathcal{J}[y(n+1)y(n)^2] = \frac{1}{2\pi j} \int_\Gamma p^{-1} p \left[\sum_{\alpha=0}^{\infty} \frac{A_\alpha}{1 - a_\alpha p^{-1}} - y(0) \right]$$

$$\times \left[\sum_{\alpha,\beta=0}^{\infty} \frac{A_\alpha A_\beta}{1 - a_\alpha a_\beta z^{-1} p} \right] dp \quad (5.27)$$

where Γ encloses the singularities of

$$p^{-1} p \left[\sum_{\alpha=0}^{\infty} \frac{A_\alpha}{1 - a_\alpha p^{-1}} - y(0) \right]$$

This equation becomes

$$\mathcal{J}[y(n+1)y(n)^2] = \sum_{\alpha,\beta,\gamma=0}^{\infty} \frac{A_\alpha A_\beta A_\gamma a_\gamma}{1 - a_\alpha a_\beta a_\gamma z^{-1}} \quad (5.28)$$

Substituting this transforms into equation (5.25) and dividing by z, we get

$$8\sum_{\alpha=0}^{\infty} \frac{A_\alpha}{1 - a_\alpha z^{-1}} + \frac{8}{z} \left[\sum_{\alpha,\beta,\gamma=0}^{\infty} \frac{A_\alpha A_\beta A_\gamma a_\gamma}{1 - a_\alpha a_\beta a_\gamma z^{-1}} \right.$$

$$\left. - \sum_{\alpha,\beta=0}^{\infty} \frac{A_\alpha A_\beta}{1 - a_\alpha a_\beta z^{-1}} \right] = \frac{3}{z-1} + 8y(0) \quad (5.29)$$

Comparing coefficients of $1/(z-1)$ and writing $z/(z-\alpha) = [\alpha/(z-\alpha) + 1]$, we obtain

$$8A_0 + 8A_0^3 - 8A_0^2 = 3 \quad (5.30)$$

The equilibrium solution A_0 can be obtained, which is

$$A_0 = 0.5 \quad (5.31)$$

The solution around this point is obtained as follows. Comparing the coefficients of $1/(z - a_1)$,

$$8A_1 + \frac{8}{a_1}(A_0^2 A_1 a_1 + 2A_0^2 A_1) - \frac{8}{a_1}(2A_0 A_1) = 0 \tag{5.32}$$

Rearranging this equation,

$$A_1(a_1 + A_0^2 a_1 + 2A_0^2 - 2A_0) = 0 \tag{5.33}$$

For the nontrivial solution of A_1, the term inside the parentheses must be zero.

$$a_1 + A_0^2 a_1 + 2A_0^2 - 2A_0 = 0 \tag{5.34}$$

Substituting $A_0 = \frac{1}{2}$ in this equation, we obtain $a_1 = \frac{2}{5}$. Comparing coefficients of $1/(z - a_1^2)$, the following relation is obtained:

$$8a_1^2 A_2 + 8(A_2 A_0^2 a_1^2 + 2A_2 A_0^2 + 2A_1^2 A_0 a_1 + A_1^2 A_0)$$
$$- 8(A_1^2 + 2A_0 A_2) = 0 \tag{5.35}$$

which, when simplified, yields

$$A_2 = -\tfrac{1}{3}A_1^2 \tag{5.36}$$

In the preceding manner, by comparing coefficients with the other terms, $A_3, A_4, \ldots$ can be determined in terms of A_1. To obtain the nonlinear relation for A_1, compare the constant term on both sides of equation (5.29). This gives

$$\sum_{\alpha=0}^{\infty} A_\alpha = y(0) \tag{5.37}$$

Thus

$$\mathscr{Y}(z) = \frac{1}{2(1 - z^{-1})} + \frac{A_1}{1 - \frac{2}{5}z^{-1}} - \frac{1}{3}\frac{A_1^2}{(1 - \frac{4}{25}z^{-1})} + \ldots \tag{5.38}$$

which, upon inverse, yields

$$y(n) = \tfrac{1}{2} + A_1(\tfrac{2}{5})^n - \tfrac{1}{3}A_1^2(\tfrac{4}{25})^n + \ldots \tag{5.39}$$

If $y(0)$ is specified, A_1 can be determined from this equation, providing (5.39) converges for the given value of $y(0)$.

EXAMPLE 2

In this example a sampled-data system with a small nonlinearity in the feedback path is considered. The nonlinearity is generally incidental and may represent a slight deviation from otherwise normal linear feedback. The problem is (if such a system is stable) how to get an explicit solution for the output when the forcing function is a step input. The stability of the system is determined from the stability of the "linearized" system, with nonlinearities neglected. By referring to Fig. 5.1, the difference equation relating the output to the input is first derived. An explicit relation is possible between the sampled output and input. The input is assumed to be a unit step function. The nonlinearity is represented as a finite power series, as indicated in Fig. 5.1.

Let $r(t) = u(t)$, where $u(t)$ is a unit step function

$$E(s) = R(s) - \mathscr{L}\left(m_1c + \sum_{q=2}^{N} m_q c^q\right) \tag{5.40}$$

where $\mathscr{L}$ indicates the operation of taking the Laplace transform of the function in the parentheses. The sampled form of equation (5.40) is

$$E^*(s) = R^*(s) - \mathscr{Z}\left[\mathscr{L}\left(m_1c + \sum_{q=2}^{N} m_q c^q\right)\right]_{z=e^{Ts}} \tag{5.41}$$

where $\mathscr{Z}$ indicates z-transform operation. In equation (5.41) the $\mathscr{L}$-transform operation can also be omitted. The output transform is given as

$$C^*(s) = G^*(s)E^*(s)$$

$$= G^*(s)\left\{R^*(s) - \mathscr{Z}\left[\mathscr{L}\left(m_1c + \sum_{q=2}^{N} m_q c^q\right)\right]_{z=e^{Ts}}\right\} \tag{5.42}$$

Now

$$C^*(s)\big|_{z=e^{Ts}} = \mathscr{C}(z) \tag{5.43}$$

Therefore in z-transform notation,

$$\mathscr{C}(z)[1 + m_1\mathscr{G}(z)] + \mathscr{G}(z)\mathscr{Z}\left[\mathscr{L}\left(\sum_{q=2}^{N} m_q c^q\right)\right] = \mathscr{R}(z)\mathscr{G}(z) \tag{5.44}$$

It is easy to see that in the absence of nonlinearity and $m_1 = 1$, we obtain the linear sampled-data system with unity feedback.

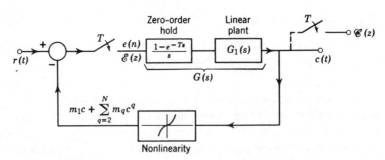

FIGURE 5.1 Nonlinear sampled-data feedback system.

Choose a first-order linear plant with $G_1(s) = 1/(s + 1)$,

$$\mathcal{G}(z) = \mathcal{Z}\left[\frac{1}{s + 1} \frac{1 - e^{-Ts}}{s}\right]$$

$$= \frac{1 - e^{-T}}{z - e^{-T}} \qquad (5.45)$$

With $T = 1$

$$\mathcal{G}(z) = \frac{0.632}{z - 0.368} \qquad (5.46)$$

and

$$\mathcal{C}(z)[z - 0.368 + 0.632m_1]$$

$$+ 0.632\mathcal{Z}\left[\mathcal{L}\left(\sum_{q=2}^{N} m_q c^q\right)\right] = \frac{0.632z}{z - 1} \qquad (5.47)$$

This corresponds to the nonlinear difference equation

$$c(n + 1) + (0.632m_1 - 0.368)c(n) + 0.632\sum_{q=2}^{N} m_q c^q(n)$$

$$= 0.632r(n) \qquad (5.48)$$

If $m_q = 0$ (for all q), in equation (5.48) and $m_1 = 1$, it reduces to the linear system with unity feedback, as explained before. Equation (5.48) then reduces to

$$\mathcal{C}(z)(z + 0.264) = \frac{0.632z}{z - 1} \qquad (5.49)$$

Taking the inverse z-transform or making use of tables, the solution for linearized system is obtained as

$$c(nT) = \tfrac{1}{2}[1 - (-0.264)^n] \qquad (5.50)$$

By inspection it is seen that for n approaches infinity, $c(nT)$ tends to $\tfrac{1}{2}$ and hence the linearized system is stable.

For the nonlinear system, assume that $m_q = 0$ for all q in equation (5.48) except $q = 3$ and $m_1 = 1$, and m_3 is "small" compared to 1. Since the linearized system is stable, assume*

$$\mathcal{C}(z) = \sum_{\alpha=0}^{\infty} \frac{A_\alpha}{1 - a_\alpha z^{-1}} \qquad (5.51)$$

with $a_0 = 1$ (from steady-state conditions), $a_2 = a_1^2$, $a_3 = a_1^3, \ldots, a_q = a_1^q \ldots$. With $\mathcal{C}(z)$ assumed as earlier, it readily follows from the discussion

---

* This form of solution is the basis of the convolution z-transform used in this example.

of the previous section that

$$
\begin{aligned}
\mathscr{J}[c(n)^3] = \Bigg(& \frac{A_0^3}{1-z^{-1}} + \frac{3A_0^2A_1}{1-a_1z^{-1}} + \frac{3A_0^2A_2 + 3A_1^2A_0}{1-a_1^2z^{-1}} \\
& + \frac{3A_0^2A_3 + 6A_1A_2A_0 + A_1^3}{1-a_1^3z^{-1}} \\
& + \frac{3A_0^2A_4 + 3A_1^2A_2 + 3A_2^2A_0 + 6A_1A_3A_0}{1-a_1^4z^{-1}} \\
& + \frac{3A_1A_2^2 + 3A_1^2A_3 + 6A_1A_4A_0 + 6A_2A_3A_0 + 3A_0^2A_5}{1-a_1^5z^{-1}} \\
& + \frac{\begin{aligned}3A_0^2A_6 + 6A_1A_5A_0 + 3A_1^2A_4 \\ + A_2^3 + 6A_1A_2A_3 + 6A_0A_2A_4 + 3A_3^2A_0\end{aligned}}{1-a_1^6z^{-1}} \\
& + \ldots + \ldots \Bigg)
\end{aligned}
\tag{5.52}
$$

Take z-transform of equation (5.48) assuming zero initial conditions and use equation (5.52) to get

$$
\mathscr{C}(z) + \frac{0.632m_3}{z + 0.264}\left(\frac{A_0^3}{1-z^{-1}} + \ldots\right) = \frac{0.632z}{(z-1)(z+0.264)}
\tag{5.53}
$$

Comparison of coefficients is now possible. Comparing the coefficients of $z/(z-1)$, $z/(z-a_1)$, $z/(z-a_1^2)\ldots z/(z-a_1^q)$, and finally $z/(z+0.264)$, the following relations are obtained:

$$
A_0 + \frac{0.632m_3}{1.264}A_0^3 = 0.5
\tag{5.54}
$$

$$
A_1 + \frac{0.632m_3}{a_1 + 0.264}(3A_0^2A_1) = 0
\tag{5.55}
$$

$$
A_2 + \frac{0.632m_3}{a_1^2 + 0.264}(3A_0^2A_2 + 3A_1^2A_0) = 0
\tag{5.56}
$$

.
.
.

$$
\begin{aligned}
A_6 + \frac{0.632m_3}{a_1^6 + 0.264}\big(3A_0^2A_6 + 6A_1A_5A_0 + 3A_1^2A_4 + A_2^3 \\
+ 6A_3A_2A_1 + 6A_2A_4A_0 + 3A_3^2A_0\big) = 0
\end{aligned}
\tag{5.57}
$$

.
.
.

$$
0.632m_3\left(-\frac{A_0^3}{1.264} - \frac{3A_0^2A_1}{a_1 + 0.264} - \frac{(3A_0^2A_2 + 3A_1^2A_0)}{a_1^2 + 0.264} - \ldots\right)
$$
$$
= -0.5
\tag{5.58}
$$

Equation (5.54), when solved for A_0, gives the steady-state value of $c(nT)$. Substituting this value of A_0 in equation (5.55) gives

$$A_1(a_1 + 0.264 + 0.632m_3 3A_0^2) = 0 \tag{5.59}$$

For nontrivial solution of A_1, it follows that

$$a_1 + 0.264 + 0.632m_3 3A_0^2 = 0 \tag{5.60}$$

from which a_1 can be readily computed. If $|a_1| < 1$, the system is locally stable around the equilibrium point. The other equations can be successively solved for $A_2, A_3, A_4 \ldots$ in terms of A_1. Using equations (5.54), (5.55), (5.56), and (5.57), equation (5.58) can be written in the form

$$A_0 + A_1 + A_2 + \ldots = 0 \tag{5.61}$$

This is merely the initial condition requirement (assuming zero initial condition) which can be written by inspection of the form of $\mathscr{C}(z)$ in equation (5.51). By knowing A_0 and $A_2, A_3 \ldots$ in terms of A_1, equation (5.61) can be solved for A_1 for whatever accuracy desired. $A_2, A_3, \ldots$ can also be then computed. By taking a few trial values of A_1 convergence can be easily ascertained. It is now a simple matter to take the inverse z-transform of equation (5.51) to get the time domain solution. The actual numerical calculations are now carried out.

Assuming* $m_3 = 0.1$, solution of equation (5.54) yields

$$A_0 = 0.494 \tag{5.62}$$

With these values of A_0 and m_3, a_1 is calculated from equation (5.59) as

$$a_1 = -0.31 \tag{5.63}$$

Since $|a_1| < 1$, the system is stable for a unit step function input.

From equations (5.56) and (5.57), $A_2, A_3 \ldots$ are obtained as follows:

$$A_2 = -\frac{A_1^2}{4.35}, \quad A_3 = -\frac{A_1^3}{13.95}, \quad A_4 = \frac{A_1^4}{6.14},$$

$$A_5 = -\frac{A_1^5}{10.25}, \quad A_6 = -\frac{A_1^6}{26.7} \ldots \tag{5.64}$$

Substituting equation (5.64) in (5.61) gives

$$0.494 + A_1 - \frac{A_1^2}{4.35} - \frac{A_1^3}{13.95} + \frac{A_1^4}{6.14}$$

$$- \frac{A_1^5}{10.25} - \frac{A_1^6}{26.7} + \ldots = 0 \tag{5.65}$$

---

* For $m_3 = -0.1$, which indicates a saturation type nonlinearity, it will be found that convergence of equation (5.44) is poor. However, by shifting time axis (using the difference equation as a recurrence relation) by one sampling period, quicker convergence can be expected. This is illustrated later.

Solution by trial and error of equation (5.65) yields

$$A_1 \approx -0.461 \tag{5.66}$$

Hence

$$A_2 = -0.0489 \qquad A_3 = 0.007025 \qquad A_4 = 0.00735$$
$$A_5 = 0.002015 \qquad A_6 = -0.000359 \tag{5.67}$$

Therefore

$$\mathscr{C}(z) = \frac{0.494}{1 - z^{-1}} - \frac{0.461}{1 + 0.31z^{-1}} - \frac{0.0489}{1 - 0.096z^{-1}} + \frac{0.007025}{1 + 0.0298z^{-1}}$$
$$+ \frac{0.00735}{1 - 0.0092z^{-1}} + \frac{0.002015}{1 + 0.00285z^{-1}}$$
$$- \frac{0.000359}{1 - 0.000884z^{-1}} + \cdots \tag{5.68}$$

Corresponding to

$$c(nT) = 0.494 - 0.461(-0.31)^n - 0.0489(0.096)^n$$
$$+ 0.007025(-0.0298)^n + 0.00735(0.0092)^n$$
$$+ 0.002015(-0.00285)^n - 0.000359(0.000884)^n \tag{5.69}$$

It should be noted that some of the modes are oscillatory decaying unlike the continuous case which are exponentially decaying. The nonlinear difference equation of this system is

$$c(n + 1) + 0.264c(n) + 0.0632c(n)^3 = 0.632r(n) \tag{5.70}$$

With $c(0) = 0$, this can be solved as a recurrence relation to get an exact solution. A comparison of this exact solution with the approximate closed form solution in equation (5.69) is given and it is seen that agreement is good up to the third decimal place. The output between sampling instants could be easily obtained by minor modification of equation (5.51).

Sampled Output	Exact Solution	Closed Form Solution
$c(0)$	0	0.000131
$c(1)$	0.632	0.6323
$c(2)$	0.4491	0.44925
$c(3)$	0.50779	0.50767
$c(4)$	0.48970	0.48975
$c(5)$	0.4955	0.4953
$c(6)$	0.4935	0.4936
$c(7)$	0.4942	0.4941
.	.	.
.	.	.
.	.	.

EXAMPLE 2a

If we take in Example 2 $m_3 = -0.1$, the difference equation that describes the system is now

$$c(n + 1) + 0.264c(n) - 0.0632c(n)^3 = 0.632 \qquad (5.71)$$

For this equation, the coefficients are

$$
\begin{aligned}
A_0 &= 0.5065 & A_4 &= 0.93A_1^4 \\
A_2 &= 0.356A_1^2 & A_5 &= 1.7A_1^5 \\
A_3 &= 0.64A_1^3 & A_6 &= 3.74A_1^6
\end{aligned}
\qquad (5.72)
$$

It is noticed from the preceding that the convergence is rather poor. However, it can be improved if we shift the time axis by one sampling period so that the difference equation is the same but the new initial value is 0.632 (instead of zero); this can be done by using the difference equation as a recurrence relationship. For instance, if we let $c(n)|_{n=0} = 0$ in Equation (5.71), we readily obtain the new initial value as 0.632.

The amplitude determining equation is

$$0.632 = 0.5065A_1 + 0.356A_1^2 + 0.64A_1^3 + 0.93A_1^4$$
$$+ 1.7A_1^5 + 3.34A_1^6 \quad (5.73)$$

which gives

$$
\begin{aligned}
A_1 &= 0.1191 & A_2 &= 0.00506 \\
A_3 &= 0.001 & A_4 &= 0.0001
\end{aligned}
\qquad (5.74)
$$

The solution is then

$$c(nT) = 0.5065 + 0.1191(-0.2155)^{n-1} + (0.00506)(0.0465)^{n-1}$$
$$+ (0.001)(-0.01)^{n-1} \quad n \geq 1, \text{ for } n = 0, c(0+) = 0. \quad (5.75)$$

It is evident that this solution is rapidly convergent. Comparing the output amplitude with the exact solution, we notice

Approximate	Exact
$c(1) = 0.632$	$c(1) = 0.632$
$c(2) = 0.4811$	$c(2) = 0.4809$
$c(3) = 0.512$	$c(3) = 0.512$
$c(4) = 0.5053$	$c(4) = 0.5054$
.	.
.	.
.	.

In conclusion, we could deduce that better convergence is expected if the new initial value is near the equilibrium point. The new initial value can be easily obtained for the discrete case by using the difference equation as a recurrence relationship. Such an advantage is not possible in the continuous case. A compromise between using the difference equation as a recurrence relationship and the labor involved in the convergence is required in any problem amenable to solution.

REFERENCES

1. Jury, E. I., and M. A. Pai, "Convolution z-Transform Method Applied to Certain Non-linear Discrete Systems," *IRE Trans. PGAC*, Vol. AC-7, No. 1, January 1962, pp. 57–64.

2. Weber, E., "Complex Convolution Method Applied to Non-linear Problems," *Proceedings of the Symposium on Non-linear Circuit Analysis*, Polytechnic Institute of Brooklyn, Brooklyn, New York, Vol. 6, 1956.

3. Montel, Paul, *Leçons sur les Recurrences et Leurs Applications*, Gauthier-Villars, Paris, France, 1957.

4. Levy, H., and F. Lessman, *Finite Difference Equations*, Macmillan Co., New York, 1961.

5. Pai, M. A., "The Analysis of Non-linear Feedback Sampled-Data Systems," Ph.D. Dissertation, Dept. of Electrical Engineering, University of California, Berkeley, September 1961.

6. Torng, H. C., "Second-Order Non-linear Difference Equations Containing Small Parameters," *J. Franklin Inst.*, Vol. 269, February 1960, pp. 97–104.

7. Norlund, N. E., "Nichtlineare Differenzgleichungen," Encyklopedie der Mathematischen Wissenschaften, Leipzig, Germany, Vol. II, No. 3, 1927.

8. Trijinsky, W. J., "Non-linear Difference Equations," *Composita Mathematica*, Vol. 5, 1937, pp. 1–66.

9. Tsypkin, Y., *Theory of Pulse Systems*, State Press for Physics and Mathematical Literature, Moscow, 1958.

10. Strodt, W., "Analytic Solutions of Nonlinear Difference Equations," *Annals Math.*, Vol. 44, No. 3, July 1943, pp. 375–396.

11. Wasow, W., "Solution of Certain Nonlinear Differential Equations, by Series of Exponential Functions," *Illinois J. Math.*, Vol. 2, No. 2, June 1958, pp. 254–260.

12. Dewey, A. G., "On the Convergence of a Series Solution of Certain Nonlinear Difference Equations," Electronics Research Laboratory Technical Memo No. TM-18, University of California, Berkeley, July 11, 1963.

13. Alper, P., "Higher-Dimensional Z-Transforms and Nonlinear Discrete Systems," Technological University, Electronics Laboratory, Delft-Netherlands, August 1963.

14. Alper, P.: "A consideration of the discrete volterra series," IEEE Trans. Automat. Contr., Vol. AC-10, July 1965, pp. 322–327.

15. Rault, A. and Jury, E. I.: "Nonlinear sampled-data systems and multidimensional z-transform," Electrn. Res. Lab, University of California, Berkeley, Memo 1121, February 1965.

16. Lavi, A. and Narayan, S.: "Analysis of a class of nonlinear discrete system using multidimensional modified z-transform," IEEE Trans. Automat. Contr. (short papers) Vol. AC-13, February 1968, pp. 90–93.

6

PERIODIC MODES OF

OSCILLATION IN NONLINEAR

DISCRETE SYSTEMS

In this chapter a study is made of periodic modes of oscillation of autonomous discrete systems. The types of nonlinear systems to be studied are pulse-width modulated, relay, nonlinear gain amplifier, and quantized level systems. The method given is also applicable to obtaining the periodic modes of oscillation for nonlinear difference equations as indicated briefly toward the end.

In addition, the stability study of limit cycles as well as the limitation on the period of limit cycles for relay mode of oscillations is presented. Finally, a certain analytical technique for examining the existence and stability of forced oscillation in a sampled-data system is discussed. Again the method presented is based on the z-transform, and the examples are chosen from the widely used field of sampled-data and digital control systems.

6.1 Limit cycle analysis of nonlinear discrete systems

When a periodic forcing function is applied to a nonlinear discrete system or a spontaneous oscillation is excited within the feedback system, the system will frequently move into a limit cycle, that is, sustained periodic oscillations then arise in the system.

Once the feedback system shown in Fig. 6.1 is forced into a limit cycle, the output from the nonlinear component $e'_{n,h}(t)$ will have a periodic feature similar to the other variables of the system such as the output $c_n(t)$ or the control error $e_n(t)$. This constitutes the basic assumptions for the analysis which is common to all other studies of periodic oscillations.

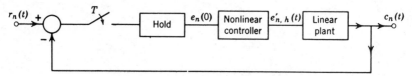

FIGURE 6.1   Nonlinear discrete feedback system.

In our study we shall also assume that these oscillations are periodic with period an integer multiple of the sampling period T. With the pulse width modulated feedback system, as will be discussed later, the signal $e'_{n,h}(t)$ will actually be a train of finite pulses with periodic features as shown in Fig. 6.2. Therefore the application of the theory of the finite-pulsed system shown in Fig. 6.3 is immediately suggested for the analysis. To obtain the basic equations that yield the limit cycles, we shall review first some of the pertinent concepts of finite-pulsed systems.[15-21]

Let $e'_{n,h}(t)$ be the output of the finite pulse width sampler as indicated in Fig. 6.4c during the $(n + 1)$th sampling period. This output is represented mathematically by the product of $e'_{n,h}(t)$ and a unit pulse $u_h(t)$ as indicated in Fig. 6.4a, b.

$$e'_{n,h}(t) = e'_n(t)u_h(t) \tag{6.1}$$

where

$$u_h(t) = 1 \qquad \text{for } 0 \leq t \leq h$$
$$= 0 \qquad \text{elsewhere} \tag{6.2}$$

The incremental response transform, $\Delta C'_n(s)$ is defined as the product of the transfer function $KG(s)$ and the Laplace transform of the pulsed input to the linear system $\mathscr{L}[e'_{n,h}(t)]$

$$\Delta C'_n(s) = KG(s)E'_{n,h}(s) \tag{6.3}$$

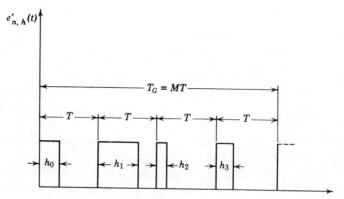

FIGURE 6.2   Sampling pattern for a global period T_g.

$$E'(s) \quad\quad T \quad\quad KG(s) \quad\quad C(s)$$

$$h_n$$

FIGURE 6.3   Open loop finite pulse-width system.

The term $\Delta C_n'(s)$ represents a fraction of the response transform effected by the input which is supplied to the linear system during the $(n + 1)$th sampling period. This incremental response is shown in Fig. 6.4d. Let

$$n = Mk, Mk + 1, \ldots, Mk + l \ldots, M(k + 1) - 1 \qquad (6.4)$$

in equation (6.3) where M is given by $T_{ti} = MT$. We then add $\Delta C_n'(s)$ from $n = Mk$ up to $n = M(k + 1) - 1$, multiplied by the relative delay

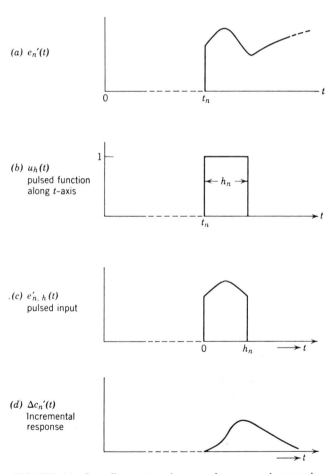

(a) $e_n'(t)$

(b) $u_h(t)$
pulsed function
along t-axis

(c) $e_{n, h}'(t)$
pulsed input

(d) $\Delta c_n'(t)$
Incremental
response

FIGURE 6.4   Sampling pattern, input, and response along t-axis.

factor. The relative delay is the delay with respect to the Mkth sampling instant, and the delay factor is given by

$$e^{-lsT} \quad \text{where} \quad l = 0, 1, 2, \ldots, M - 1 \tag{6.5}$$

Then equation (6.3) gives

$$\Delta C_k(s) = \sum_{l=0}^{M-1} e^{-lsT} \Delta C'_{Mk+l}(s) \tag{6.6}$$

Thus $\Delta C_k(s)$ gives the incremental response resulting from the input during the $(k + 1)$th global period T_G. If this incremental response $\Delta C_k(s)$ is superposed for all k from 0 to ∞ with proper time lags, the summation will give the total response $C(s)$. Hence

$$
\begin{aligned}
C(s) &= \sum_{k=0}^{\infty} e^{-ksT_G} \Delta C_k(s) \\
&= \sum_{k=0}^{\infty} e^{-ksT_G} \sum_{l=0}^{M-1} e^{-lsT} \Delta C'_{Mk+l}(s)
\end{aligned}
\tag{6.7}
$$

The z-transform of this equation is obtained by using the notation $z = e^{sT}$ and $Z = e^{sT_G} = z^M$.

$$\mathscr{C}(z) = \sum_{k=0}^{\infty} Z^{-k} \Delta \mathscr{C}_k(z) = \mathcal{Z}_d \left[\sum_{l=0}^{M-1} z^{-l} \mathcal{Z}_T[KG(s)E'_{(Mk+l),h}(s)] \right] \tag{6.8}$$

where the function $\mathcal{Z}_d[\ ]$ represents an operator that may be described as the sequence z-transformation and it is performed by multiplying the function of k by Z^{-k} and summing for all k from zero to infinity. Similarly, the response between sampling instants is given with the aid of the modified z-transform as follows:

$$\mathscr{C}(z, m) = \sum_{k=0}^{\infty} Z^{-k} \Delta \mathscr{C}_k(z, m) = \mathcal{Z}_d \left[\sum_{l=0}^{M-1} z^{-l} \mathcal{Z}_m[KG(s)E'_{(Mk+l),h}(s)] \right]$$

$$\tag{6.9}$$

The general form of (6.8) and (6.9) can be readily applicable to the analysis of finite pulsed sampled-data feedback systems. It is used in the following to aid us in obtaining the fundamental equations for the limit cycles.

After the system enters the limit cycle, the incremental response of each sampling period will be repeated for every global period T_G of the limit cycle, and thus $\Delta C_k(s)$ of equation (6.6) will become identical for every k. Thus the incremental responses of each limit cycle become independent of k. Hence Mk at the subscript of C' and E' may be removed. However, we add the subscript s to indicate the steady-state (although periodically varying) of the variable. Then the incremental response in one limit cycle is denoted as $\Delta C_s(s)$ and is given by the sum of $\Delta C_{ls}(s)$ from $l = 0$ to $l = M - 1$ with proper delay factors (where l indicates the relative location of the specified sampling period within the global period T_G of the limit cycle). It is given as

$$\Delta C_s(s) = \sum_{l=0}^{M-1} e^{-lsT} \Delta C_{ls}(s) \tag{6.10}$$

Using this notation, $\mathscr{C}(z)$ of equation (6.8) will be divided into two parts, the transient-state and the steady-state (limit cycle)

$$\mathscr{C}(z) = \sum_{k=0}^{N-1} Z^{-k} \Delta \mathscr{C}_k(z) + \sum_{k=N}^{\infty} Z^{-k} \Delta \mathscr{C}_s(z) \tag{6.11}$$

where

$$\Delta \mathscr{C}_s(z) = \mathscr{Z}_T[\Delta C_s(s)] \quad \text{and} \quad \Delta \mathscr{C}_k(z) = \mathscr{Z}_T[\Delta C_k(s)]$$

Equation (6.11) can also be written as

$$\mathscr{C}(z) = \sum_{k=0}^{N-1} Z^{-k} \Delta \mathscr{C}_k(z) + \frac{Z^{-N+1}}{Z - 1} \Delta \mathscr{C}_s(z) \tag{6.12}$$

At this point the skip sampling operation (introduced in Section 4.3) is used to obtain the z-transform with respect to the period $T_G = MT$ from $\mathscr{C}(z)$. This operation is described as $\mathscr{Z}_s[\ ]$ and its mathematical form is given as

$$\mathscr{C}(Z) = \mathscr{Z}_s[\mathscr{C}(z)] = \frac{1}{2\pi j} \int_\Gamma \mathscr{C}(p) \frac{1}{1 - p^M Z^{-1}} \frac{dp}{p} \tag{6.13}$$

Applying the skip sampling operation to equation (6.12) yields

$$\mathscr{C}_0(Z) = \sum_{k=0}^{N-1} Z^{-k} \Delta \mathscr{C}_{0k}(Z) + \frac{Z^{-N+1}}{Z - 1} \Delta \mathscr{C}_{0s}(Z) \tag{6.14}$$

where

$$\Delta \mathscr{C}_{0s}(Z) = \mathscr{Z}_s[\Delta \mathscr{C}_s(z)], \qquad \Delta \mathscr{C}_{0k}(Z) = \mathscr{Z}_s[\Delta \mathscr{C}_k(z)] \tag{6.15}$$

If the response at the next set of sampling instants, that is, T, $T + T_G$, $T + 2T_G, \ldots$ is desired, it is obtained by two different ways as follows:

$$\mathscr{C}_1(Z) = \mathscr{Z}_s[z\mathscr{C}(z)] = \sum_{k=0}^{N-1} Z^{-k} \mathscr{Z}_s[z \Delta \mathscr{C}_k(z)] + \frac{Z^{-N+1}}{Z - 1} \Delta \mathscr{C}_{1s}(Z) \tag{6.16}$$

where

$$\Delta \mathscr{C}_{1s}(Z) = \mathscr{Z}_s[z \Delta \mathscr{C}_s(z)] \tag{6.17}$$

or by the alternate and equivalent form (since no discontinuities at the sampling instants exist)

$$\mathscr{C}_1(Z) = \sum_{k=0}^{N-1} Z^{-k} \mathscr{Z}_s[\Delta \mathscr{C}_k'(z)] + \frac{Z^{-N+1}}{Z - 1} \Delta \mathscr{C}_{1s}(Z) \tag{6.18}$$

where

$$\Delta \mathscr{C}'_k(z) = \mathscr{Z}_T[KG(s)E'_{(Mk+l+1),h}(s)] \qquad (6.19)$$

and

$$\Delta \mathscr{C}_{1s}(Z) = \mathscr{Z}_s\left[\mathscr{Z}_T\left[\sum_{l=0}^{M-1} e^{-ls T}KG(s)E'_{l+1,h}(s)\right]\right] \qquad (6.20)$$

The responses at other sets of sampling instants can be obtained in a similar fashion. The relationships (6.16) and (6.17) with 6.18 through 6.20 will be utilized to arrive at two equivalent forms of the fundamental equation for the limit cycles.

At this point, the assumption is made that the transfer function does not contain any integrator and that all its poles possess negative real parts. This restriction on $KG(s)$ will be relaxed and $KG(s)$ with a single integrator will be discussed later. Then it is observed that neither $\Delta \mathscr{C}_{0k}(Z)$ nor $\Delta \mathscr{C}_{0s}(Z)$ possesses poles at $Z = 1$ because neither $KG(s)$ not $E'_{i,h}(s)$ has poles at the origin of the s-plane. Hence the first term under the summation in equation (6.14) has no pole at $Z = 1$, and the last term has a single pole at $Z = 1$.

Now the final value theorem is applied to equation (6.14) to obtain the output c_{0s} as follows:

$$c_{0s} = \lim_{Z \to 1} (Z-1) \ \mathscr{C}_0(Z) = \lim_{Z \to 1} \Delta \mathscr{C}_{0s}(Z) \qquad (6.21)$$

In general, the final value of $\mathscr{C}_i(Z)$ is denoted as c_{is} and is given by

$$c_{is} = \lim_{Z \to 1} (Z-1) \ \mathscr{C}_i(Z) = \lim_{Z \to 1} \Delta \mathscr{C}_{is}(Z)$$

$$= \lim_{Z \to 1} \mathscr{Z}_s\left\{z^i \sum_{l=0}^{M-1} z^{-l} \mathscr{Z}_T[E'_{l,h}(s)KG(s)]\right\},$$

$$i = 0, 1, 2, \ldots, M-1 \quad (6.22)$$

This is one form of the fundamental equation to be used for the limit cycle analysis. Another form which is very convenient consists of equations (6.18) through (6.20). Following the same manipulation used in (6.14) and (6.15), we finally obtain

$$c_{is} = \lim_{Z \to 1} \mathscr{Z}_s\left[\sum_{l=0}^{M-1} z^{-l} \mathscr{Z}_T[KG(s)E'_{l+i,h}(s)]\right],$$

$$i = 0, 1, 2, \ldots, M-1 \quad (6.23)$$

It may be noted that $E'_{l+i,h}(s) = E'_{l+i-M,h}(s)$, when $l + i \geq M$.

The response between sampling instants is derived by applying the final value theorem to $\mathscr{C}_i(Z, m)$:

$$c_{is}(mT) = \lim_{Z \to 1} \mathcal{Z}_s \left[\sum_{l=0}^{M-1} z^{-l} \mathcal{Z}_m [KG(s)E'_{l+i,h}(s)] \right],$$

$$i = 0, 1, 2, \ldots, M - 1 \qquad 0 \le m \le 1 \quad (6.24)$$

When no discrete processing units are included in the plant, equation (6.23) can be more conveniently and simply written as

$$c_{is} = \lim_{Z \to 1} \mathcal{Z}_{T_G} \left[\sum_{l=0}^{M-1} e^{-lsT} KG(s)E'_{l+i,h}(s) \right],$$

$$i = 0, 1, 2, \ldots, M - 1 \quad (6.25)$$

We note that the skip sampling process is removed, and instead we use the regular z-transform with respect to the global period $T_G = MT$.

The evaluation of equation (6.25) can be performed by using the integral theorem which gives

$$c_{is} = \lim_{Z = e^{MsT} \to 1} \mathcal{Z}_{T_G} \left\{ e^{MsT} \left[\sum_{l=0}^{M-1} e^{-lsT} KG(s)E'_{l+i,h}(s) \right] \right\} Z^{-1}$$

$$= \lim_{\substack{e^{MTs} = Z \to 1 \\ s \to 0}} \frac{Z^{-1}}{2\pi j} \int_{\Gamma} \frac{e^{MpT} KG(p) \sum_{l=0}^{M-1} e^{-lpT} E'_{l+i,h}(p)}{1 - e^{-MT(s-p)}} \, dp,$$

$$i = 0, 1, 2, \ldots, M - 1 \quad (6.26)$$

The multiplication of the expression within the bracket by e^{MsT} is done to insure the convergence of the integral along the infinite semicircle in the left half plane. This does not cause any change in the final result; we compensated for this by multiplying by Z^{-1}.

We can interchange the limiting process and the integration if we take the path of the latter sufficiently close to the imaginary axis of the p-plane. Hence equation (6.26) reduces to

$$c_{is} = \frac{1}{2\pi j} \int_{\Gamma} \frac{e^{MpT} KG(p) \sum_{l=0}^{M-1} e^{-lpT} E'_{l+i,h}(p)}{1 - e^{MpT}} \, dp,$$

$$i = 0, 1, 2, \ldots, M - 1 \quad (6.27)$$

Further simplification of this equation is possible, when the oscillations are symmetrical. Symmetrical oscillation results when the same shape of oscillations is repeated for every half period of the limit cycle with an opposite sign.

If we let $M = 2\mu$ (μ = number of samples in the half period of limit cycle) and

$$E'_{l,h}(s) = -E'_{l+\mu,h}(s) \qquad \text{for } l = 0, 1, 2, \ldots, \mu - 1 \qquad (6.28)$$

then, since $E'_{l+\mu+i,h}(s) = -E'_{l+i,h}(s)$, equation (6.27) can be written as

$$c_{is} = \frac{1}{2\pi j} \int_{\Gamma} \frac{e^{2\mu pT} KG(p) \sum_{l=0}^{\mu-1} e^{-lpT} E'_{l+i,h}(p)(1 - e^{-\mu pT})}{1 - e^{2\mu pT}} \, dp$$

or

$$c_{is} = \frac{-1}{2\pi j} \int_{\Gamma} \frac{e^{\mu pT} KG(p) \sum_{l=0}^{\mu-1} e^{-lpT} E'_{l+i,h}(p)}{1 + e^{\mu pT}} \, dp \qquad (6.29)$$

We note that half the zeros of the denominator of the integrand which include the zero at the origin are canceled by the zeros of $(1 - e^{-\mu pT})$ in the numerator by introducing the symmetry condition. In some cases the symmetry condition requires that the summation of $e'_{l,h}(0)$ over one global period is equal to zero. It should be noted that the elimination of the pole at the origin simplifies consideration of the analysis of the system when $KG(s)$ contains an integrator. The symmetry condition is a valid assumption for relay and PWM systems when the plant has an integrator and low-pass filter characteristic as is usually so.

In summarizing the preceding, equation (6.26) is a general form to obtain the response at the sampling instants when the system is in the limit cycle. It could be used for either free oscillation or forced oscillations (when the forcing function is periodic with the period an integer multiple of the sampling period). Equation (6.29) is a simplified form of (6.26) when the symmetry condition exists. It yields the oscillations with zero d-c components* (because the constant value of the limit of the summation in equation (6.18) is ignored).

6.2 Application of the fundamental equation to specific examples[22]

In this section we shall apply the theory to three examples representing a pulse-width modulated feedback system, a nonlinear gain amplifier, and a quantized level system. In the first two examples, symmetry condition is assumed, whereas, in the last, asymmetrical oscillation is considered.

---

* The d-c component implies the average value of the response at the sampling instants during one period of the limit cycle.

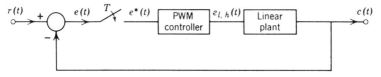

FIGURE 6.5   Pulse-width modulated system.

Pulse-width modulated feedback system

In this system as shown in Fig. 6.5, the signal pulse-width modulation is indicated in Fig. 6.6.

$$E'_{l,h}(s) = \gamma(l) \frac{1 - e^{-sh_l}}{s} = \mathscr{L}[e'_{l,h}(t)] = \mathscr{L}[\gamma(l)u_h(t)] \qquad (6.30)$$

where

$$\gamma(l) = \frac{e_l(0)}{|e_l(0)|} \qquad \text{(and this takes only the values } +1 \text{ and } -1)$$

and

$$h_l = \alpha |e_l(0)| = \alpha |r_l(0) - c_l(0)|, \qquad \text{for } \alpha |e_l(0)| \leq T \quad (6.31)$$

Substituting for $E'_{l,h}(s)$ in equation (6.29), we readily obtain for this case

$$c_{is} = \frac{-1}{2\pi j} \int_\Gamma \frac{e^{\mu p T} KG(p)}{1 + e^{\mu p T}} \sum_{l=0}^{\mu-1} \frac{\gamma(l + i)e^{-lpT}(1 - e^{-ph_{l+i}})}{p} dp \quad (6.32)$$

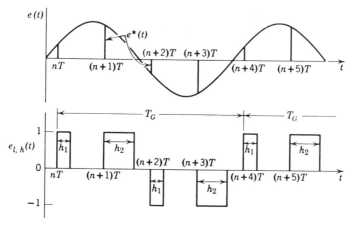

e(t), e*(t): input and sampled input
to controller

$e_{l,h}(t)$: output of controller

FIGURE 6.6   Input and output of PWM controller.

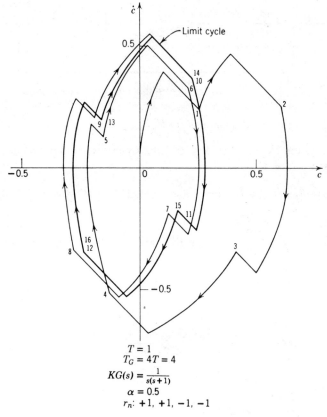

$$T = 1$$
$$T_G = 4T = 4$$
$$KG(s) = \frac{1}{s(s+1)}$$
$$\alpha = 0.5$$
$$r_n: +1, +1, -1, -1$$

FIGURE 6.7 Phase plane analysis of PWM system ($M = 4$).

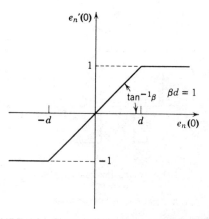

FIGURE 6.8 Characteristic of saturating amplifier.

We assume for this example that $KG(s) = K/s(s + b)$, and the input has a period of four examples, $r_0, r_1, -r_0, -r_1$. Since the input is symmetric and $KG(s)$ has an integrator, we can assume that the output is also symmetric. So we have

$$\mu = 2, \qquad \gamma(0) = \gamma(1) = +1, \qquad \gamma(2) = \gamma(3) = -1 \qquad (6.33)$$

Using the equation for c_{is} and noting that

$$\gamma(l + i) = +1, \qquad \text{for } l = 0, 1, 2, \ldots, \mu - 1 - i$$
$$= -1, \qquad \text{for } l = \mu - i, \mu - i + 1, \ldots, \mu - 1$$

$$(6.34)$$

we obtain for the response at the sampling instants on the limit cycle,

$$c_{0s} = -\frac{K}{b}\left\{\frac{h_0 + h_1}{2} - \frac{e^{-bT}}{b(1 + e^{-2bT})}\left[e^{-bT}(e^{bh_0} - 1) + (e^{bh_1} - 1)\right]\right\}$$

$$(6.35)$$

$$c_{1s} = -\frac{K}{b}\left\{\frac{h_1 - h_0}{2} - \frac{e^{-bT}}{b(1 + e^{-2bT})}\left[e^{-bT}(e^{bh_1} - 1) - (e^{bh_0} - 1)\right]\right\}$$

$$(6.36)$$

From equation (6.31) we know that

$$h_0 = \alpha(r_0 - c_{0s}) \qquad h_1 = \alpha(r_1 - c_{1s}) \qquad (6.37)$$

These equations can be solved for h_0 and h_1 and consequently for c_{0s} and c_{1s}.

When $b = 1$, $K = 1$, $\alpha = 0.5$, $T = 1$ and $r_0 = r_1 = +1$, c_{0s} and c_{1s} can be solved numerically to yield

$$c_{0s} = -0.238 \qquad c_{1s} = -0.162 \qquad (6.38)$$

The limit cycle obtained in the phase plane of Fig. 6.7 verifies these calculated values.

Nonlinear gain amplifier[21,22]

For the nonlinear gain amplifier, a saturating amplifier with linear zone is chosen, as shown in Fig. 6.8. The use of this nonlinearity in a discrete feedback system is shown in Fig. 6.9.

The description of the nonlinear gain is the following:

$$e'_n(t) = 1, \qquad d < e_n(0)$$
$$= \beta e_n(0), \qquad -d < e_n(0) < d$$
$$= -1, \qquad e_n(0) < -d \qquad (6.39)$$

We examine the mode $M = 4$, where the output of the saturating amplifier is the sequence $1, k, -1, -k$. For this case the response falls in

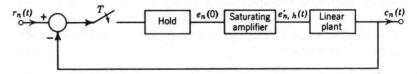

FIGURE 6.9 Saturating gain sampled-data system.

the saturated region at the first sampling instant and in the linear region at the next sampling instant. The same feature is repeated with opposite sign. No input is applied.

The plant is

$$KG(s) = \frac{1}{s(s+1)} \tag{6.40}$$

The sampling period is $T = 2$, $\beta = 2$, and $d = 0.5$.

The outputs of the saturating amplifier are assumed as follows:

$$e'_{0s}(0) = 1, \qquad e'_{1s}(0) = k, \qquad e'_{2s}(0) = -1,$$
$$e'_{3s}(0) = -k, \qquad |k| < 1 \tag{6.41}$$

For a saturating amplifier the pulse width h is equal to T, since there is no pulse-width modulation and therefore the pulsed outputs from the hold denoted as $e'_{j,h}(t)$, $j = 0, 1, 2, 3$ will have the following Laplace transforms:

$$E'_{0,h}(s) = \frac{1 - e^{-sT}}{s}, \qquad E'_{1,h}(s) = k\frac{1 - e^{-sT}}{s}$$

$$E'_{2,h}(s) = -\frac{1 - e^{-sT}}{s}, \qquad E'_{3,h}(s) = -k\frac{1 - e^{-sT}}{s} \tag{6.42}$$

This sequence of oscillations is symmetrical and equation (6.29) can be used for the solution provided T is substituted for h. We ultimately get the following response:

$$c_{0s} = -\frac{k}{2b}\left[T(e'_{0s} + e'_{1s}) + \frac{1 - e^{-bT}}{b(1 + e^{-2bT})}(e'_{0s}e^{-bT} + e'_{1s})\right] \tag{6.43}$$

$$c_{1s} = -\frac{k}{2b}\left[T(e'_{1s} - e'_{0s}) + \frac{1 - e^{-bT}}{b(1 + e^{-2bT})}(e'_{0s} - e'_{1s}e^{-bT})\right] \tag{6.44}$$

Substituting the given numerical values, we get

$$c_{0s} = -0.885 - 0.150k \tag{6.45}$$

$$c_{1s} = 0.150 - 0.885k \tag{6.46}$$

Since it is assumed that the system is operating in the linear region at the sampling instant corresponding to c_{1s}, we get from equation (6.39),

$$\beta e_{1s} = -\beta c_{1s} = e'_{1s}(t) = k \tag{6.47}$$

or

$$c_{1s} = -\frac{k}{\beta} \tag{6.48}$$

Substituting this into equation (6.46), we obtain

$$k = 0.390 < 1$$

Using this value of k, c_{0s} and c_{1s} can be calculated.

$$c_{0s} = -0.943 < -d \tag{6.49}$$

$$c_{1s} = -0.195 > -d \tag{6.50}$$

The results show that c_{0s} falls in the saturating region producing unity as the output of the saturating amplifier and c_{1s} falls in the linear region producing k ($= 0.390$ in this case) as the output. Thus the assumption of the sequence $1, k, -1, -k$ is verified and the existence of such a limit cycle of the mode $M = 4$ is proved.

Quantized level amplifier

In this example, the nonlinear gain amplifier has a characteristic of two quantized levels as shown in Fig. 6.10. Such a quantization appears in digital control systems where analog-to-digital converters are used.

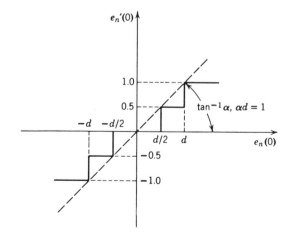

FIGURE 6.10   Characteristic of quantized level amplifier.

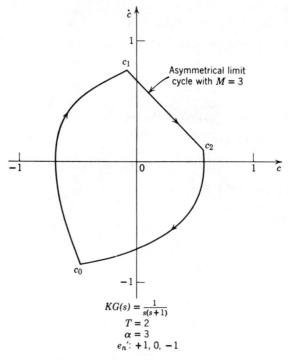

$$KG(s) = \frac{1}{s(s+1)}$$
$$T = 2$$
$$\alpha = 3$$
$$e_n': +1, 0, -1$$

FIGURE 6.11 Asymmetrical limit cycle of quantized level amplifier system.

The characteristic of this quantization is represented as follows:

$$e_n'(t) = 1 \qquad d < e_n(0)$$

$$= 0.5 \qquad \frac{d}{2} < e_n(0) < d$$

$$= 0 \qquad -\frac{d}{2} < e_n(0) < \frac{d}{2}$$

$$= -0.5 \qquad -d < e_n(0) < -\frac{d}{2}$$

$$= -1 \qquad e_n(0) < -d \qquad (6.51)$$

where $\alpha d = 1$ and the linear plant is the same as the previous example.

The existence of an asymmetrical oscillation with $M = 3$ can be ascertained for this case.

We let $M = 3$, and assume that the output of the nonlinear component has a sequence of $+1, 0, -1$; hence $\gamma(0) = 1$, $\gamma(2) = -1$. Substituting these values in equation (6.26) with the preceding characteristics and letting $h_n \rightarrow T$, we obtain

$$c_{0s} = -\frac{K}{b}\left[\frac{2T}{3} - \frac{1 - e^{-2bT}}{b(1 + e^{-bT} + e^{-2bT})}\right] \tag{6.52}$$

$$c_{1s} = \frac{K}{b}\left[\frac{T}{3} - \frac{1 - e^{-bT}}{b(1 + e^{-bT} + e^{-2bT})}\right] \tag{6.53}$$

$$c_{2s} = \frac{K}{b}\left[\frac{T}{3} - \frac{e^{-bT} - e^{-2bT}}{b(1 + e^{-bT} + e^{-2bT})}\right] \tag{6.54}$$

Letting $T = 2, b = 1, K = 1$, and $d = \frac{1}{3}$ ($\alpha = 3$), these values yield

$$c_{0s} = -0.482, \qquad c_{1s} = -0.083, \qquad c_{2s} = 0.565 \tag{6.55}$$

The outputs of the quantized level amplifier corresponding to c_{0s}, c_{1s}, and c_{2s} are $+1$, 0 and -1, which satisfy the original assumption of the sequence. This limit cycle is shown in Fig. 6.11.

In another example of asymmetrical oscillations, if we let $d = \frac{1}{2}$ ($\alpha = 2$) and assume the sequence $+1$, 0, $-\frac{1}{2}$, 0, $\frac{1}{2}$, 0, -1 as the output of the nonlinear component, then a limit cycle of $M = 7$ is sustained, as shown in Fig. 6.12.

Extension of the method to other types of nonlinearities such as relay sampled-data systems is feasible and could be handled by the same procedure. A discussion of the maximum period and the stability of the limit cycles obtained follows.

6.3 Limitation on the period of limit cycles of relay mode oscillations[22]

In this section, a derivation of the fundamental equation that yields the limits of modes of oscillation is obtained. It is based on the assumption of symmetry of the oscillations and is valid for (autonomous) relay discrete systems. The equation for the response during the limit cycle can be obtained from equation (6.32) of the previous section by replacing all the h_{l+i} by T. Thus

$$c_{is} = -\frac{1}{2\pi j}\int_{\Gamma} \frac{e^{\mu pT}KG(p)}{1 + e^{\mu pT}} \sum_{l=0}^{\mu-1} \frac{\gamma(l + i)e^{-lpT}(1 - e^{-pT})}{p}\,dp \tag{6.56}$$

From the symmetry condition, $e'_{ls}(0)$ is positive for the first half period and negative for the other half period. This implies that the response $c_{ls}(0)$ is negative for the first half period and positive for the second half since no input is applied. Therefore

$$\begin{aligned}\gamma(l) &= +1 & l &= 0, 1, 2, \ldots, \mu - 1 \\ &= -1 & l &= \mu, \mu + 1, \ldots, M - 1\end{aligned}$$

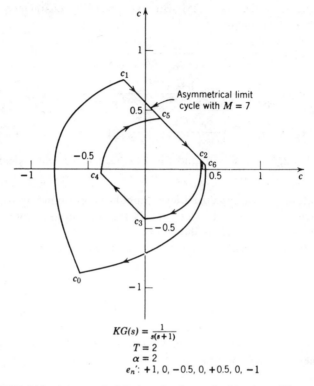

$$KG(s) = \frac{1}{s(s+1)}$$
$$T = 2$$
$$\alpha = 2$$
$$e_n': +1, 0, -0.5, 0, +0.5, 0, -1$$

FIGURE 6.12   Asymmetrical limit cycle of quantized level amplifier system.

and

$$c_{ls} < 0 \qquad l = 0, 1, 2, \ldots, \mu - 1$$
$$c_{ls} > 0 \qquad l = \mu, \mu + 1, \ldots, M - 1 \tag{6.57}$$

By investigating the polarity of $c_{\mu-1,s}$ which is the response at the last sampling instant contained in the first half period of the limit cycle, we can obtain the maximum number $\mu_{\max}$ or $M_{\max}$. This is done by letting $i = \mu - 1$ in equation (6.56).

$$c_{\mu-1,s} = -\frac{1}{2\pi j} \int_\Gamma \frac{e^{\mu pT} KG(p)}{1 + e^{\mu pT}} \frac{(1 - e^{-pT})}{p} \sum_{l=0}^{\mu-1} \gamma(l + \mu - 1) e^{-lpT} \, dp \tag{6.58}$$

Since c_{0s} is negative by the original assumption, the polarity of $c_{\mu-1,s}$ is tested starting from $\mu = 2$, that is, from c_{1s}. The response $c_{\mu-1,s}$ may be negative up to a certain $\mu = \mu'$, but it may become positive for all $\mu \geq \mu' + 1$. Then this critical μ' is taken as $\mu_{\max}$.

This general formulation and procedure is applied to the following examples.

EXAMPLE 1

The plant transfer is of first order, that is, $KG(s) = K/(s + b)$. The response $c_{\mu-1,s}$ at the margin of the first half period is obtained by letting $i = \mu - 1$ in equation (6.34) to give

$$\gamma(l + \mu) = +1 \quad \text{for } l = 0$$
$$= -1 \quad \text{for } l = 1, 2, \ldots, \mu - 1 \tag{6.59}$$

and

$$c_0, c_1, c_2, \ldots, c_{\mu-1} < 0 \tag{6.60}$$

Equation (6.58) becomes

$$c_{\mu-1,s} = -\frac{1}{2\pi j} \int_\Gamma \frac{e^{\mu p T} KG(p)}{1 + e^{\mu p T}} \frac{1 - e^{-pT}}{p} \left(1 - \sum_{l=1}^{\mu-1} e^{-lpT} \right) dp$$

$$= \frac{K}{b} \frac{1 - e^{-bT}}{1 + e^{-\mu bT}} [1 + e^{-bT} + \ldots e^{-(\mu-2)bT} - e^{-(\mu-1)bT}]$$

$$\tag{6.61}$$

It is evident from equation (6.61) that $c_{\mu-1,s}$ is positive for all $\mu \geq 2$, thus violating the assumption of equation (6.60). Therefore it can be concluded that the first-order relay sampled-data system can maintain only the relay mode of oscillations of two sampling periods ($M = 2$ or $\mu = 1$) and that longer periods cannot be sustained. This holds for any K, b, and sampling period T.

EXAMPLE 2

We shall consider a second-order plant with integrator in this example, that is, $KG(s) = K/s(s + b)$. Letting $h_{l+i} \to T$ in equation (6.29) yields a set of solutions $c_{0s}, c_{1s}, \ldots, c_{\mu-1,s}$ for the responses at all sampling instants of the limit cycle.

$$c_{is} = -\frac{K}{b} \left\{ \sum_{l=0}^{\mu-i-1} \left[\frac{T}{2} - \frac{e^{-(\mu-l-1)bT}(1 - e^{-bT})}{b(1 + e^{-\mu bT})} \right] \right.$$

$$\left. - \sum_{l=\mu-i}^{\mu-1} \left[\frac{T}{2} - \frac{e^{-(\mu-l-1)bT}(1 - e^{-bT})}{b(1 + e^{-\mu bT})} \right] \right\} \tag{6.62}$$

For $\mu = 1$ and $i = \mu - 1 = 0$,

$$c_{0s} = -\frac{K}{b} \left[\frac{T}{2} - \frac{1 - e^{-bT}}{b(1 + e^{-bT})} \right]$$

$$= -\frac{K}{2b^2} \left[\frac{bT(1 + e^{-bT}) - 2(1 - e^{-bT})}{1 + e^{-bT}} \right] \tag{6.63}$$

It can be proved that the numerator inside the bracket is positive for all $bT > 0$. Hence it may be concluded that c_{0s} is negative for all T.

For $\mu = 2$ and $i = \mu - 1 = 1$,

$$c_{1s} = -\frac{K}{b^2}\frac{(1 - e^{-bT})^2}{1 + e^{-2bT}} < 0, \qquad \text{for all } bT > 0 \qquad (6.64)$$

Therefore c_{1s} is negative for any sampling period T.

For $\mu = 3$ and $i = \mu - 1 = 2$

$$c_{2s} = \frac{K}{b}\left[\frac{T}{2} - \frac{(1 - e^{-bT})}{b(1 + e^{-3bT})}(1 + e^{-bT} - e^{-2bT})\right] \qquad (6.65)$$

Simple trial shows that c_{2s} is negative for small T and becomes positive for larger T, thus violating the original assumption. We can find the critical T_c by solving equation (6.65) for T when c_{2s} is equated to zero. Therefore the oscillations of $\mu = 3$ or $M = 6$ can exist for $T < T_c$, but it cannot be sustained for $T \geq T_c$. A similar observation is obtained for larger μ.

To derive the fundamental equation that relates the maximum μ and the sampling period T for any second-order system, we let $i = \mu - 1$ in equation (6.62).

$$
\begin{aligned}
c_{\mu-1\,s} &= -\frac{K}{b}\left\{\frac{T}{2} - \frac{e^{-(\mu-1)bT}(1 - e^{-bT})}{b(1 + e^{-\mu bT})}\right.\\
&\qquad \left. - \sum_{l=1}^{\mu-1}\left[\frac{T}{2} - \frac{e^{-(\mu-l-1)bT}(1 - e^{-bT})}{b(1 + e^{-\mu bT})}\right]\right\}\\
&= \frac{K}{b^2}\left[\frac{bT}{2}(\mu - 2) - e^{bT}\frac{1 - e^{-\mu bT}}{1 + e^{-\mu bT}} + e^{bT} - 1\right] \qquad (6.66)
\end{aligned}
$$

By the original assumption, $c_{\mu-1,s} < 0$. Hence $\mu_{\max}$ is obtained by finding the maximum integer μ which satisfies the following inequality:

$$\frac{bT}{2}(\mu - 2) - e^{-bT}\frac{1 - e^{-\mu bT}}{1 + e^{-\mu bT}} + e^{bT} - 1 < 0 \qquad (6.67)$$

To conclude, we may state that limit cycles of two and four sampling periods can exist in the relay system for any sampling period T, but that for $\mu \geq 3$ the maximum number of sampling periods or the mode of oscillations is restricted by the system parameters b and T. Figure 6.13 indicates $\mu_{\max}$ as a function of bT.

These discussions can be applied to any order plant and to other types of nonlinearities.[20-22] An important application of the maximum number of modes of limit cycles is in the stability study of nonlinear discrete systems. It yields the boundary stability curves for various nonlinear discrete systems.

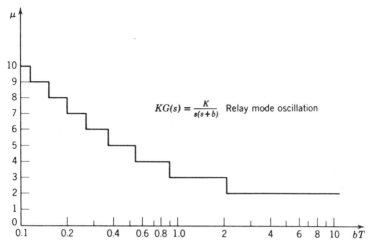

FIGURE 6.13   Maximum number of sampling periods contained in half period of limit cycle.

6.4 Stability study of limit cycles[2,20,27]

In the preceding section a method was presented for obtaining the periodic oscillations (or limit cycles) of a system without information as to their stability. We shall now discuss the stability by first defining a stable limit cycle.

A *limit cycle* is considered to be asymptotically stable if any *small* perturbation around the limit cycle approaches 0 as n approaches ∞. By following this definition, the following two theorems can be applied for testing the stability.

THEOREM 1:   Assume that the nonlinear difference equation in vector form

$$x_{n+1}] = F(x_n)]$$ (6.68)

has a periodic solution $s_n]$ of period M, and that the functions $F(x_n)$ are single valued and possess continuous first partial derivatives. The first approximation of the difference equation for small perturbations about the periodic solution $s_n]$ is

$$Y_{n+1}] = [A_n]Y_n]$$ (6.69)

and the solution of this equation determines the stability of the periodic solution $s_n]$ if $[A_n]$ is nonsingular at all the solution points. In this equation $Y_n]$ is the perturbation about $s_n]$ and the components of $[A_n]$ are

$$a_{ij,n} = \frac{\partial F_i(x_n)}{\partial x_j}\bigg|_{x_n]=s_n]}$$ (6.70)

THEOREM 2: The system of equation (6.69) is asymptotically stable if all the eigenvalues of the matrix

$$[A_G] = \prod_{n=0}^{M-1} [A_n] = [A_{M-1}][A_{M-2}] \cdots [A_0] \tag{6.71}$$

lie inside the unit circle. Then all the solutions tend to 0 as n becomes large. If one of the values lies outside the unit circle, the solution is unstable. Finally, if all the values lie on the unit circle, the linearized solution $Y_n]$ of equation (6.69) can be considered as stable.*

Combining the two theorems, the condition for the asymptotic stability of limit cycles is reduced to the following statement. All the eigenvalues of the matrix $[A_G]$ which is the product of all the matrices which consist of the first partial derivatives of $F(x_n)$ lie inside the unit circle at all the periodic solution points $s_n]$.

The application of this theorem is shown in the following discussion.

6.5 Forced oscillations in nonlinear discrete systems[4,23,27]

In this section, a particular example of the nonlinear sampled-data system discussed in the preceding chapter is analyzed for a sinusoidal forcing function. Since only harmonic oscillations (oscillations having the same frequency as input frequency) are considered, it is necessary to put suitable restrictions on the parameters of the system in order for such oscillations to exist. Furthermore, the ratio of the sampling frequency to signal frequency is assumed to be an integer.

EXAMPLE[23]

Consider the sampled-data system shown in Fig. 6.14, where $G_1(s) = K/s(s + 1)$ and $r(t)$ is a sinusoidal input. The nonlinear characteristic is described by

$$c' = c + m_3 c^3 \qquad m_3 \ll 1 \tag{6.72}$$

where c' is the output of the nonlinearity and

$$\mathcal{G}(z) = \mathcal{Z}\left[\frac{1 - e^{-Ts}}{s} G_1(s)\right] = \frac{K(0.368z + 0.264)}{(z^2 - 1.368z + 0.368)},$$
$$T = 1 \tag{6.73}$$

---

* It should be noted that even if the linearized solution of the perturbation is *stable*, the limit cycle is not *asymptotically stable* since the perturbation will not decay in this case.

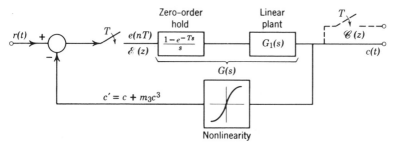

FIGURE 6.14   A nonlinear discrete system with nonlinearity in feedback path.

The difference equation relating output to input is easily derived as follows:

$$c(n + 2) - 1.368c(n + 1) + 0.368c(n)$$
$$= K[0.368e(n + 1) + 0.264e(n)]$$
$$= K\{0.368[r(n + 1) - c'(n + 1)] + 0.264[r(n) - c'(n)]\}$$

$$(6.74)$$

Choosing $m_3 = -0.1$ and substituting for c' in terms of c, the following difference equation is obtained:

$$c(n + 2) + c(n + 1)[0.368K - 1.368] + c(n)[0.264K + 0.368]$$
$$- K[0.0368c(n + 1)^3 + 0.0264c(n)^3]$$
$$= 0.368Kr(n + 1) + 0.264Kr(n) \quad (6.75)$$

If the peak value of $r(n)$ is not chosen very large, it can be assumed that the harmonic oscillations will be the dominant term in the periodic response. Let $r(n) = B \sin (\pi/3)n$. For the periodic steady-state output the following form can be assumed:

$$c(n) = p(n) \sin \frac{\pi}{3} n + q(n) \cos \frac{\pi}{3} n \qquad (6.76)$$

where $p(n)$ and $q(n)$ are slowly varying discrete functions of n. We substitute for $r(n)$ and $c(n)$ in equation (6.75) and equate coefficients of $\sin (\pi/3)n$ and $\cos (\pi/3)n$, noting the fact that $\sin^3 \theta = \frac{1}{4}(3 \sin \theta - \sin 3\theta)$ and $\cos^3 \theta = \frac{1}{4}(3 \cos \theta + \cos 3\theta)$. Since $p(n)$ and $q(n)$ are slowly varying with n, it can be assumed that

$$p(n + 2) = 2p(n + 1) - p(n) \quad \text{(that is, } \Delta^2 p(n) = 0) \quad (6.77)$$

and in terms involving m_3, $p(n + 1)$ could be replaced by $p(n)$. These simplifications are legitimate so long as consideration is restricted to the harmonic oscillations. With these assumptions, the comparison of coefficients of $\sin(\pi/3)n$ and $\cos(\pi/3)n$ in equation (6.75) yields the following two relations:

$$p(n+1)(0.184K - 1.684) + q(n+1)(-0.547 - 0.319K)$$
$$= p(n)(-0.868 - 0.264K + 0.0336A^2K)$$
$$+ q(n)(-0.866 - 0.0239KA^2) + 0.448B. \quad (6.78)$$

$$p(n+1)(0.547 + 0.319K) + q(n+1)(0.184K - 1.684)$$
$$= p(n)(0.866 + 0.0239KA^2) + q(n)(-0.868 - 0.264K$$
$$+ 0.0336A^2K) + 0.3185B \quad (6.79)$$

where $A^2 = p^2(n) + q^2(n)$. These are the key equations in the study of periodic solutions and their stability.

After the transients have disappeared, the solution will tend toward one of the periodic states given by the substitution of $p(n+1) = p(n) = p_s$ and $q(n+1) = q(n) = q_s$ in equations (6.78) and (6.79).

Define

$$\begin{bmatrix} 0.184K - 1.684 & -0.547 - 0.319K \\ 0.547 + 0.319K & 0.184K - 1.684 \end{bmatrix} = \mathbf{C} \quad (6.80)$$

and let

$$\begin{bmatrix} p(n) \\ q(n) \end{bmatrix} = \mathbf{y}(n) \quad (6.81)$$

Equations (6.78) and (6.79) are then rewritten in a simplified notation as

$$\mathbf{C}\mathbf{y}(n+1) = \mathbf{H}[\mathbf{y}(n)] \quad (6.82)$$

where $\mathbf{H}[\mathbf{y}(n)]$ is the nonlinear term appearing on the right-hand sides of equations (6.78) and (6.79). Equation (6.82) is further simplified as

$$\mathbf{y}(n+1) = \mathbf{C}^{-1}\mathbf{H}[\mathbf{y}(n)]$$
$$= \mathbf{F}[\mathbf{y}(n)] \quad (6.83)$$

The equilibrium points of this equation are given by

$$\boldsymbol{\xi} = \mathbf{F}(\boldsymbol{\xi}) \quad \text{where } \boldsymbol{\xi} = \begin{bmatrix} p_s \\ q_s \end{bmatrix} \quad (6.84)$$

which reduces to the following two equations:.

$$p_s(-0.816 + 0.448K - 0.0336KA^2) + q_s(0.319 - 0.319K$$
$$+ 0.0239KA^2) = 0.448KB \quad (6.85)$$

$$p_s(0.319K - 0.319 - 0.0239KA^2) + q_s(-0.816 + 0.448K$$
$$- 0.0336KA^2) = 0.3185KB \quad (6.86)$$

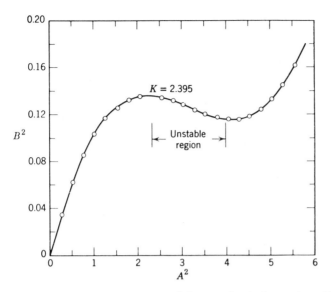

FIGURE 6.15   Amplitude characteristic curve for the harmonic oscillation.

These equations when solved for p_s, q_s and using the fact that $p_s^2 + q_s^2 = A^2$ yield the amplitude characteristic

$$A^2[(-0.816 + 0.448K - 0.0336KA^2)^2 + (0.319K - 0.319$$
$$- 0.0239KA^2)^2] = 0.448K^2A^2 + 0.3185K^2B^2 \quad (6.87)$$

For a given value of K the functional relation A^2 versus B^2 can be plotted. It will be seen that for some values of K the system has more than one periodic state for a certain range of values of B^2. Figure 6.15 shows B^2 plotted as a function of A^2 with $K = 2.395$. Computation shows that for values of K greater than 2.25 multivalued regions are obtained.

Let us choose $K = 2.395$. This will make the poles of the linear part of the difference equation just lie on the unit circle. The characteristic equation for the linear portion is

$$z^2 - 0.488z + 1 = 0$$

which gives

$$z = \rho e^{\pm i\theta}, \quad \text{where } \rho = 1 \quad \text{and} \quad \theta = \frac{2\pi}{5} \quad (6.88)$$

This gives the period as $2\pi/\theta = 5$ seconds. The period of the sinusoidal input is 6 seconds and since the difference between the natural frequency and signal frequency is small, a locking phenomenon or a frequency entrainment takes place—a phenomenon similar to that in continuous systems. Calculation of the response using the difference equation as a recurrence relation indicates a response of period 6 as expected.

The amplitude characteristic has a region, for values of A^2 between 2.25 and 4, where $dB^2/dA^2 < 0$. From the theory for nonlinear continuous systems, in particular, works of Hayashi,[36] and more recently, that of Klotter and Pinney,[25] we would expect the periodic solution in this region to be unstable. That this is true is proved by considering the variational equation around the periodic state.

Let the components of the vector $\mathbf{F}[\mathbf{y}(n)]$ in equation (6.83) be denoted by $\begin{bmatrix} f_1 \\ f_2 \end{bmatrix}$ If the eigenvalues of the matrix

$$\begin{bmatrix} \dfrac{\partial f_1}{\partial p} & \dfrac{\partial f_1}{\partial q} \\[2mm] \dfrac{\partial f_2}{\partial p} & \dfrac{\partial f_2}{\partial q} \end{bmatrix}_{\mathbf{y}(n)=\boldsymbol{\xi}} \tag{6.89}$$

lie inside the unit circle, then the equilibrium point is stable; otherwise it is unstable. For the region in Fig. 6.15 where $dB^2/dA^2 < 0$, the equilibrium point is unstable and if the system is slightly disturbed at this point, it will ultimately settle down to one of the other two stable periodic solutions. In the numerical example discussed in this section, and for $B^2 = 0.125$ from Fig. 6.15, three periodic states with $A^2 = 1.495,\ 3.25,$ and 4.84 are obtained. From equations (6.85) and (6.86), $p_s,\ q_s$ are computed for each of these values and then the characteristic equation for the variational equation at each point is computed. Stability of this characteristic equation is then examined. A summary of the results are given.

$$K = 2.395$$
$$B = 0.354$$

Equilibrium Points		Characteristic Equation for Variational Equation	Stable or Unstable
$p_s = \quad 1.012$	$q_s = -0.69$	$\lambda^2 - 1.793\lambda + 0.809$	Stable
$p_s = \quad 1.015$	$q_s = -1.5$	$\lambda^2 - 1.738\lambda + 0.73$	Unstable
$p_s = -0.0505$	$q_s = -2.2$	$\lambda^2 - 1.688\lambda + 0.706$	Stable

These results were arrived at through laborious numerical computation. It is seen that the roots of the characteristic equation lie very near the unit circle. Hence it is to be expected that the periodic solution will settle down to its steady-state value after a very long time. The closeness of the numerical values is attributed to the small slope of the amplitude characteristic. For example, for the input magnitude of $B = 0.294$, which has only one stable periodic solution, the characteristic equation is $\lambda^2 - 1.816\lambda + 0.86$ which is clearly stable.

6.6 Direct z-transform for
determining true oscillation[23]

In addition to what has been discussed in the preceding section, other methods exist for determining oscillation in nonlinear discrete systems. These methods constitute both graphical procedures such as the phase plane (space) and the describing function, and analytical procedures such as the use of orthogonal discrete frequency functions or Fourier polynomials, the state-vector approach, and the direct z-transform. In the following, we shall discuss only the latter method, which is closely related to the contents of this book; however, the other techniques are important and have been extensively elaborated in the literature.

In the direct z-transform method, the type of nonlinearity assumed is either a relay or a saturating gain amplifier with straight-line characteristics, as shown in Fig. 6.8. The method is based on specifying a certain mode of oscillation for zero input and obtaining the conditions that sustain these oscillations. This technique will now be explained and later applied to a specific example.

Let the output of the nonlinearity be assumed as in Fig. 6.16, where the period of oscillation, for sake of illustration, is assumed to be four sampling periods, the sequence being m_0, m_1, m_2, m_3. In the steady state the z-transform of this repetitive sequence can be defined as

$$\frac{m_0}{1 - z^{-4}} + \frac{m_1 z^{-1}}{1 - z^{-4}} + \frac{m_2 z^{-2}}{1 - z^{-4}} + \frac{m_3 z^{-3}}{1 - z^{-4}} \tag{6.90}$$

The output of the system with a repetitive sequence c_0, c_1, c_2, c_3 has similarly a steady-state z-transform of

$$\frac{c_0}{1 - z^{-4}} + \frac{c_1 z^{-1}}{1 - z^{-4}} + \frac{c_2 z^{-2}}{1 - z^{-4}} + \frac{c_3 z^{-3}}{1 - z^{-4}} \tag{6.91}$$

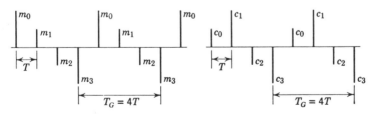

FIGURE 6.16   Input-output description of linear plant under limit cycle operation.

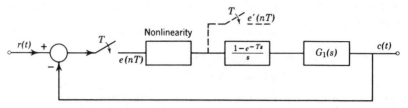

FIGURE 6.17   Mathematical equivalent of system in Fig. 6.18.

Next take the z-transform of the difference equation describing the linear plant and substitute the z-transform expression (6.90) and (6.91) for the input and output, respectively. Comparison of coefficients of like powers of z will yield four linear relations involving c_0, c_1, c_2, c_3. It is found that not all these relations are linearly independent. For the limit cycle with period four, only three relations are linearly independent. The fourth relation appears as a constraint which should be satisfied so that the specified output of the nonlinearity is maintained. The solution of these equations will yield bounds on the initial values of the output which are the conditions that are necessary (but not sufficient) to sustain the specified mode of oscillation. The following example will illustrate the procedure.

EXAMPLE

Let Fig. 6.17 be the mathematical equivalent of the sampled-data system shown in Fig. 6.18. Let $G_1(s)$ be

$$G_1(s) = \frac{0.305s + 0.695}{s(s + 0.695)} \tag{6.92}$$

and the nonlinearity be an ideal relay as shown in Fig. 6.19. The z-transform of $G_1(s)$ is

$$\mathscr{G}_1(z) = \mathscr{Z}\left[\frac{1 - e^{-Ts}}{s} G_1(s)\right] \qquad \text{where } T = 1$$

$$= \frac{0.5z}{(z - 1)(z - 0.5)} \tag{6.93}$$

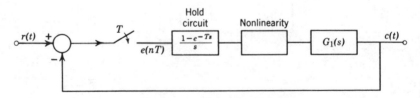

FIGURE 6.18   A nonlinear discrete system.

Thus the difference equation for the linear portion can at once be written as

$$c(n + 2) - 1.5c(n + 1) + 0.5c(n) = 0.5e'(n + 1) \qquad (6.94)$$

where n takes on integer values $0, 1, 2, \ldots$.

It is required to find initial conditions corresponding to periodic solutions of period two.

The z-transform of equation (6.94) in the steady state is

$$(z^2 - 1.5z + 0.5)\mathscr{C}(z) - z^2c(0) - zc(1) + 1.5zc(0)$$
$$= 0.5z\mathscr{E}'(z) - 0.5ze'(0) \quad (6.95)$$

In the steady state, let the relay output be -1, $+1$, and output of the system be c_0, c_1. Then the z-transform of relay output in the steady state is given by

$$\frac{-1}{1 - z^{-2}} + \frac{z^{-1}}{1 - z^{-2}} = \frac{-z}{z + 1} = \mathscr{E}'(z) \quad (6.96)$$

The z-transform of the output $c(t)$ is

$$(c_0 + c_1z^{-1})/(1 - z^{-2}) = \mathscr{C}(z).$$

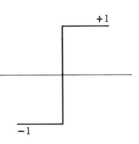

FIGURE 6.19   Ideal relay.

We substitute these expressions in equation (6.95), clear the fractions, and equate coefficients of like powers of z. Coefficients of z^3 and z^2 drop out and the coefficient of z and the constant term yield identical relation

$$c_0 - c_1 = \tfrac{1}{3} \qquad (6.97)$$

If the relay output is to be maintained -1, $+1$, it is necessary that $-c_0 < 0$ and $-c_1 > 0$; that is, $c_0 > 0$, $c_1 < 0$. Combining this with the relation (6.97) between c_0 and c_1, it is immediately seen that $-\tfrac{1}{3} < c_1 < 0$ and $0 < c_0 < \tfrac{1}{3}$, which agrees with the results obtained using other methods.

6.7 Periodic solution of certain nonlinear difference equations[27,37]

In the preceding sections, the z-transform method has been applied to obtain the periodic oscillations of nonlinear discrete systems. The systems discussed are those usually encountered in control engineering applications. The mathematical description of these systems represents the field of nonlinear difference equations. Hence the z-transform as shown in this chapter can be readily used to obtain the periodic solution of certain nonlinear difference equations. The type of difference equation that can be solved by this method is

$$\sum_{k=0}^{l} \beta_k c(n + k) = \sum_{k=0}^{l_1} \alpha_k f(n + k),$$

$$\text{with } l_1 \leq l \quad \text{and} \quad n = 0, 1, 2, \ldots \quad (6.98)$$

In equation (6.98), the nonlinear term $f(n)$ represents

$$f(n) = \Phi[c(n)] \tag{6.99}$$

where Φ is a nonlinear single-valued symmetrical function and α_k, β_k are constants.

In applying the z-transform method, we can establish a set of nonlinear algebraic equations which give the general solution for any period. In particular, solution for the periodic oscillation $c_s(n)$ can be determined. If we restrict the symmetrical solution to that for even periods only, we can obtain the exact solution for periodic modes with half-periods less than or equal to two. For higher harmonic oscillations approximate solutions could be obtained. A detailed discussion of the solution of equation (6.98) is beyond the scope of this text; however, the method that can be used is similar to that applied in the preceding sections. Furthermore, the stability study of the periodic solution of equation (6.98) can be readily studied as discussed in Section 6.4.

In concluding this chapter, it should be indicated that the z-transform method is also applicable for obtaining the periodic modes of oscillation in continuous nonlinear feedback systems. As mentioned earlier, other methods exist for determining the periodic modes of oscillation. The purpose of this chapter is not to discuss and compare all these methods but to propose in detail the application of one particular method, the z-transform for obtaining a solution to these problems.

REFERENCES

1. Kalman, R. E., "Nonlinear Aspects of Sampled-Data Control Systems," *Proceedings of the Symposium on Non-linear Circuit Analysis*, Polytechnic Institute of Brooklyn, Brooklyn, New York, April 1956.

2. Nease, R. F., "Analysis and Design of Nonlinear Sampled-Data Control Systems," WADD Technical Note 57-162, Servomechanism Laboratory, M.I.T., June 1957.

3. Mullin, F. J., "The Stability and Compensation of Saturation Sampled-Data Systems," *AIEE Trans.*, Vol. 78, Part 1, July 1959, pp. 270–278.

4. Mullin, F. J., and E. I. Jury, "A Phase Plane Approach to Relay Sampled-Data Feedback Systems," *AIEE Trans.*, Vol. 78, Part 2, 1959, pp. 517–524.

5. Izawa, K., and L. E. Weaver, "Relay-Type Feedback Control Systems with Dead Time and Sampling," *AIEE Trans.*, Vol. 78, Part 2, 1959, pp. 49–54, and discussion by K. Izawa in reference (4).

6. Cypkin, J., *Theory of Pulse Systems* (in Russian), State Press for Physics and Mathematical Literature, Moscow, USSR, 1958.

7. Nelson, W. L., "Pulse Width Control of Sampled-Data Systems," Technical Report T-35/B, Columbia University, July 1959.

8. Kadota, T. T., "Asymptotic Stability of Some Nonlinear Feedback Systems," ERL Report Series No. 60, Issue No. 264, University of California, Berkeley, January 1960.

9. Pyshkin, I. V., *Self-Oscillation in Pulse-Width-Modulated Systems*, Theory and Application of Discrete Automatic Systems (in Russian), Academy of Science, Moscow, USSR, 1960, pp. 134–150.

10. Andeen, "Analysis of Pulse Duration Sampled-Data Systems with Linear Elements," *IRE Trans. Automatic Control*, Vol. AC-5, No. 4, September 1960, pp. 306–313.

11. Andeen, R., "Analysis of Sampled-Data Systems with Nonlinear Elements," *Automatic and Remote Control, Proceedings First Int. Congress IFAC*, Butterworths, London, 1961, pp. 314–320.

12. Torng, H. C., "A Study of Nonlinear Sampled-Data Systems Containing a Relay, a Saturating, or a Backlash Element," Ph.D Thesis, Cornell University, February 1960.

13. Torng, H. C., and W. C. Meserve, "Determination of Periodic Modes in Relay Servomechanisms Employing Sampled-Data," *IRE Transactions on Automatic Control*, Vol. AC-5, No. 4, September 1960.

14. Meserve, W. E., and H. C. Torng, "Investigation of Periodic Modes of Sampled-Data Control Systems Containing a Saturating Element," *Trans. ASME*, Series D, *J. Basic Eng.*, Vol. 83, 1961, pp. 77-81.

15. Jury, E. I., and T. Nishimura, "Analysis of Finite Pulsed Systems with Periodically-Varying Sampling Rate and Pulse Width," *AIEE*, CP 60-866, June 1960.

16. Nishimura, T., "Operational Analysis of Finite Pulsed Sampled-Data Systems," ERL Report Series No. 60, Issue No. 279, University of California, Berkeley, May 1960.

17. Jury, E. I., *Sampled-Data Control Systems*, John Wiley and Sons, New York, 1958, Chapters 1 and 9.

18. Jury, E. I., "A Note on the Steady-State Response of Linear Time-Invariant Systems to General Periodic Inputs," *IRE Proc.* Vol. 48, No. 5, May 1960.

19. Jury, E. I., "Contribution to the Modified z-Transform Theory," *J. Franklin Inst.*, Vol. 270, No. 2, August 1960, pp. 114–129.

20. Jury, E. I. and T. Nishimura, "On the Periodic Modes of Oscillations in Pulse-Width-Modulated Feedback Systems," ERL Report No. 60, Issue 328, University of California, Berkeley, November 29, 1960; also, *Trans. ASME*, Series E, *J. Basic Eng.*, March 1962, pp. 71-84.

21. Nishimura, T. "Stability Analysis of Pulse-Width-Modulated Feedback Systems," ERL Report Series No. 60, Issue 353, University of California, Berkeley, April 4, 1961.

22. Jury, E. I., and T. Nishimura, "Stability Study of PWM Feedback Systems," presented at the JACC meeting in Minnesota, June 1963. To appear in the *Trans. ASME*, 1964.

23. Pai, M. A., "Oscillations in Nonlinear Sampled-Data Systems," *AIEE Trans.*, Vol. 81, Part II (Applications and Industry), January 1963, pp. 350–355.

24. Chow, C. K., "Contactor Servomechanism Employing Sampled-Data," *AIEE Trans.*, Vol. 73, Part II, 1954, pp. 51–64.

25. Klotter, K., and E. Pinney, "A Comprehensive Stability Criterion for Forced Vibrations in Nonlinear Systems," *J. of Appl. Mech., Trans. ASME,* Vol. 75, 1953, pp. 9–12.

26. Da-Chuan, Shao, "On the Possibility of Certain Types of Oscillations in Sampled-Data Control Systems," *Automation and Remote Control,* Vol. 10, June 1959, pp. 85–89.

27. Tsypkin, Y. Z., "Periodic Solutions of Nonlinear Finite Difference Equations and their Stability," International Union of Theoretical and Applied Mechanics, Institute of Mathematics, Academy of Science of the Ukranian SSR, Kiev, 1961.

28. Delfeld, F. R., and G. J. Murphy, "Analysis of Pulse-Width-Modulated Control Systems," *IRE Trans. A.C.,* Vol. AC-6, No. 3, September 1961, pp. 283–292.

29. Tsypkin, Y. Z., "Elements of Theory of Numerical Automatic Systems," *Automatic and Remote Control, Proceedings First Int. Congress IFAC,* Butterworths, London, 1961, pp. 286–294.

30. Jury, E. I., "Contribution to the Modified z-Transform Theory," *J. Franklin Inst.,* Vol. 270, No. 2, August 1960, pp. 114–129.

31. Monroe, J., *Digital Processes for Sampled-Data Systems,* John Wiley and Sons, New York, 1962.

32. Torng, H. C., "Complete and Exact Identification of Self-Sustained Oscillations in Relay Sampled-Data Control Systems," *AIEE Trans.* Vol. 81, part II, 1962, pp. 355–361.

33. Jury, E. I., Discussion of Reference (32).

34. Guichet, P. L., "Oscillations Periodiques dans les Systemes Echantillonnes Non-Lineaires," *Automatisme,* No. 6, June 1963, pp. 229–239.

35. Kuo, B. C., *Analysis and Synthesis of Sampled-Data Control Systems,* Prentice-Hall, Englewood Cliffs, New Jersey, 1963.

36. Hayashi, C., *Forced Oscillations in Nonlinear Systems,* Nippon Printing and Publishing Co., Japan, 1953.

37. Pasteur, Franceline, "Self-Sustained Oscillations in Nonlinear Sampled-Data Systems," Master of Science Project, Dept. of Electrical Engineering, University of California, Berkeley, June 1963.

38. Kaplan, W., "Stability Theory," *Proceedings of the Symposium on Non-linear Circuit Analysis,* Polytechnic Institute of Brooklyn, Brooklyn, New York, Vol. 4, April 1956.

39. Kalman, R. E., and J. E. Bertram, "Control System Analysis and Design Via the Second Method of Lyapunov," Parts I and II, *Trans. ASME (J. Basic Eng.),* Vol. 82, June 1960, pp. 371–400.

40. Tsypkin, Y. Z., "Investigation of Stability of Periodic States in Nonlinear Pulse Automatic Systems," *Automatic and Remote Control,* Academic Press, New York, Vol. 22, No. 6, June 1961, pp. 614–623.

7

z-TRANSFORM METHOD IN

APPROXIMATION TECHNIQUES

The z-transform method discussed in the preceding chapters was applied for the most part to the exact solution of difference equations or to discrete systems which are describable by difference or difference-differential equations. One of the basic advantages of the z-transform method is that the time response can be obtained by power series or long division method. This procedure circumvents the evaluation of the poles of the system transfer function or the characteristic roots of the difference equation. This advantage could and has been utilized for the approximate solution of differential equations or continuous systems. Furthermore, the z-transform could also be used for time domain synthesis of networks to yield certain responses, or for identifying the linear plant transfer function. The material of this chapter deals mainly with the various approximation techniques which utilize the z-transform theory.

7.1 Approximation methods

Approximating a differential equation by a difference equation is not new. Mathematicians have been in the past and are at present engaged in doing extensive work toward this approximation, which is called numerical analysis. With the advent of digital computers, approximation is becoming increasingly important for programming the solution of differential equations. In the following discussion this subject is only briefly indicated by the important techniques for approximating a continuous system by a discrete model.

To illustrate one aspect of the approximation procedure, assume that the continuous system shown in Fig. 7.1 is represented by a continuous

219

input and a transfer function $G(s)$, and that the output is obtained at all times. An approximate system using sampled-data techniques[1-3] is presented in Fig. 7.2. By using the z-transform or the modified z-transform, the approximate output of the system of Fig. 7.1 can be obtained. It is noticed from Fig. 7.2 that an interpolator (or a mathematical hold) is used. The purpose of the interpolator is to reconstruct as closely as possible the continuous function which has been fictitiously sampled.

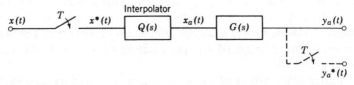

$x(t)$		$y(t)$
$X(s)$	$G(s)$	$Y(s)$

FIGURE 7.1 Continuous system.

Shown in Fig. 7.3a to e are the various forms of the interpolator function commonly used. The approximation $x_a(t)$ is the sum of a number of impulse responses, that is,

$$x_a(t) = \sum_{n=0}^{\infty} x_n q(t - nT) \qquad (7.1)$$

where $q(t) = \mathscr{L}^{-1}[Q(s)]$.

For the cases a, b, d, and e, equation (7.1) applies, whereas for case c, in which the values of $x(t)$ at midpoints of the interval are used, the following is used:

$$x_a(t) = \sum_{n=0}^{\infty} x_{n+\frac{1}{2}} q(t - \tfrac{1}{2}T - nT) \qquad (7.1a)$$

If we impose the condition $x_a(nT) = x(nT)$ [or $\mathscr{X}_a(z) = \mathscr{X}(z)$] in a, d, and e, by applying the z-transformation to equation (7.1) we obtain

$$\mathscr{J}[q(t)] = 1 \qquad (7.1b)$$

The same relationship also holds for case c with the imposed condition $x_a(nT + T/2) = x(nT + T/2)$. These conditions are not imposed on b where the pulse heights are the average of the ordinates $x(t)$ on either side of the pulse.

If we put

$$\mathscr{L}[q(t)] = Q(s) = \frac{F_{k+1}(z^{-1})}{s^{k+1}} \qquad (7.1c)$$

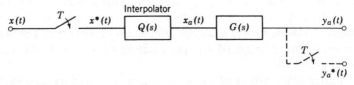

FIGURE 7.2 A sampled-data approximation of Fig. 7.1.

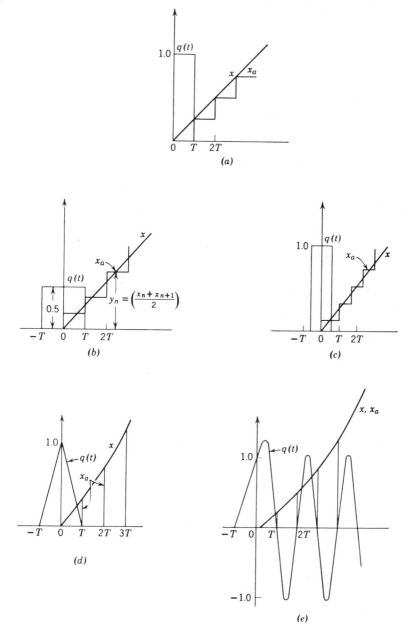

FIGURE 7.3 Approximation of a time function.

$F_{k+1}(z^{-1})$ (a certain function of (z^{-1})) can be determined by applying the z-transformation to equation (7.1c) and using the results of 7.1b to obtain

$$F_{k+1}(z^{-1}) = \frac{1}{z\left[\dfrac{1}{s^{k+1}}\right]} \tag{7.1d}$$

and

$$Q(s) = \frac{1}{s^{k+1}z\left[\dfrac{1}{s^{k+1}}\right]} \tag{7.1e}$$

The interpolator transfer functions $Q(s)$ which result from equation (7.1e) will be termed normal interpolators of order 0, 1, 2, by putting $k = 0, 1, 2$. For instance, the zero-order normal interpolator transfer function can be readily obtained by letting $k = 0$ in equation (7.1e) to obtain

$$Q_0(s) = \frac{(1 - z^{-1})}{s}\bigg|_{z=e^{Ts}} \tag{7.1f}$$

Similarly, higher-order normal interpolator transfer functions can be readily obtained.

To summarize the various interpolation schemes shown in Fig. 7.3, we use Table 7.1, introduced by Cruickshank,[4] to indicate the transfer function of each interpolator.

TABLE 7.1 CLASSIFICATION OF INTERPOLATION[4]

Interpolator	Transfer Function	Name of Approximation
Zero-order normal (a)	$Q_0(s) = \dfrac{(1 - z^{-1})}{s}$	Rectangular
First-order normal (d)	$Q_1(s) = \dfrac{z(1 - z^{-1})^2}{Ts^2}$	Triangular
Second-order normal (e)	$Q_2(s) = \dfrac{2z(1 - z^{-1})^3}{T^2(1 + z^{-1})s^3}$	Parabolic
Zero-order midinterval (c)	$Q(s) = \dfrac{z^{1/2}(1 - z^{-1})}{s}$	Midinterval rectangular
Zero-order mean (b)	$Q(s) = \dfrac{z(1 - z^{-2})}{2s}$	Mean rectangular

It should be noted that the second-order normal interpolation case e gives exact representation of parabolas, whereas case d gives exact fitting of straight lines. The mean rectangular and midinterval rectangular approximations give a relatively coarse fit to any curve except stepped functions.

Having obtained the transfer functions of the interpolators, we can write the approximate output z-transform from Fig. 7.2 as follows:

$$\mathscr{Y}_a(z) = \mathscr{X}(z)\mathscr{Z}[QG] \qquad (7.1g)$$

For integrating operators of any order n, we can readily obtain from tables of z-transforms the transform $\mathscr{Z}[Qs^{-n}]$. These transforms are given in the second column of Table 7.2.

By using the division method, the approximate output sequence $y_a(nT)$ can be readily obtained. The normal interpolators may be combined to represent accurately functions with given initial conditions, which is explained in the next section.

7.2 Initial conditions nonzero[4]

The problem of initial conditions can be incorporated by combining the normal operators. Thus we can have linear or quadratic interpolation, depending on the number of terms used in the Taylor's series expansion of $x(t)$ of Fig. 7.1 around the origin. This is illustrated as follows.

Let the Taylor's series expansion of $x(t)$ be presented

$$x(t) = x(0) + tx'(0) + \frac{t^2}{2!} x''(0) + \ldots + x_m(t) \qquad (7.2)$$

where $x_m(t)$ is the remainder after m terms.

Taking the z-transform of this equation, we obtain

$$\mathscr{X}(z) = \frac{x(0)}{1 - z^{-1}} + \frac{x'(0)Tz^{-1}}{(1 - z^{-1})^2}$$

$$+ \frac{x''(0)T^2 z^{-1}(1 + z^{-1})}{2(1 - z^{-1})^3} + \ldots + \mathscr{X}_m(z) \quad (7.2a)$$

We can replace $\mathscr{Y}_a(z)$ from Fig. 7.2 by the following approximation:

$$\mathscr{Y}_a(z) = \frac{x(0)}{1 - z^{-1}} \mathscr{Z}[Q_0 G]$$

$$+ \frac{x'(0)Tz^{-1}}{(1 - z^{-1})^2} \mathscr{Z}[Q_1 G]$$

$$+ \frac{x''(0)T^2 z^{-1}(1 + z^{-1})}{2(1 - z^{-1})^3} \mathscr{Z}[Q_2 G] + \ldots + \mathscr{X}_m(z)\mathscr{Z}[Q_m G]$$

$$(7.3)$$

TABLE 7.2 INTEGRATING OPERATORS

Function $G(s)$	Zero-Order Normal Interpolation	Linear Interpolation
$\dfrac{1}{s}$	$\dfrac{Tz^{-1}}{1 - z^{-1}}$	$\dfrac{T}{2}\dfrac{(1 + z^{-1})}{(1 - z^{-1})} - \dfrac{Tx(0)}{2(1 - z^{-1})}$
$\dfrac{1}{s^2}$	$\dfrac{T^2 z^{-1}(1 + z^{-1})}{2(1 - z^{-1})^2}$	$\dfrac{T^2}{6}\dfrac{(1 + 4z^{-1} + z^{-2})}{(1 - z^{-1})^2} - \dfrac{T^2(1 + 2z^{-1})x(0)}{6(1 - z^{-1})^2}$
$\dfrac{1}{s^3}$	$\dfrac{T^3 z^{-1}(1 + 4z^{-1} + z^{-2})}{6(1 - z^{-1})^3}$	$\dfrac{T^3(1 + 11z^{-1} + 11z^{-2} + z^{-3})}{24(1 - z^{-1})^3} - \dfrac{T^3(1 + 8z^{-1} + 3z^{-2})x(0)}{24(1 - z^{-1})^3}$
$\dfrac{1}{s^4}$	$\dfrac{T^4 z^{-1}(1 + 11z^{-1} + 11z^{-2} + z^{-3})}{24(1 - z^{-1})^4}$	$\dfrac{T^4(1 + 26z^{-1} + 66z^{-2} + 26z^{-3} + z^{-4})}{120(1 - z^{-1})^4} - \dfrac{T^4(1 + 22z^{-1} + 33z^{-2} + 4z^{-3})x(0)}{120(1 - z^{-1})^4}$
$\dfrac{1}{s^5}$	$\dfrac{T^5 z^{-1}(1 + 26z^{-1} + 66z^{-2} + 26z^{-3} + z^{-4})}{120(1 - z^{-1})^5}$	$\dfrac{T^5(1 + 57z^{-1} + 302z^{-2} + 302z^{-3} + 57z^{-4} + z^{-5})}{720(1 - z^{-1})^5} - \dfrac{T^5(1 + 52z^{-1} + 198z^{-2} + 104z^{-3} + 5z^{-4})x(0)}{720(1 - z^{-1})^5}$

Using only the first three terms on the right side of equations (7.2a) and (7.3) and neglecting the remainder terms, we obtain the following relationship:

$$\mathscr{Y}_a(z) = \mathscr{X}(z)\mathscr{Z}[Q_2 G] + \frac{x(0)}{1 - z^{-1}}\{\mathscr{Z}[Q_0 G] - \mathscr{Z}[Q_2 G]\}$$

$$+ \frac{x'(0)Tz^{-1}}{(1 - z^{-1})^2}\{\mathscr{Z}[Q_1 G] - \mathscr{Z}[Q_2 G]\} \quad (7.4)$$

As an illustration, if we let $G(s) = 1/s$, then from (7.4) and from Table 7.1 we obtain

$$\mathscr{Y}_a(z) = \mathscr{X}(z)\frac{T(1 + 4z^{-1} + z^{-2})}{3(1 + z^{-1})(1 - z^{-1})}$$

$$+ \frac{x(0)}{1 - z^{-1}}\left[\frac{Tz^{-1}}{1 - z^{-1}} - \frac{T(1 + 4z^{-1} + z^{-2})}{3(1 + z^{-1})(1 - z^{-1})}\right]$$

$$+ \frac{x'(0)Tz^{-1}}{(1 - z^{-1})^2}\left\{\frac{T(1 + z^{-1})}{2(1 - z^{-1})} - \frac{T(1 + 4z^{-1} + z^{-2})}{3(1 + z^{-1})(1 - z^{-1})}\right\}$$

$$(7.5)$$

Combining these expressions, we finally obtain the quadratic operator of $1/s$ with initial conditions as follows:

$$\mathscr{Y}_a(z) = \mathscr{X}(z)\frac{T(1 + 4z^{-1} + z^{-2})}{3(1 + z^{-1})(1 - z^{-1})}$$

$$- \frac{x(0)T(1 + 2z^{-1})}{3(1 + z^{-1})(1 - z^{-1})} + \frac{x'(0)T^2 z^{-1}}{6(1 - z^{-1})(1 + z^{-1})} \quad (7.6)$$

which is seen to be identical to the entry in Table 7.3 for $1/s$.

Similarly, we can obtain the linear or higher-order interpolation as the situation requires. Table 7.2 gives zero-order normal and linear interpolations [using only Q_0 and Q_1 terms in equation (7.3)] for $G(s)$ up to $1/s^5$. These are also known as point slope and trapezoidal rule interpolations. Table 7.3 lists these forms of $G(s)$ for quadratic (Simpson's rule) interpolation.

EXAMPLE 1

In this example we apply Table 7.1 to a linear system described by the following differential equation with constant coefficients:

$$\frac{d^2 x}{dt^2} + 3\frac{dx}{dt} + 2x = 4u(t) \quad (7.7)$$

TABLE 7.3　INTEGRATING OPERATORS (quadratic interpolation[4])

$\dfrac{1}{s}$	$\dfrac{T(1 + 4z^{-1} + z^{-2})}{3(1 + z^{-1})(1 - z^{-1})} - \dfrac{T(1 + 2z^{-1})x(0)}{3(1 + z^{-1})(1 - z^{-1})} + \dfrac{T^2 z^{-1} x'(0)}{6(1 + z^{-1})(1 - z^{-1})}$
$\dfrac{1}{s^2}$	$\dfrac{T^2(1 + 10z^{-1} + z^{-2})}{12(1 - z^{-1})^2} - \dfrac{T^2(1 + 5z^{-1})x(0)}{12(1 - z^{-1})^2} + \dfrac{T^3 z^{-1} x'(0)}{12(1 - z^{-1})^3}$

$$\frac{1}{s^3} \quad \frac{T^3(1 + 26z^{-1} + 66z^{-2} + 26z^{-3} + z^{-4})}{60(1 + z^{-1})(1 - z^{-1})^3}$$

$$- \frac{T^3(1 + 17z^{-1} + 33z^{-2} + 9z^{-3})x(0)}{60(1 + z^{-1})(1 - z^{-1})^3}$$

$$+ \frac{T^4 z^{-1}(3 + 14z^{-1} + 3z^{-2})x'(0)}{(1 + z^{-1})(1 - z^{-1})^3}$$

$$\frac{1}{s^4} \quad \frac{T^4(1 + 56z^{-1} + 246z^{-2} + 56z^{-3} + z^{-4})}{360(1 - z^{-1})^4}$$

$$- \frac{T^4(1 + 42z^{-1} + 123z^{-2} + 14z^{-3})x(0)}{360(1 - z^{-1})^4}$$

$$+ \frac{T^5 z^{-1}(1 + 13z^{-1} + z^{-2})x'(0)}{180(1 - z^{-1})^4}$$

$$\frac{1}{s^5} \quad \frac{T^5(1 + 120z^{-1} + 1191z^{-2} + 2416z^{-3} + 1191z^{-4} + 120z^{-5} + z^{-6})}{2520(1 + z^{-1})(1 - z^{-1})^5}$$

$$- \frac{T^5(1 + 100z^{-1} + 724z^{-2} + 1208z^{-3} + 467z^{-4} + 20z^{-5})x(0)}{2520(1 + z^{-1})(1 - z^{-1})^5}$$

$$+ \frac{T^6 z^{-1}(5 + 176z^{-1} + 478z^{-2} + 176z^{-3} + 5z^{-4})x'(0)}{5040(1 + z^{-1})(1 - z^{-1})^5}$$

where $u(t)$ is a unit step and the given initial conditions are $x(0) = 3$, $x'(0) = -4$. The following steps are indicated for the solution.

1. Apply the Laplace transform to equation (7.7) and divide by s^2 (in general, by s^n, where n is the order of the equation) to get

$$\left(1 + \frac{3}{s} + \frac{2}{s^2}\right)X(s) = \frac{4}{s^3} + \frac{5}{s^2} + \frac{3}{s} \tag{7.8}$$

2. Substitute integrating operators for the left side. In this case we choose quadratic operators from Table 7.3. We note equation (7.1g) and apply the z-transform to the right side of equation (7.8) by using Table II or Table I of the Appendix.

3. Carry out the algebraic manipulation to bring the form of $\mathscr{X}_a(z)$ to a ratio of two polynomials in z^{-1} as follows

$$\mathscr{X}_a(z) = \frac{\begin{array}{l}(18 + 18T + 3T^2) + (-18 + 30T + 39T^2 + 4T^3)z^{-1} \\ \quad + (-18 - 54T - 3T^2)z^{-2} \\ \quad\quad + (18 + 6T + 9T^2 - 4T^3)z^{-3}\end{array}}{\begin{array}{l}(6 + 6T + T^2) + (-12 + 12T + 10T^2)z^{-1} \\ \quad + (-36T)z^{-2} + (12 + 12T - 10T^2)z^{-3} \\ \quad\quad + (-6 + 6T - T^2)z^{-4}\end{array}}$$

(7.8a)

4. Choose a certain T; let $T = 0.1$. The initial choice of T will be discussed later. Divide the numerator by denominator to obtain an expression in powers of z^{-1}. We then obtain

$$\mathscr{X}_a(z) = 3.00 + 2.646z^{-1} + 2.373z^{-2} + 2.164z^{-4} + \ldots \quad (7.9)$$

The coefficients of z^{-n} yield the time response at the sampling instants. By use of the modified z-transform, we can extend the preceding methods to obtain the response between the sampling instants if desired.

EXAMPLE 2

To illustrate the application of the z-transform method to the approximate analysis of continuous feedback system,[1] consider the system shown in Fig. 7.4 where

$$G_1(s) = \frac{s + 0.3}{s^2}, \quad (7.10)$$

and

$$e^{-\Delta s} \Delta = 1 = e^{-s} \quad (7.11)$$

This example has been analyzed exactly for ramp input in Section 2.3. In this discussion we shall compare the approximate response with the exact one at the sampling instants.

If the ramp response is determined by analyzing the sampled-data system shown in Fig. 7.5, the first step is to choose an approximate sampling period. The Laplace transform of the output is $R(s)$ times the

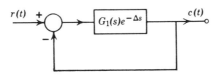

FIGURE 7.4   Continuous closed-loop system with delay.

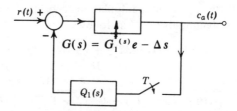

FIGURE 7.5   Sampled-data system approximation of Fig. 7.4.

overall transfer function; therefore, for a unit ramp input,

$$C(s) = \frac{(s + 0.3)e^{-s}}{s^2[s^2 + (s + 0.3)e^{-s}]} \qquad (7.12)$$

The relative real-frequency composition of the output can be obtained by replacing s by $j\omega$ in equation (7.12), which yields

$$C(j\omega) = \frac{(j\omega + 0.3)e^{-j\omega}}{-\omega^2[-\omega^2 + (j\omega + 0.3)e^{-j\omega}]} \qquad (7.13)$$

As will be explained in Section 7.5, for obtaining an initial value of T, we let $|C(j\omega)|$ be approximately 0.01 or about −40 db. Thus equating the absolute amplitude of $C(j\omega)$ to 0.01 yields

$$|C(j\omega)| = \frac{|j\omega + 0.3| \, |e^{-j\omega}|}{|-\omega^2| \, |-\omega^2 + (j\omega + 0.3)e^{-j\omega}|} = 0.01 \qquad (7.14)$$

An exact solution of equation (7.14) could be difficult, especially in complicated systems. Fortunately, an exact solution is not necessary since any convenient ω yielding an absolute value near 0.01 will be satisfactory. Such a ω can be obtained by recognizing that for large ω equation (7.14) becomes approximately

$$|C(j\omega)| \cong \frac{1}{\omega^3} = 0.01 \qquad (7.15)$$

from which an upper frequency limit of 4.64 radians per second is obtained. Evaluation of equation (7.14) for ω equal to 4.64 yields an absolute value of $C(j\omega)$ of 0.0128, and therefore the approximation made in equation (7.14) is satisfactory. As explained in Section 7.5, a sampling frequency of twice 4.64 radians per second (twice because of the sampling theorem) corresponds to a sampling period of 0.675. This sampling period can be used, but a T of 0.5 seconds is more convenient (also more accurate) since the delay is 1 second. It is not necessary for the delay to be an integer value of the sampling period since a sampled-data system can be analyzed for any arbitrary delay.

With a period of 0.5 second, the approximate transient response at the sampling instants to a ramp input can be found from the following expression, if we use the fictitious triangular hold $Q_1(s)$ in the feedback path as shown in Fig. 7.5.

$$\mathscr{C}_a(z) = \mathscr{RG}(z)\left[\frac{1}{1 + \mathscr{Q}_1\mathscr{G}(z)}\right] \tag{7.16}$$

where

$$\mathscr{RG}(z) = \mathcal{Z}[R(s)G(s)] = \frac{0.125(2.1z^2 + 0.4z - 1.9)}{2z(z - 1)^4} \tag{7.17}$$

and

$$\mathscr{Q}_1\mathscr{G}(z) = \mathcal{Z}[Q_1(s)G(s)] = \frac{0.25(2.1z^2 + 0.4z - 1.9)}{2z^2(z - 1)^2} \tag{7.18}*$$

Substitution of equations (7.17) and (7.18) into (7.16) yields

$$\mathscr{C}_a(z) = \frac{(1.05z^2 + 0.2z - 0.95)z}{(z - 1)^2(8z^4 - 16z^3 + 10.1z^2 + 0.4z - 1.9)} \tag{7.19}$$

Long division of the denominator into the numerator yields the power series

$$\begin{aligned}\mathscr{C}_a(z) = {}&0.131z^{-3} + 0.550z^{-4} + 1.26z^{-5} + 2.18z^{-6} + 3.17z^{-7} \\ &+ 4.10z^{-8} + 4.86z^{-9} + 5.41z^{-10} + 5.78z^{-11} \\ &\qquad\qquad\qquad\qquad + 6.05z^{-12} + \ldots \end{aligned} \tag{7.20}$$

The response at the sampling instants is given by the coefficients of equation (7.20) and it is noticed that it compares favorably with the exact response obtained in equation (2.60). By using the modified z-transform we may readily obtain the continuous response if desired. The accuracy may be increased by reducing T and repeating the process. A negligible error between the first and second choice makes certain that the result is within engineering approximation. This is true provided the division process is performed exactly without any approximation.

7.3 Integrating operators[2,3,27]

The interpolating schemes indicated in Fig. 7.3 represent also the integrating operators used by mathematicians in numerical analysis. These integrating operators can also be classified as follows.

(a). INTEGRATION BY RECTANGULAR RULE. Here the interpolator form is as shown in Fig. 7.3a.

---

* It may be noted that $Q_1(s) = \dfrac{(1 - e^{-Ts})^2 e^{Ts}}{Ts^2}$

(*b*). INTEGRATION BY THE TRAPEZOIDAL RULE. This is similar to linear interpolation given in Table 7.2.

(*c*). INTEGRATION BY SIMPSON'S ONE-THIRD RULE. This is similar to quadratic interpolation shown in Table 7.3.

(*d*). INTEGRATION BY SIMPSON'S THREE-EIGHTH RULE. In this case the interpolation transfer function for $1/s$ is

$$\frac{1}{s} \to \frac{3T}{8} \frac{1 + 3z^{-1} + 3z^{-2} + z^{-3}}{1 - z^{-3}} \qquad (7.21)$$

(*e*). INTEGRATION BY WEDDLE'S RULE.

$$\frac{1}{s} \to \frac{3T}{10} \frac{1 + 5z^{-1} + z^{-2} + 6z^{-3} + z^{-4} + 5z^{-5} + z^{-6}}{1 - z^{-6}} \qquad (7.22)$$

Comparison of the relative amplitude-characteristics curves of cases *b*, *c*, *d*, *e*, and the ideal integrator is shown in Fig. 7.6. It is seen that *b* is of simple form and can be used effectively because it also introduces high attenuation at high frequency, thus minimizing the effect of an external disturbance. The discussion and derivation of these integrating operators are available in any standard text on numerical analyses,[27] and thus only a brief mention for comparison is described in this section.

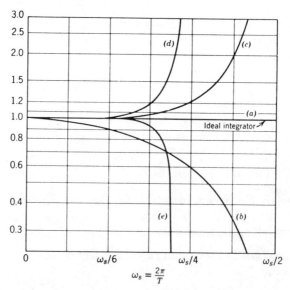

FIGURE 7.6   Relative amplitude-characteristic curves of the integration operators. (From J. M. Salzer, "Frequency Analysis of Digital Computers Operating in Real Time," *Proc. IRE*, Vol. 42, February 1954, p. 463.)

7.4 z-Forms and modified z-forms[1,6,11,23]

The z-form method of analysis is similar to the integrating operator method discussed in the preceding section. This numerical method is useful in obtaining the responses of continuous linear or nonlinear systems. It is very useful for digital-computer approach to the solution of automatic control problems. This method was proposed by Boxer and Thaler and, in recent years, Wasow[22] has put this method on a rigorous mathematical basis. We shall discuss this method both as proposed originally and with the justifications indicated by Wasow. A closely related method to the z-forms is that proposed by M. Cuenod.[7,14] The latter algorithm deals directly with the sequence $f(nT)$ as an approximation to $f(t)$, whereas the z-form deals directly with the Laplace transform, $\mathcal{L}[f(t)] = F(s)$. Wasow has

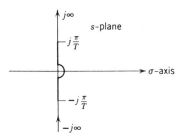

FIGURE 7.7 Path of integration in s-plane.

shown that the resulting two methods have the same accuracy as far as the order of magnitude of the error of approximation is concerned.

z-Forms relationships

The inverse Laplace transform of a rational function of s with higher-degree denominator in s than the numerator is given by the following contour integral:

$$f(t) = \mathcal{L}^{-1}[F(s)] = \frac{1}{2\pi j} \int_{c-j\infty}^{c+j\infty} F(s)e^{ts}\,ds \qquad (7.23)$$

We assume for simplicity that c is zero (that is, all poles of $F(s)$ lie in the left half of the s-plane with the permissible location of a simple pole at the origin). This condition assures that the response of a physically realizable system is bounded. The contour integration can then be performed as shown in Fig. 7.7.

Equation (7.23) can be written as the sum of the following three integrals:

$$f(t) = \frac{1}{2\pi j} \int_{-j(\pi/T)}^{j(\pi/T)} F(s)e^{ts}\,ds$$

$$+ \frac{1}{2\pi j}\left[\int_{j(\pi/T)}^{j\infty} F(s)e^{ts}\,ds - \int_{-j(\pi/T)}^{-j\infty} F(s)e^{ts}\,ds\right] \qquad (7.24)$$

If T is chosen sufficiently small, the first integral will yield a good approximation for $f(t)$, and the second and the third integrals may be ignored. The error involved in this approximation will be discussed later. Provided T is chosen very small and letting $t = nT$, we obtain

$$f(t) \cong f_a(nT) = \frac{1}{2\pi j} \int_{-j(\pi/T)}^{j(\pi/T)} F(s)e^{nTs} \, ds \qquad (7.25)$$

By substituting for $s = (1/T) \ln z$ (with $z = e^{Ts}$) in this equation and noting that by this change of variable the imaginary axis becomes the unit circle, we obtain

$$f_a(nT) = \frac{1}{2\pi j} \int_\Gamma \frac{1}{T} F\left(\frac{1}{T} \ln z\right) z^{n-1} \, dz \qquad (7.26)$$

The contour Γ is the unit circle in the z-plane. Equation (7.26) will be recognized as similar to the relation for the inverse z-transform, with the exception of the factor $1/T$. Indeed, Wasow has shown that if $F[(1/T) \ln z]$ is considered as the z-transform of $f(nT)$, the difference between the Laplace transform $F(s)$ and the z-transform $\mathscr{F}(z)$ times T (which is referred to as the Riemann sum corresponding to $\mathscr{L}$ f) can be expressed by the Euler-Maclaurin formula. A pertinent form is given.[26]

$$\mathscr{L}f - T\mathscr{Z}f = \sum_{v=1}^{m} \frac{T^v}{v!} B_v \left\{ \frac{d^{v-1}}{dt^{v-1}} [f(t)e^{-st}] \right\}_{t=0} + R_m \qquad (7.27)$$

where m is an arbitrary integer, B_v is the vth Bernoulli number, and R_m is the remainder that can be expressed by a Bernoulli polynomial. Furthermore, it can be shown that there exists a positive number A such that

$$|\mathscr{L}f - T\mathscr{Z}f| \le AT \qquad (7.28)$$

Thus the error involved in the discretization of the Laplace transform is proportional to the sampling period T. A better approximation is obtained if a refinement of the z-transformation is used as follows. Let

$$\mathscr{Z}^*f = \mathscr{Z}f - \tfrac{1}{2}f(0) \qquad (7.29)$$

Then Wasow has shown that

$$|\mathscr{L}f - T\mathscr{Z}^*f| \le A^*T^2 \qquad (7.30)$$

The transformation $\mathscr{Z}^*$ amounts to approximating the Laplace transformation by means of the trapezoidal rule.

Based on this motivation, Boxer and Thaler have proposed still another modification which as will be shown later, yields even better approximation.

It is noticed from equation (7.26) that $F[(1/T) \ln z]$ is a transcendental function of z, which makes it impossible to expand in powers of $1/z$ by synthetic division. Thus an approximation is made for $\ln z$. Of the several possible, the following approximation will be chosen:

$$\ln z = 2(u + \tfrac{1}{3}u^3 + \tfrac{1}{5}u^5 + \ldots) \tag{7.31}$$

where

$$u = \frac{1 - z^{-1}}{1 + z^{-1}} \tag{7.32}$$

The series in (7.31) converges rather rapidly and the approximation yields a minimum phase error.

In the final application of this method, $F(s)$ is expanded in descending powers of s, that is,

$$F(s) = a_1 s^{-1} + a_2 s^{-2} + a_3 s^{-3} + \ldots \tag{7.33}$$

Thus a substitution for s^{-k} is required. This can be obtained if we rewrite equation (7.31) as

$$\frac{1}{s} = \frac{T}{\ln z} = \frac{T/2}{u + u^3/3 + u^5/5 + \ldots} \tag{7.34}$$

By synthetic division, the Laurent series is obtained.

$$s^{-1} = \frac{T}{2}\left(\frac{1}{u} - \frac{u}{3} - \frac{4u^3}{45} - \frac{44\,u^5}{945} \cdots\right) \tag{7.35}$$

Series expansions of s^{-k} can be obtained by raising both sides of this equation to the kth power. Retaining the principal part and the constant term gives

$$s^{-k} \approx \frac{N_k(z^{-1})}{(1 - z^{-1})^k} = F_k(z^{-1}) \tag{7.36}$$

where N_k is a polynomial in powers of z^{-1}. These approximate expressions for s^{-k} are called z-*forms* and are given in Table 7.4. If we denote the z-forms as $T\mathscr{z}^{**}$, they are related to the z-transform as follows:

$$T\mathscr{z}^{**}\frac{t^{k-1}}{(k-1)!} = T\mathscr{z}\frac{t^{k-1}}{(k-1)!} + T^k\frac{B_k}{k!} \tag{7.37}$$

Based on these notations, Wasow has shown that

$$\left|\mathscr{L}\frac{t^{k-1}}{(k-1)!} - T\mathscr{z}^{**}\frac{t^{k-1}}{(k-1)!}\right| \leq A_k T^{k+1} \tag{7.38}$$

where A_k is a constant. Hence the z-forms or $(T\mathscr{z}^{**})$ leads to a still better approximation to the Laplace transformation for these special functions, provided $k > 1$.

In applying the z-form method to the solution of linear differential equations with constant coefficients, Wasow[22] has shown that the error

TABLE 7.4

	z-Forms
s^{-k}	$F_k(z^{-1})$
s^{-1}	$\dfrac{T}{2}\dfrac{1 + z^{-1}}{1 - z^{-1}}$
s^{-2}	$\dfrac{T^2}{12}\dfrac{1 + 10z^{-1} + z^{-2}}{(1 - z^{-1})^2}$
s^{-3}	$\dfrac{T^3}{2}\dfrac{z^{-1} + z^{-2}}{(1 - z^{-1})^3}$
s^{-4}	$\dfrac{T^4}{6}\dfrac{z^{-1} + 4z^{-2} + z^{-3}}{(1 - z^{-1})^4} - \dfrac{T^4}{720}$
s^{-5}	$\dfrac{T^5}{24}\dfrac{(z^{-1} + 11z^{-2} + 11z^{-3} + z^{-4})}{(1 - z^{-1})^5}$
s^{-6}	$\dfrac{T^6}{120}\dfrac{(z^{-1} + 26z^{-2} + 66z^{-3} + 26z^{-4} + z^{-5})}{(1 - z^{-1})^6} + \dfrac{T^6}{30{,}240}$
s^{-7}	$\dfrac{T^7}{720}\dfrac{(z^{-1} + 57z^{-2} + 302z^{-3} + 302z^{-4} + 57z^{-5} + z^{-6})}{(1 - z^{-1})^7}$
.	.
.	.
.	.
s^{-k}	$T\mathscr{F}_k(z) + \dfrac{T^k}{k!}B_k$ where $\mathscr{F}_k(z) = \mathscr{Z}\left[\dfrac{1}{s^k}\right]^{\dagger}$

magnitude between the exact solution at sampling instants $f(nT)$ and the approximate solution $f_a(nT)$ for ($n > 1$, or $t > 0$) is proportional to T^2, that is,

$$|\delta_n| = |f_a(nT) - f(nT)| \le kT^2 \tag{7.39}$$

Furthermore, if $F(s)$ is written in the following form:

$$F(s) = \frac{P(s)}{1 + Q(s)} \tag{7.40}$$

where

$$P(s) = \sum_{r=1}^{\infty} a_r s^{-r} \tag{7.41}$$

$$Q(s) = \sum_{r=1}^{\infty} b_r s^{-r} \tag{7.42}$$

and if $p(t) = \mathcal{L}^{-1}P(s)$ and $q(t) = \mathcal{L}^{-1}Q(s)$ have their first k $(k > 0)$ derivatives equal to zero at $t = 0$, then the error of approximation is proportional to T^{2+k}. This indicates that by using the z-forms a better approximation is obtained than with z-transform or its modified form $\mathscr{z}^*$.

z-Form procedure

The following steps are involved in obtaining the approximate response $f_a(nT)$ from $F(s) = \mathcal{L}[f(t)]$.

1. Express the function $F(s)$ as a rational fraction in powers of $1/s$.

2. Substitute for each s^{-k} a rational fraction in z^{-1} obtained from Table 7.4 and arrange $\mathscr{F}_a(z)$ as a rational fraction in z^{-1}.

3. Divide the resulting expression by T. The initial choice of T will be discussed later.

4. Expand the fraction as a power series by using the synthetic division or other methods to obtain

$$f_a(0T) + f_a(1T)z^{-1} + f_a(2T)z^{-2} + \ldots + f_a(nT)z^{-n} + \ldots$$
$$(7.43)$$

The coefficients $f_a(nT)$ are the approximate value of $f(t)$ at the sampling instants. To obtain the approximate response between the sampling instants, if required, the method to be discussed on p. 236 can be used.

If $F(s)$ has one degree higher denominator than the numerator in s, we can improve the degree of approximation using the z-forms by writing $F(s)$ in the following form:

$$F(s) = \frac{A}{s} + F_1(s)$$

By obtaining first the inverse Laplace transform of A/s, $Au(t)$, and then applying the z-forms into $F_1(s)$ and carrying out the procedure given, we can improve on the approximate response to $f(t)$. Finally, if initial values do exist, the z-forms could be easily modified to cover this case as well.

---

† See Table IV for higher values of k. The values of B_k are the Bernoulli numbers, some of which are given below:[26]

$$B_0 = 1,\ B_1 = -\tfrac{1}{2},\ B_2 = \tfrac{1}{6},\ B_4 = -\tfrac{1}{30},\ B_6 = \tfrac{1}{42},\ B_8 = -\tfrac{1}{30},$$
$$B_{10} = \tfrac{5}{66},\ B_{12} = -\tfrac{691}{2730},\ B_{11} = \tfrac{7}{6},\ \ldots \quad \text{with } B_{2k\,1} = 0,$$
$$\text{for } k > 0.$$

Modified z-forms[11]

As with the z-forms, we can also obtain approximate relations for the continuous response by using other relations; these relations are called modified z-forms and are derived as follows. Assume the Laplace transform of a continuous output is given as

$$F(s) = \frac{c_0 + c_1 s + c_2 s^2 + \ldots + c_n s^n}{d_0 + d_1 s + d_2 s^2 + \ldots + d_k s^k} \tag{7.44}$$

If this equation is multiplied by e^{smT}, the inverse Laplace transform will be $f(t + mT)$. By letting m vary between zero and unity, we obtain the response between the sampling instants if $f(t)$ is approximated by $f_a(nT)$ as discussed earlier.

The use of these relations requires rewriting equation (7.44) as

$$F(s) = \frac{c_0(1/s^k) + c_1(1/s^{k-1}) + \ldots + c_n(1/s^{k-n})}{d_0(1/s^k) + d_1(1/s^{k-1}) + \ldots + d_k} \tag{7.45}$$

The numerator of equation (7.45) is multiplied by the Taylor series expansion of e^{smT}; that is, by

$$e^{msT} = 1 + smT + \frac{(smT)^2}{2!} + \frac{s^3 m^3 T^3}{3!} + \ldots \tag{7.46}$$

If each term in the numerator is multiplied by the series and we carry terms that yield only the principal part plus a constant term, then

$$F(s)e^{smT}$$
$$= \frac{g_0(1/s^k, s, mT) + g_1(1/s^{k-1}, s, mT) + \ldots + g_n(1/s^{k-n}, s, mT)}{d_0(1/s^k) + d_1(1/s^{k-1}) + \ldots + d_k} \tag{7.47}$$

Substituting the z-forms for $1/s^k$, we obtain the modified z-forms.* These modified z-forms are tabulated in Table 7.5.

---

* For instance, if $F(s) = 1/s$, we have from equation (7.46),

$$F(s)e^{msT} = \frac{1}{s} + mT + s\frac{(mT)^2}{2!} + \ldots \tag{7.47a}$$

To obtain the modified z-forms, we substitute the z-forms for the first two terms to obtain

$$F(m, z) = \frac{T}{2}\frac{z+1}{z-1} + mT = \frac{T}{2}\frac{(1+2m)z + (1-2m)}{z-1}$$

TABLE 7.5 MODIFIED z-FORMS[11]

$\dfrac{1}{s^n}$	$F(m, z)$
$\dfrac{1}{s}$	$\dfrac{T}{2} \dfrac{(1 + 2m)z + (1 - 2m)}{z - 1}$
$\dfrac{1}{s^2}$	$\dfrac{T^2}{12} \dfrac{(1 + 6m + 6m^2)z^2 + (10 - 12m^2)z + (1 - 6m + 6m^2)}{(z - 1)^2}$
$\dfrac{1}{s^3}$	$\dfrac{T^3}{12} \dfrac{(m + 3m^2 + 2m^3)z^3 + (6 + 9m - 3m^2 - 6m^3)z^2 + (6 - 9m - 3m^2 + 6m^3)z + (-m + 3m^2 - m^3)}{(z - 1)^3}$

If $m \to 0$, the modified z-forms reduce to the z-forms. The accuracy of the calculations is improved if m is allowed to vary in the range $-\frac{1}{2} \le m \le \frac{1}{2}$ to obtain the total response.

The procedures to be followed using the modified z-forms are

1. The modified z-forms are substituted into the numerator of the Laplace transform expression.

2. The z-forms are substituted into the denominator of the Laplace transform expression.

3. Divide the resulting ratios of polynomials in z^{-1} by T. To obtain the time function, carry on the synthetic division method by first choosing a particular value of T.

ILLUSTRATIVE EXAMPLE FOR z-FORMS

In this example we consider the feedback control system shown in Fig. 7.8. Assume the input as a unit step, $R(s) = 1/s$; the output transform $C(s)$ is given by

$$C(s) = \frac{1}{s^3 + s^2 + s} \tag{7.48}$$

The following procedure is used to obtain the approximate response using the z-forms.

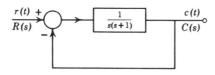

FIGURE 7.8 Continuous feedback system.

1. Divide the numerator and denominator by the highest power of s; then

$$C(s) = \frac{s^{-3}}{s^{-1} + s^{-2} + 1} \qquad (7.49)$$

2. Substitute for each term the z-form from Table 7.4 and divide by T to obtain

$$\mathscr{C}_a(z) = \frac{6T^2(z^{-1} + z^{-2})}{(12 + 6T + T^2) - (36 + 6T - 9T^2)z^{-1}} \\ + (36 - 6T - 9T^2)z^{-2} + (12 - 6T + T^2)z^{-3}$$

$$(7.50)$$

3. Choose the sampling period T on the basis of frequency response. Here T is chosen as 0.5, based on the criterion that frequency components below -30 db are negligible. Therefore $\mathscr{C}_a(z)$ becomes

$$\mathscr{C}_a(z) = \frac{1.5z^{-1} + 1.5z^{-2}}{15.25 - 36.75z^{-1} + 30.75z^{-2} - 9.25z^{-3}} \qquad (7.51)$$

4. Dividing the numerator by the denominator, we obtain the time sequence response $c_a(n)$ as the coefficient of z^{-n}. Hence

$$\mathscr{C}_a(z) = 0.0984z^{-1} + 0.335z^{-2} + 0.610z^{-3} + 0.853z^{-4} + \dots$$

$$(7.52)$$

In comparing the approximate with exact response, we would find that the difference is negligibly small.

7.5 The choice of the sampling period[1,10]

The error of approximation depends to a large extent on the sampling period. For instance, if the sampling period T is zero in the limit, the approximate system is exactly equivalent to the original system before approximation. On the other hand, if T is large, the error of approximation is increased although the number of computations required to obtain the time response is considerably less than for small T. Furthermore, if a digital computer is used in connection with z-forms, as the number of computations increases the round-off error also increases. Thus the choice of the sampling period requires a compromise between the error of approximation and the number of computations required.

The criterion for the initial choice of T is rather difficult. Several criteria are advocated, among which is the one considered here based on the frequency response of the output. For instance, if the output magnitude as a function of real frequency is written as

$$|C(j\omega)| \tag{7.53}$$

we can choose a value of frequency ω_k that gives a small value of $|C(j\omega)|$, that is, around -30 db or about 0.01. By obtaining such a frequency, then from the sampling theorem, the value of T is given by[1]

$$T = \frac{\pi}{\omega_k} \tag{7.54}$$

To obtain an approximate value of ω_k, $|C(j\omega)|$ is approximated for large ω, which avoids any exact calculations. This procedure is explained in Example 2. Another procedure for choosing T (as used in obtaining the transfer function of a system or network when both the input and the output $f_i(t)$, $f_o(t)$ are given) is based on the fact that both $f_o(t)$ and $f_i(t)$ should change on the average by about 10% of their maximum values within successive intervals of the chosen sampling time.

7.6 Analysis of the error[6,22,24,25]

The error entailed in such an approximate analysis, discussed in the preceding sections, cannot be formulated exactly. The formulation of the error bound which can be obtained for linear systems is generally quite elaborate. The error bound becomes significant only when many samples are considered, as is done in the analysis using digital computers. However, the error can be readily estimated if the sampling period is halved or subdivided to calculate a few transient terms. If by so changing the sampling period the original solution is essentially unchanged or the change is small for engineering approximation, the original solution is satisfactory. This, of course, is based on the fact that round-off error is not considered, that is, when the computation is carried on without digital computers. If the initial choice of the sampling period is unsatisfactory, this procedure has to be repeated until the change in the response is insignificant. Both Wasow[22] and Bridgland[24] have discussed the error of approximation involved in the use of the z-forms and other rules indicated earlier. The complete discussion of this subject is beyond the scope of this text.

In some cases Simpson's (quadratic) rule is numerically unstable when used for the integration of the differential equation $dy/dx = \lambda y$ when the real part of λ is negative. This is because the characteristic equation in z has a root of modulus greater than unity. The stability criterion established in Chapter 3 can be readily used to determine such a situation. To avoid such a difficulty, we may use a small interval over the initial and steep part of the response and continue with a much longer interval over the more slowly changing part. Thus the adjustable sampling interval plays an important role in minimizing the error of approximation.

7.7 Low-pass transformation for z-transforms[20,21]

In certain applications, in which the output of a linear time-invariant system $f_0(t)$ as well as its input $f_i(t)$ are given as experimental data, the z-transform method could be easily used to obtain the system transfer function $\mathscr{H}(z)$ as follows:

$$\mathscr{H}(z) = \frac{\mathscr{F}_o(z)}{\mathscr{F}_i(z)} \tag{7.55}$$

Using the synthetic division method $\mathscr{H}(z)$, the impulsive response at discrete intervals of time, can be easily determined.

The data of the input and output are usually not exact in practice but are subject to error or noise and the division method of the z-transform will yield erroneous results. Error in the series for $\mathscr{H}(z)$ is introduced if the leading (or initial) term of $\mathscr{F}_o(z)$, that is, $f_o(0)$ is much smaller than the subsequent terms.

To avoid this difficulty, the z-variable may be replaced, before performing the synthetic division, by the variable λ, where

$$\lambda + 1 = z^{-1} \tag{7.56}$$

It is done by simple substitution of $\lambda + 1$ for $1/z$, in the expressions for $\mathscr{F}_o(z)$ and $\mathscr{F}_i(z)$, followed by expansion and regrouping of terms to form a power series in λ; thus $\mathscr{F}_o(z)$ and $\mathscr{F}_i(z)$ become $\tilde{\mathscr{F}}_o(\lambda)$ and $\tilde{\mathscr{F}}_i(\lambda)$. By this process, known as low-pass transformation, the leading term of $\tilde{\mathscr{F}}_o(\lambda)$, that is, $\tilde{\mathscr{F}}_o(\lambda)|_{\lambda=0}$ is much larger and thus the division method is less sensitive to the errors in the individual terms. By dividing $\tilde{\mathscr{F}}_o(\lambda)$ by $\tilde{\mathscr{F}}_i(\lambda)$ and transforming back to the z-plane by this low-pass transformation, we readily obtain $\mathscr{H}(z)$ or the system transfer function. It should be noted that only when we consider noisy data do the advantages of λ-domain become apparent. Solution of Problem 7.3 illustrates the procedure and the advantage of this transformation. The λ-transform leads to a match for

$$H(s) = \frac{F_o(s)}{F_i(s)} \tag{7.57}$$

at low frequency, whereas the z-transform leads to a match for the system transfer function at higher frequencies and therefore exaggerates the effect of the noise. Another kind of transformation, known as the two-sided z-transform, has also been advocated for this particular case.[21] However, we shall not elaborate on this technique.

7.8 Application to time-varying differential equations[6,11]

Boxer and Thaler have advocated use of the z-forms method for the approximate solution of time-varying or nonlinear differential equations. Wasow has shown in a rigorous way the validity of this method and the underlying assumptions required to obtain a fairly good approximation. In this section, we shall briefly indicate the procedure to be applied to the following:

$$\frac{d^n}{dt^n}[f_n(t)y] + \frac{d^{n-1}}{dt^{n-1}}[f_{n-1}(t)y] + \ldots f_o(t)y = f(t) \tag{7.58}$$

where $f_n(t), f_{n-1}(t), \ldots, f_o(t)$ are functions of the independent variable t.

The procedure for the approximate solution is

1. Obtain the Laplace transform of (7.58) after substituting for $f_n(t) = c_n, \ldots, f_i(t) = c_i$ and inserting the initial condition.

2. Proceed with the division as in the constant coefficient case. However, change the values of $c_n, c_{n-1}, \ldots, c_0$ at each step in the division process to the values of the functions at the corresponding times.

The minimum limitation on the form of the functions in (7.58) is that they be Laplace transformable. The procedure for inserting the initial conditions is illustrated in Problem 7.4.

EXAMPLE

To illustrate the procedure, we choose the following example:

$$\frac{dy}{dt} + ty = t, \quad \text{with } y(0) = 0 \tag{7.59}$$

Equation (7.59) is written as

$$\frac{dy}{dt} + cy = t, \quad \text{where } c = t = nT \tag{7.60}$$

When we take the Laplace transform, considering c as constant and $y(0) = 0$,

$$Y(s) = \frac{1}{s^3 + cs^2} \tag{7.61}$$

or

$$Y(s) = \frac{s^{-3}}{1 + cs^{-1}}$$

By substituting the z-forms of Table 7.4 and dividing by T, we obtain

$$\mathscr{Y}_a(z) = \frac{T^2(z^{-1} - z^{-2})}{(2 + cT) - (6 + cT)z^{-1} + (6 - cT)z^{-2} - (2 - cT)z^{-3}} \tag{7.62}$$

Letting $T = 0.4$,

$$\mathscr{Y}_a(z) = \frac{0.16\,z^{-1} + 0.16\,z^{-2}}{(2 + 0.4\,c) - (6 + 0.4\,c)\,z^{-1} + (6 - 0.4\,c)\,z^{-2} - (2 - 0.4\,c)\,z^{-3}} \tag{7.63}$$

The long division process is carried out letting $c = 0.4$ during the first step of the division, 0.8 during the second step, and so forth, yielding

$$\mathscr{Y}_a(z) = 0.0741z^{-1} + 0.266z^{-2} + 0.503z^{-3} + 0.714z^{-4} + \ldots \tag{7.64}$$

The approximate solution can be compared with the exact solution for this example. The latter solution is

$$y = 1 - e^{-t^2/2} \tag{7.65}$$

This procedure is also applicable to differential equation of the following form if the $f_i(t)$ are slowly varying as in some physical systems.

$$f_n \frac{d^n}{dt^n} y + \ldots + f_{n-1} \frac{d^{n-1}}{dt^{n-1}} y + \ldots + f_0 y = f(t) \tag{7.66}$$

This can be justified if we notice that

$$\frac{d^n(f_n y)}{dt^n} = \sum_{k=0}^{n} \binom{n}{k} \frac{d^k f_n}{dt^k} \frac{d^{n-k} y}{dt^{n-k}} \tag{7.67}$$

where $\binom{n}{k}$ are the binomial coefficients. If f_n is slowly varying, the contributions of the derivatives of f_n are negligible, so that the approximation

$$\frac{d^n(f_n y)}{dt^n} \simeq f_n \frac{d^n y}{dt^n} \tag{7.68}$$

can be justified. It should be cautioned that with this procedure information on the stability of these equations cannot be obtained.

7.9 Application to nonlinear differential equations[9,11-13,16]

In the preceding sections the methods of integrating operators and the z-form have been applied to obtain the approximate solution of linear differential equations with or without initial conditions. In this section, the method of sequential computation, which consists in approximating a given differential equation by its discrete version, is employed. Furthermore, the method of integrating operators and the z-transform will be employed to obtain an approximate solution of a nonlinear differential equation.

EXAMPLE 1

Consider, for illustration purposes, the nonlinear differential equation

$$\frac{di}{dt} + i + i^2 = 1, \quad \text{with } i(0) = 0 \tag{7.69}$$

We approximate this equation by means of a difference equation as follows. Let

$$\frac{i_{n+1} - i_n}{T} \simeq \frac{di}{dt}, \quad \text{where } T = \text{sampling interval} \tag{7.70}$$

Then,

$$i_{n+1} - i_n + Ti_n + Ti_n^2 = T. \tag{7.71}$$

If we choose $T = 0.2$, we get

$$5i_{n+1} - 4i_n + i_n^2 = 1 \tag{7.72}$$

The series solution of this equation for $T = 0.4$ by the method of complex convolution discussed in Chapter 5 does not converge. However, we obtain a convergent solution for $T = 0.2$. The solution as a recurrence relationship compared with the exact solution of the differential equation is shown in Table 7.6.

TABLE 7.6 COMPARISON OF EXACT AND APPROXIMATE SOLUTION FOR EXAMPLE 1

$t = nT$	Recurrence Equation Solution	Exact Solution of Differential Equation
0	0	0
5	0.2230	0.217
10	0.3780	0.370
15	0.4783	0.467
20	0.5383	0.529
40	0.6093	0.606

EXAMPLE 2

In this example we employ the linear interpolation operators to solve the following nonlinear equation:

$$\frac{d^2x}{dt^2} + 2\frac{dx}{dt} + x = -0.9\frac{dv}{dt}, \quad \text{with } x(0) = 0,\ x'(0) = 1$$

where $v = f(x)$ and $v(0) = 0$ (7.73)

1. Apply the Laplace transform to equation (7.73).

$$(s^2 + 2s + 1)X(s) = -0.9[sV(s) - v(0)] + 2x(0)$$
$$+ x'(0) + sx(0) \quad (7.74)$$

2. Divide by s^2 and insert initial conditions

$$\left(1 + \frac{2}{s} + \frac{1}{s^2}\right)X(s) = -0.9\frac{V(s)}{s} + \frac{1}{s^2} \quad (7.75)$$

3. Substitute linear interpolation operators from Table 7.2 and the z-transform for $1/s^2$ in the right-hand side.

$$\mathscr{X}_a(z)\left[1 + \frac{2T(1 + z^{-1})}{2(1 - z^{-1})} + \frac{T^2}{6}\frac{(1 + 4z^{-1} + z^{-2})}{(1 - z^{-1})^2}\right]$$
$$= -0.9\mathscr{V}(z)\frac{T}{2}\frac{1 + z^{-1}}{1 - z^{-1}} + \frac{Tz^{-1}}{(1 - z^{-1})^2} \quad (7.76)$$

4. With $T = 0.4$, the regression (or difference) equation of the above transform is

$$8.56x_n - 11.36x_{n-1} + 3.76x_{n-2} = -1.08v_n + 1.08v_{n-2} + 2.4,$$

for $n = 1$, $= -1.08v_n + 1.08v_{n-2}$,   for $n > 1$ (7.77)

If we let $v_n = x_n^2$, we can solve this equation as a recurrence relationship for each value of n starting with $n = 1$ and putting $v_n = x_n^2 = 0$, for $n < 1$. The response is shown in Fig. 7.9.

In conclusion it should be pointed out that the division method using the z-forms can also be used to obtain an approximate solution of such

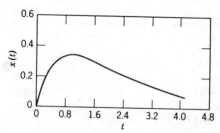

FIGURE 7.9 Response of Example 2 for initial velocity $x'(0) = 1$.

equations. This method is based on adjusting the divisor at each step of the division, as illustrated by the following example.

EXAMPLE 3

$$\frac{dy}{dt} + y^2 = 1, \qquad \text{with } y(0) = 0 \tag{7.78}$$

This equation is written as

$$\frac{dy}{dt} + cy = 1$$

where c is considered constant in this operation and adjusted at each step of the division.

The Laplace transform in powers of s^{-1} is given as

$$Y(s) = \frac{s^{-2}}{1 + cs^{-1}} \tag{7.79}$$

By substituting the z-forms and dividing by T,

$$\mathscr{Y}_a(z) = \frac{T(1 + 10z^{-1} + z^{-2})}{(12 + 6cT) - 24z^{-1} + (12 - 6cT)Z^{-2}}$$

Letting $T = 0.1$,

$$\mathscr{Y}_a(z) = \frac{0.1(1 + 10z^{-1} + z^{-2})}{(12 + 0.6c) - 24z^{-1} + (12 - 0.6c)z^{-2}} \tag{7.80}$$

Carrying out the long division and letting $c = 0$ for the step first and adjusting it after each division, we get

$$\mathscr{Y}_a(z) = 0.00833 + 0.100z^{-1} + 0.199z^{-2} + 0.295z^{-3}$$
$$+ 0.390z^{-4} + \ldots \tag{7.81}$$

The exact solution of the original equation is

$$y = \tanh t \tag{7.82}$$

The approximate solution compares favorably with the exact one. This method can be used for the approximate solution of the following differential equation:

$$\frac{d^n}{dt^n}\left[f_n\left(y, \frac{dy}{dt}, \ldots\right)y\right] + \frac{d^{n-1}}{dt^{n-1}}\left[f_{n-1}\left(y, \frac{dy}{dt}, \ldots\right)y\right]$$
$$+ \ldots + f_o\left(y, \frac{dy}{dt}, \ldots\right)y = f(t) \tag{7.83}$$

with

$$c_i = f_i\left(y, \frac{dy}{dt}, \ldots\right) \tag{7.84}$$

We proceed for the approximation as in the constant coefficient case. However, in performing the long division process, we change the values of $c_n, \ldots, c_0$ at each step in the division process to the most recent values available of $c_i = f_i\left(y, \dfrac{dy}{dt}, \ldots\right)$.

7.10 Other numerical techniques[8,9,14,17-19]

To obtain an exhaustive study of all the numerical techniques is beyond the scope of these discussions, and can be readily studied in any of the standard books on numerical analysis. In this chapter, we have used several of the integrating operators which are closely related to the subject matter, that is, the z-transform method. The main emphasis has been in using these to solve systems (linear or nonlinear) which are usually encountered in engineering applications. Rigorous application of the theory to approximation problems in mathematical terms is not attempted. In trying to limit the discussion, it was necessary to ignore other numerical techniques. Among those not discussed in detail are the works of Madwed,[9] Cuénod,[7,14] Tustin,[8] and Heizman et al.[13] However, the techniques discussed are closely related to these and other methods.

The main emphasis of these numerical techniques is to obtain approximate solutions for systems in which exact solutions in a closed form are not possible. This is often true in a complicated nonlinear or time-varying continuous system. It is for solving such problems that this method could be advantageously used. Furthermore, the use of digital computers to solve differential equations requires the formulation of the problem in terms of difference equations. Hence the z-transform method plays an important part in obtaining an approximate solution.

REFERENCES

1. Jury, E. I., *Sampled Data Control Systems*, John Wiley and Sons, New York, 1958.

2. Ragazzini, J. R., and G. F. Franklin, *Sampled-Data Control Systems*, McGraw-Hill Book Co., New York, 1958.

3. Tou, J. T., *Digital and Sampled-Data Control Systems*, McGraw-Hill Book Co., New York, 1959.

4. Cruickshank, A. J. O., "Time Series and Z-Transform Methods of Analysis of Linear and Nonlinear Control Systems," *Automatic and Remote Control, Proc. of First Int. IFAC Congress*, Moscow, 1960, Butterworths, London, 1961, pp. 277–285.

5. Robertson, H. H., Discussion of Reference (4), p. 285.

6. Boxer, R., and S. Thaler, "A Simplified Method for Solving Linear and Nonlinear Systems," *Prod. Inst. Radio Engineers*, Vol. 44, 1956, p. 89.

7. Cuénod, M., "Contribution à L'etude de Phénoménes Transitoires à l'aide des Suites de Temps," *Bull. Tech. Suisse rom.*, Vol. 75, 1949, p. 201.

8. Tustin, A., "A Method of Analysing the Effect of Certain Kinds of Nonlinearity in Closed Cycle Control Systems," *J. Inst. Elect. Engrs.*, Vol. 94, Part II, 1947, p. 152.

9. Madwed, A., "Numerical Analysis by the Number Series Transformation Method," *Proceedings Symposium on Nonlinear Circuit Analysis*, New York, 1953, Edwards Publishing Company, Ann Arbor, Michigan, p. 320.

10. Truxal, J. G., "Numerical Analysis for Network Design," *Proceeding Institute of Radio Engineers*, Professional Group on Circuit Theory, CT-1, 1954, p. 49.

11. Boxer, R., and S. Thaler, "Extension of Numerical Transform Theory," Report RADC-TR-56-115, Rome Air Development Center, New York.

12. Naumov, B. N., "Eine Näherungmethode zur Berechnung der Übergangsprozesse in Selbsttätigen Regelungssystemen mit nichtlinearen Elementen," *Rep. Conf. Automatic Control*, Heidelberg, 1956, Oldenbourg, Munich, 1956, p. 184.

13. Heizman, C., J. Millman, and A. Vagant, "Comparison of the X-Transform Method with Other Numerical Methods," Technical Report T-8/C, E. R. L., Columbia University Engineering Center, New York, September, 1956.

14. Cuénod, M., "Principe de L'analyse impulsionelle et de son application à la Theorie des Servo-méchanismes," *Onde élect.* Vol. 37, 1957, p. 723.

15. Jury, E. I., and F. J. Mullin, "A Note on the Operational Solution of Linear Difference Equations," *J. Franklin Inst.*, Vol. 266, 1958, p. 189.

16. Mishkin, E., M. S. Goldstein, and J. G. Truxal, "Nonlinear Feedback Systems with Sampling," Research Report R-450-55, PIB-380, Polytechnic Institute of Brooklyn, New York.

17. Hellman, O., "On the Iterative Solution of the Equations of a Single-Loop System with One Non-linearity," *J. Electronics and Control*, Vol. 6, 1959, p. 186.

18. Brown, B. M., *The Mathematical Theory of Linear Systems*, John Wiley and Sons, New York, 1961.

19. Raymond, F. H., "Regimes Transitoires et Techniques des Impulsions," *Onde Eletriques*, Vol. 28, 1948, p. 222.

20. Huggins, W. H., "A Low Pass Transformation for Z-Transforms," *IRE Trans. Circuit Theory*, Vol. 1, September, 1954, pp. 69–70.

21. Thomson, W. E., "On Two Sided Z-Transform," *IRE Trans. Circuit Theory*, Vol. 3, June 1956, p. 156.

22. Wasow, W., "Discrete Approximation to the Laplace Transformation," *Z. angew. Math. u. Phys.*, Vol. 8, 1957 pp. 401–407.

23. Boxer, R., "A Note onNumerical Transform Calculus," *Proc. IRE*, Vol. 45, 1957.

24. Bridgland, T. F., Jr., "A Note on Numerical Integrating Operators," *J. Soc. Industrial and Appl. Math.*, Vol. 6, No. 3, September 1958, pp. 240–256.

25. Gibson, J. E., *Nonlinear Automatic Control*, McGraw-Hill Book Co., New York, 1963.

26. Jordan, C., *Calculus of Finite Differences*, Chelsea Publishing Co., New York (2nd Ed.), 1960.

27. Scarborough, J. B., *Numerical Mathematical Analysis*, The Johns Hopkins Press, Baltimore, 1958, Chapter 7.

28. Salzer, J. M., "Frequency Analysis of Digital Computers Operating in Real Time," *Proc. IRE*, Vol. 42, No. 2, 1954, pp. 457–466.

29. Weiss, L., and R. N. McDonough, "Prony's Method, Z-Transforms, and Padé Approximation," *SIAM Rev.*, Vol. 5, No. 2, April 1963, pp. 145–149.

8

APPLICATIONS TO VARIOUS

AREAS OF SYSTEM THEORY

In the preceding chapters the z-transform theory has been extensively discussed and developed. Several examples from physical systems were considered to indicate the applications of the theory.

This chapter is concerned mainly with the application of the material developed. The examples chosen show the wide spectrum of application of the z-transform method. To limit the material, only six examples are discussed in detail. The problems section at the end of the book will give the reader a greater indication of the extensive applications.

The examples are chosen from the following areas of system theory: sampled-data feedback systems,[1,2,5] antenna theory,[7–9] economic systems,[11–13] information and filtering theory,[27–32] sequential circuits,[14–17] and finite-state Markov processes.[18–20] The examples are formulated mainly in terms of difference equations, both linear and nonlinear, and the z-transform with the other theorems developed earlier are used to obtain the required solutions.

8.1 Nonlinear sampled-data feedback systems[3,5,6,23]

Because the later examples are concerned for the most part with linear theory, it is advisable for the sake of completeness to choose a saturating-type, nonlinear sampled-data system as an illustration. In the following discussion the convolution z-transform theory discussed in Chapters 4 and 5 will be applied to a second-order nonlinear system.[5]

Consider the sampled-data system shown in Fig. 8.1, where the non-linearity consists of a saturating amplifier in the feed-forward path. We will obtain the response of this system using the convolution z-transform.

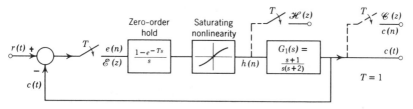

FIGURE 8.1 Nonlinear sampled-data feedback system.

We now derive the difference equation of the system. Since $h(n)$ is constant over a sampling interval (in view of the zero-order hold), we obtain the pulse transfer function for the linear part as

$$\mathcal{G}(z) = \mathcal{Z}\left[\frac{1 - e^{-Ts}}{s}G_1(s)\right] = \frac{0.716z - 0.284}{z^2 - 1.135z + 0.135} = \frac{\mathcal{C}(z)}{\mathcal{H}(z)}$$

(8.1)

This equation gives the following difference equation:

$$c(n + 2) - 1.135c(n + 1) + 0.135c(n) = 0.716h(n + 1)$$
$$- 0.284h(n) \quad (8.2)$$

Now $h(n)$ is given as

$$h(n) = \begin{cases} 40 & e(n) \geq 40 \\ e(n) & -40 \leq e(n) \geq 40 \\ -40 & e(n) \leq -40 \end{cases} \quad (8.3)$$

The power series representation of this nonlinearity over $-65 \leq e(n) \leq 65$ is

$$h(n) = 1.111e(n) - 0.1234 \times 10^{-3}e(n)^3 \quad (8.4)$$

From Fig. 8.1 we note

$$e(n) = r(n) - c(n) \quad (8.5)$$

By substituting for $e(n)$ in equation (8.4) from equation (8.5) and inserting the results in equation (8.2), we obtain

$$c(n + 2) - 1.135c(n + 1) + 0.135c(n)$$
$$= 0.795[r(n + 1) - c(n + 1)] - 0.0884 \times 10^{-3}$$
$$\times [r(n + 1)^3 - c(n + 1)^3 + 3r(n + 1)c(n + 1)^2$$
$$- 3r(n + 1)^2c(n + 1)] - 0.316[r(n) - c(n)] + 0.035$$
$$\times 10^{-3}[r(n)^3 - c(n)^3 + 3r(n)c(n)^2 - 3r(n)^2c(n)] \quad (8.6)$$

If we assume that $r(n) = 60u(n)$, where $u(n)$ is a unit step function, then $r(n + k) = r(n)$ and equation (8.6) becomes

$$c(n + 2) - 1.295c(n + 1) + 0.197c(n) + 10^{-3}$$
$$\times [-6.3c(n)^2 + 15.9c(n + 1)^2 - 0.0884c(n + 1)^3$$
$$+ 0.035c(n)^3] = 0.2865 \times 60u(n) \quad (8.7)$$

If the system is stable around the equilibrium point as assumed, then $\mathscr{C}(z)$ can be written in the form

$$\mathscr{C}(z) = \sum_{\alpha=0}^{\infty} \frac{A}{1 - a_\alpha z^{-1}}, \quad (8.8)$$

$$a_0 = 1 > |a_1| > |a_2| > |a_3| > |a_4|, \ldots \quad (8.9)$$

where a_α for $\alpha \geq 3$ is of the form $a_1^\gamma \, a_2^\delta$, where γ, δ are positive integers (including zero) and $\gamma + \delta \geq 2$.

Taking the z-transform of equation (8.7), we obtain

$$\mathscr{C}(z) + \frac{(15.9z - 6.3)}{z^2 - 1.295z + 0.197} \{\mathscr{Z}[c(n)^2] - 0.00555\mathscr{Z}[c(n)]^3\}$$

$$= (0.2865) \frac{60z}{z - 1}$$

$$+ \frac{c(0)(z^2 - 1.295z) + zc(1) + (15.9)10^{-3}zc(0)^2 - 10^{-3}(0.0884)zc(0)^3}{z^2 - 1.295z + 0.197} \quad (8.10)$$

The demoninator of the last term of this equation can be written

$$z^2 - 1.295z + 0.197 = (z - a_1')(z - a_2') \quad (8.11)$$

where

$$a_1' = 1.12, \qquad a_2' = 0.175 \quad (8.11a)$$

That $|a_1'| > 1$ should not be of concern because it is due to simplification of terms of the form $r(n + 1)c(n + 1)^2$ to $60c(n + 1)^2$ and $r(n + 1)^2c(n + 1)$ to $3600 \, c(n + 1)$. This stems from the fact that $r(n + k) = r(n) = 60$.

From equation (8.8) we assume the following solution for $\mathscr{C}(z)$:

$$\mathscr{C}(z) = \frac{A_0}{1 - z^{-1}} + \frac{A_1}{1 - a_1 z^{-1}} + \frac{A_2}{1 - a_2 z^{-1}} + \frac{A_{20}}{1 - a_1^2 z^{-1}}$$

$$+ \frac{A_{30}}{1 - a_1^3 z^{-1}} + \ldots + \frac{A_{02}}{1 - a_2^2 z^{-1}} + \frac{A_{03}}{1 - a_2^3 z^{-1}}$$

$$+ \ldots + \frac{A_{11}}{1 - a_1 a_2 z^{-1}} + \frac{A_{21}}{1 - a_1^2 a_2 z^{-1}}$$

$$+ \frac{A_{12}}{1 - a_1 a_2^2 z^{-1}} + \ldots \quad (8.12)$$

Similarly, from equation (8.8), the z-transforms of $c(n)^2$ and $c(n)^3$ can be written as

$$\mathcal{Z}[c(n)^2] = \frac{A_0^2}{1 - z^{-1}} + \frac{2A_0A_1}{1 - a_1z^{-1}} + \frac{2A_0A_2}{1 - a_2z^{-1}} + \frac{2A_0A_{20} + A_1^2}{1 - a_1^2z^{-1}}$$

$$+ \frac{2A_0A_{30} + 2A_1A_{20}}{1 - a_1^3z^{-1}} + \frac{2A_0A_2 + A_2^2}{1 - a_2^2z^{-1}} + \cdots$$

$$+ \frac{2A_0A_{11} + 2A_1A_2}{1 - a_1a_2z^{-1}} + \frac{2A_0A_{21} + 2A_2A_{20} + 2A_1A_{11}}{1 - a_1^2a_2z^{-1}}$$

$$+ \cdots \tag{8.13}$$

and

$$\mathcal{Z}[c(n)^3] = \frac{A_0^3}{1 - z^{-1}} + \frac{3A_0^2A_1}{1 - az_1^{-1}} + \frac{3A_0^2A_2}{1 - a_2z^{-1}}$$

$$+ \frac{3A_0^2A_{20} + 3A_0A_1^2}{1 - a_1^2z^{-1}} + \cdots + \frac{3A_0^2A_{02} + 3A_0A_2^2}{1 - a_2^2z^{-1}} + \cdots$$

$$+ \frac{3A_0^2A_{21} + 3A_1^2A_2 + 6A_0A_{20}A_2}{1 - a_1^2a_2z^{-1}}$$

$$+ \frac{3A_0^2A_{11} + 6A_0A_1A_2}{1 - a_1a_2z^{-1}} + \cdots \tag{8.14}$$

Substitute equations (8.12 through 8.14) into equation (8.10) and compare coefficients of like terms of $z/(z - a_1^\gamma a_2^\delta)$, γ, $\delta = 0, 1, 2, \ldots$. The steady-state amplitude is given by

$$A_0 + \frac{(15.9 - 6.3)10^{-3}(A_0^2 - 0.00555A_0^3)}{1.197 - 1.295} = (0.2865)60 \tag{8.15}$$

which gives $A_0 = 60$. This is expected since the system is stable and the steady-state error is zero. Comparison of coefficients of $z/(z - a_1)$, $z/(z - a_2)$ yields

$$A_{1,2}\{a_{1,2}^2 - 1.295a_{1,2} + 0.197 + (15.9a_{1,2} - 6.3)(60)10^{-3}\} = 0 \tag{8.16}$$

For a nontrivial solution of A_1 and A_2 we must have the term inside the parentheses in equation (8.16) equal to zero, that is,

$$a_{1,2}^2 - 0.34a_{1,2} - 0.181 = 0 \tag{8.17}$$

or

$$a_1 = 0.6275$$
$$a_2 = -0.2872 \tag{8.18}$$

Comparison of coefficients of other terms gives

$$A_{30} = (0.0645)10^{-3}A_1; \qquad A_{03} = (0.215)10^{-3}A_2^3,$$
$$A_{50} = (0.0249)10^{-6}A_1^5$$
$$A_{70} = (0.0143)10^{-9}A_1^3, \qquad A_{05} = (0.1265)10^{-6}A_2^5,$$
$$A_{21} = (1.04)10^{-3}A_1^2A_2 \quad (8.19)$$
$$A_{41} = (0.84)10^{-6}A_1^4A_2; \qquad A_{61} = (0.61)10^{-9}A_1^6A_2;$$
$$A_{12} = (0.465)10^{-3}A_1A_2^2$$
$$A_{14} = (0.511)10^{-6}A_1A_2^4, \ldots$$

Next, we consider the coefficient of terms $z/(z - a_1')$, $z/(z - a_2')$, where a_1' and a_2' are given in equation (8.11a). We then obtain the two relations

$$20 + \frac{60A_1}{492.5} + \frac{60A_2}{1407.2} - \frac{A_{30}}{33.4} + \frac{A_{50}}{60.5} + \frac{A_{03}}{33.5} + \frac{A_{05}}{35.4} + \frac{A_{21}}{28}$$

$$+ \frac{A_{41}}{31.7} + \frac{A_{12}}{44} + \frac{A_{14}}{36.3} + \frac{A_{70}}{39.8} + \frac{A_{01}}{34.2} + \cdots$$

$$= \left\{ \frac{(0.2865)60}{0.12} + c(0)(1.12 - 1.295) + c(1) \right.$$
$$\left. + [15.9c(0)^2 - (0.0884)c(0)^3]10^{-3} \right\} \frac{1}{11.5} \quad (8.20)$$

and

$$-2.91 - \frac{60A_1}{452.5} + \frac{60A_2}{462.2} + \frac{A_{30}}{2.76} + \frac{A_{50}}{4.6} + \frac{A_{03}}{5.81} + \frac{A_{21}}{6.55}$$

$$+ \frac{A_{41}}{5.97} + \cdots = \left\{ \frac{(0.2865)60}{-0.825} + c(0)(0.175 - 1.295) \right.$$
$$\left. + c(1)[15.9c(0)^2 - 0.0884c(0)^3]10^{-3} \right\} \frac{1}{-3.52} \quad (8.21)$$

Using relations (8.19), we reduce the preceding two equations into two nonlinear relations in A_1 and A_2. The series on the left side of equations (8.20) and (8.21) must be absolutely convergent. For this problem, we know $c(0) = 0$; therefore $e(0) = 60$ and $h(0) = 40$. Also we know that $c(-1) = h(-1) = 0$, so from equation (8.2) with $n = -1$ we get $c(1) = 28.6$. A few trial values of A_1 and A_2 (A_1 and A_2 initially chosen around linear solution values) indicate divergence of the series. This indicates that the initial values are far away from the steady-state value (equilibrium point). However, if the time axis is shifted by one integer value (sampling interval), we must use the new values of $c(0) = 28.6$ and $c(1) = 43.6$, the latter being calculated from equation (8.2) by using the difference equation as recurrence relation. It should be pointed out that since this shifting can always be used in such cases, a more rapid convergence is obtainable.

A similar modification does not exist in the application of Laplace transform convolution to nonlinear differential equations. By this time axis shifting, convergence is obtained with the right-hand side of equations (8.20) and (8.21) now equal to -3.26 and 2.5, respectively. Numerical values obtained for the various coefficients are

$$A_1 = -26, \; A_2 = -1.4, \; A_3 = -1.13, \; A_{50} = -0.298,$$
$$A_{70} = -0.115, \; A_{21} = -0.985, \; A_{41} = -0.54, \; A_{61} = -0.265,$$
$$A_{12} = -0.0239 \ldots \quad (8.22)$$

The z-transform of $c(n)$ for $n \geq 1$ can now be written from equation (8.12), using the calculated A's and a's:

$$\mathcal{C}(z) = \frac{60}{1 - z^{-1}} - \frac{26}{1 - 0.6275z^{-1}} - \frac{1.4}{1 + 0.2872z^{-1}}$$
$$- \frac{1.13}{1 - 0.247z^{-1}} - \frac{0.298}{1 - 0.0974z^{-1}} - \frac{0.115}{1 - 0.038z^{-1}}$$
$$- \frac{0.985}{1 + 0.1131z^{-1}} - \frac{0.54}{1 + 0.0445z^{-1}} - \frac{0.265}{1 + 0.0175z^{-1}}$$
$$- \frac{0.0239}{1 - 0.0518z^{-1}} \ldots \quad (8.23)$$

The output $c(n)$ for $n \geq 1$ is readily obtained from the inverse z-transform of equation (8.23).

$$c(n) = 60 - 26(0.6275)^n - 1.4(-0.2872)^n - 1.13(0.247)^n$$
$$- 0.298(0.0974)^n - 0.115(0.038)^n - 0.985(-0.1131)^n$$
$$- 0.54(-0.0445)^n - 0.265(-0.0175)^n$$
$$- 0.0239(0.0518)^n \ldots \quad n \geq 1 \quad (8.24)$$

A comparison between the response of equation (8.24) and that obtained by using equation (8.7) as a recurrence relation is tabulated in Table 8.1. Agreement is satisfactory and could be improved if higher terms are considered.

This example has demonstrated that the convolution z-transform can be systematically applied to the solution of higher-order discrete systems. However, the computation becomes exceedingly involved as the order increases. In practical cases for obtaining the response for a few sampling intervals, the difference equation yields the response if used as a recurrence relationship. Where convergence is rapid by choosing the appropriate initial values, the equation for $c(n)$ consists only of a few terms or response modes. This facilitates the synthesis procedure by obtaining a system modification to cancel the troublesome modes in the response. It is from this viewpoint and for obtaining the response for larger n that the convolution z-transform procedure becomes very important. Thus the system designer should possess all the possible methods of solutions so that he can use his judgment as to the method best suited to his problem.

TABLE 8.1 COMPARISON OF EXACT AND APPROXIMATE RESPONSES

n	Convolution z-Transform	Recurrence Relationship
0	—	28.6
1	43.88	43.31
2	49.56	49.32
3	53.596	53.43
4	55.96	55.88
5	57.47	57.45
6	58.415	58.43
.	.	.
.	.	.
.	.	.

8.2 Analysis of discrete antenna array by z-transform method[8,9]

In this section, a discrete linear array will be treated as a sampled-data system and thus the z-transform method is readily applicable. Using this method we may express the array polynomial in a closed form, even for nonuniform arrays. Furthermore, the analysis of the important characteristics of the radiation pattern and other useful characteristics can be conveniently performed using the z-transform theory. This is explained in the following.

Consider the linear array of n equally spaced, identical elements in Fig. 8.2. The polynomial associated with such an array can be expressed

$$\mathcal{E}(z) = a_0 + a_1 z^{-1} + a_2 z^{-2} + \ldots + a_{n-1} z^{-(n-1)} = \sum_{k=0}^{n-1} a_k z^{-k}$$

where

$$(8.25)$$

$$z = e^{-j\psi}$$

$$\psi = \beta d \cos \phi + \alpha$$

$$\beta = \frac{2\pi}{\lambda} = \text{phase constant} \qquad (8.26)$$

and α represents the progressive phase lead of the excitation in an element compared to that with its neighbor on the left.

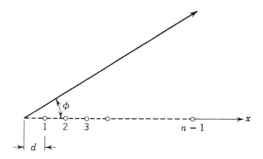

FIGURE 8.2   A linear array of n equally spaced elements.

The coefficients $a_0, a_1, \ldots, a_{n-1}$ represent the excitation of the elements. For most practical arrays, a progressive phase shift α exists along the array and the a-coefficients are used. When all the a's are equal, a uniform array results.

Suppose that the envelope of the amplitude distribution of the excitation in the n-element array can be described by a continuous function $f(x)$ within the range $0 \leq x < (n-1)d$. Then the a-coefficients in equation (8.25) can be written as

$$a_0 = f(0)$$
$$a_1 = f(d)$$
$$\cdot$$
$$\cdot$$
$$\cdot$$
$$a_{n-1} = f[(n-1)d] \tag{8.27}$$

and the array polynomial of equation (8.25) becomes

$$\mathcal{E}(z) = f(0) + f(d)z^{-1} + \ldots f[(n-1)d]z^{-(n-1)}$$
$$= \sum_{k=0}^{n-1} f(kd)z^{-k} \tag{8.28}$$

This can be written also as

$$\mathcal{E}(z) = \sum_{k=0}^{\infty} f(kd)z^{-k} - \sum_{k=n}^{\infty} f(kd)z^{-k} \tag{8.29}$$

Equation (8.29) can be expressed as

$$\mathcal{E}(z) = \mathcal{F}(z) - z^{-n}\mathcal{G}(z) \tag{8.30}$$

where

$$\mathcal{F}(z) = \mathcal{Z}[f(x)], \qquad \mathcal{G}(z) = \mathcal{Z}[f(nd + x)]$$

and d is the sampling period.

For most practical arrays the amplitudes of the excitation in the two end elements are equal and thus

$$f[(n-1)d + x] = \pm f(x) \tag{8.31}$$

By using equation (8.31), $\mathscr{G}(z)$ [from (8.30)] becomes

$$\mathscr{G}(z) = \mathscr{Z}[f(nd + x)] = \sum_{k=0}^{\infty} f(nd + kd)z^{-k}$$

$$= \sum_{k=0}^{\infty} [f(n-1)d + (k+1)d]z^{-k}$$

$$= \pm \sum_{k=0}^{\infty} f[(k+1)d]z^{-k} \tag{8.32}$$

From the shifting theorem, we have

$$\mathscr{Z}[f(x+d)] = z[\mathscr{F}(z) - f(0)] \tag{8.33}$$

where $f(0)$ is the excitation in the first element.

Substituting (8.33) in (8.30),we finally obtain

$$\mathscr{E}(z) = [1 \mp z^{-(n-1)}]\mathscr{F}(z) \pm f(0)z^{-(n-1)} \tag{8.34}$$

where the plus and minus sign follow from (8.31). Since the z-transform of many useful nonuniform envelope functions $f(x)$ exist in a closed form, $\mathscr{E}(z)$ in (8.34) is expressible as a closed function of z instead of a polynomial of n terms (if this problem was treated in the classical way). Note further that increasing the number of elements n in an array does not increase the complexity of the expression for $\mathscr{E}(z)$.

Applications

UNIFORM ARRAY OF n ELEMENTS. The amplitude of the excitation can be assumed to be unity with no loss of generality. Then,

$$f_A(x) = u(x) \tag{8.35}$$

$$f_A[(n-1)d + x] = f_A(x) \tag{8.36}$$

$$\mathscr{F}_A(z) = \mathscr{Z}[f_A(x)] = \frac{1}{1 - z^{-1}} \tag{8.37}$$

In this case $\mathscr{E}(z)$ in (8.34), using the proper sign, yields

$$\mathscr{E}_A(z) = \frac{1 - z^{-(n-1)}}{1 - z^{-1}} + z^{-(n-1)} = \frac{1 - z^{-n}}{1 - z^{-1}} \tag{8.38}$$

LINEAR ARRAY OF n ELEMENTS WITH SINUSOIDAL AMPLITUDE DISTRIBUTION. For the distribution shown in Fig. 8.3,

$$f_B(x) = \sin \beta x \tag{8.39}$$

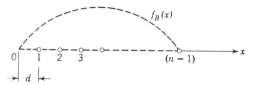

FIGURE 8.3   Linear array with sine amplitude distribution.

In this particular case, $(n - 1)\beta d = \pi$, and

$$f_B[(n - 1)d + x] = -f_B(x) \tag{8.40}$$

The z-transform of $f_B(x)$ is

$$\mathscr{F}_B(z) = \mathscr{Z}[f_B(x)] = \frac{z \sin \beta d}{z^2 - 2z \cos \beta d + 1} \tag{8.41}$$

Substituting in equation (8.34) and using the proper sign, we obtain

$$\mathscr{E}_B(z) = \frac{[1 + z^{-(n-1)}]z \sin \beta d}{z^2 - 2z \cos \beta d + 1} \tag{8.42}$$

In practical problems other properties of the array pattern are required, and among these the array factor that describes the power pattern of the array is important. The array factor $|\mathscr{E}(z)|^2$ can be obtained from $\mathscr{E}(z)$ by noting that

$$\bar{z} = z^{-1} = e^{j\psi} \tag{8.43}$$

Hence

$$|\mathscr{E}(z)|^2 = \mathscr{E}(z)\mathscr{E}(z^{-1}) = \left(\sum_{k=0}^{n-1} a_k z^{-k}\right)\left(\sum_{k=0}^{n-1} a_k z^k\right) \tag{8.44}$$

Using equation (8.34), we can obtain the general formula

$$|\mathscr{E}(z)|^2 = [2 \mp z^{(n-1)} \mp z^{-(n-1)}]\mathscr{F}(z)\mathscr{F}(z^{-1})$$
$$- f(0)\{[1 + z^{(n-1)}]\mathscr{F}(z) + [1 \mp z^{-(n-1)}]\mathscr{F}(z^{-1})\} + f^2(0) \tag{8.45}$$

To determine the array factor for the examples discussed earlier, we substitute for $\mathscr{E}_A(z)$ and $\mathscr{E}_B(z)$ in expression (8.45) to get

$$\mathscr{E}_A(z^{-1}) = \frac{1 - z^n}{1 - z} \tag{8.46}$$

$$|\mathscr{E}_A(z)|^2 = \mathscr{E}_A(z)\mathscr{E}_A(z^{-1}) = \frac{2 - (z^n + z^{-n})}{2 - (z + z^{-1})} \tag{8.47}$$

Substituting $e^{-j\psi}$ for z, we have

$$|\mathscr{E}_A'(\psi)|^2 = \left|\frac{\sin (n\psi/2)}{\sin (\psi/2)}\right|^2 \tag{8.48}$$

For the linear array of n elements with sinusoidal amplitude distribution with

$$\mathscr{E}_B(z) = \frac{[1 + z^{-(n-1)}]z \sin \beta d}{z^2 - 2z \cos \beta d + 1} \tag{8.49}$$

we get

$$|\mathscr{E}_B(z)|^2 = \frac{[2 + z^{(n-1)} + z^{-(n-1)}] \sin^2 \beta d}{(2 + z^2 + z^{-2}) - 4(z + z^{-1}) \cos \beta d + 4 \cos^2 \beta d} \tag{8.50}$$

Other properties such as nulls, maxima, and beamwidth can also be obtained from the z-transform approach to this problem.

8.3 Application to information and filtering theory[27-32]

In some practical cases, for efficiency and economy, it is necessary to transmit continuous signals over a sampled-data link. For instance, accurate transmitting of signals by short wave is reliably done in pulse-code modulation. Here the sampling operation is part of the pulse-code modulation. The sampling action causes frequency aliasing and mixing of high-frequency noise into the signal band. This effect can be remedied by using a low-pass filter $F(s)$ before sampling to filter out most of the high-frequency noise. At the receiving end, a wave-shaping filter $G(s)$ (or hold circuit) is used to reconstruct the continuous signal from the sampled signal. Such a sampled-data transmission link is shown in Fig. 8.4.

In this section, we shall indicate the method of optimizing the system in Fig. 8.4 by applying both the Laplace and z-transform theory. We can also use the modified z-transform, but for this case the former procedure is used because of ease of application.

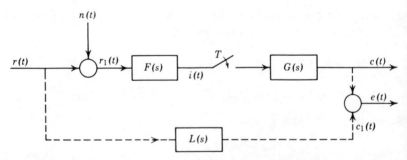

FIGURE 8.4 Block diagram of optimization of sampled-data transmission link.

The optimization procedure[27]

In this procedure, given the spectral density $\Phi_{r_1 r_1}(j\omega)$, the networks $F(s)$ and $G(s)$ are determined to give the minimum value of $\overline{[e(t)]^2}$, where the input signal $r_1(t) = r(t) + n(t)$ and the desired output is $c_1(t)$. Three cases can be considered; (1) $F(s)$ is fixed and $G(s)$ is to be optimized, (2) the contrary, (3) the general case where $F(s)$ and $G(s)$ are to be optimized simultaneously. For brevity, we shall discuss only the optimization procedure where $F(s)$ is fixed and $G(s)$ is to be optimized. The other cases can be handled in the same fashion.

We shall assume that the reader is familiar with the optimization procedure for the continuous and the discrete cases, and therefore many of the detailed derivations and explanations are omitted; references, however, will be made to standard texts on statistical design theory.

From Fig. 8.4, the mean-square error is given as

$$\overline{[e(t)]^2} = \frac{1}{2\pi j} \int_{-j\infty}^{j\infty} \Phi_{ee}(s) \, ds \tag{8.51}$$

where the spectral density $\Phi_{ee}(s)$ is obtained as follows:

$$\Phi_{ee}(s) = \Phi_{c_1 c_1} - \Phi_{c_1 c} - \Phi_{cc_1} + \Phi_{cc} \tag{8.51a}$$

In terms of z-transform the mean-square error at the sampling instants is obtained [from equation (4.92)] as follows:

$$\overline{[e(nT)]^2} = \frac{1}{2\pi j} \oint_{\substack{\text{unit} \\ \text{circle}}} \Phi_{ee}(z) z^{-1} \, dz \tag{8.51b}$$

We can also obtain the mean-square error at all times by using the modified z-transform. However, as mentioned earlier, this procedure for this example will not be used, but instead equation (8.51) will be utilized.

The various spectral densities of equation (8.51a) can be obtained from Fig. 8.4 by following certain statistical definitions and concepts, which are[27]

$$\Phi_{c_1 c_1} = L\bar{L}\Phi_{rr} \tag{8.52}$$

$$\Phi_{c_1 c} = \frac{1}{T} G\Phi_{c_1 i} = \frac{1}{T} FGL\Phi_{rr_1} \tag{8.52a}$$

$$\Phi_{cc_1} = \Phi_{c_1 c}(-s) = \frac{1}{T} F\bar{G}L\Phi_{r_1 r} \tag{8.53}$$

$$\Phi_{cc} = \frac{1}{T}(F\bar{F}\Phi_{r_1 r_1})^* \bar{G}G \tag{8.53a}$$

In equations (8.52 through 8.53a) the following symbols are used:

$$\bar{L} = L(-s), \quad \text{etc.} \tag{8.54}$$

$$(\bar{F}F\Phi_{r_1r_1})^* = \mathcal{Z}(\bar{F}F\Phi_{r_1r_1})|_{z=e^{Ts}} \tag{8.54a}$$

Substituting equations (8.52) and (8.54) in equation (8.51a), we obtain

$$\Phi_{ee} = \bar{L}L\Phi_{rr} - \frac{1}{T}FG\bar{L}\Phi_{rr_1} - \frac{1}{T}\bar{F}\bar{G}L\Phi_{r_1r} + \frac{1}{T}(\bar{F}F\Phi_{r_1r})^*\bar{G}G \tag{8.54b}$$

If we let F be fixed, we can obtain G such that the mean square error is minimized. To find this optimum G, we can use a theorem from calculus of variations which states the following.

The function G must be such that the partial derivative of Φ_{ee} with respect to $\bar{G}$ is analytic in the left half of the s-plane (LHP). Hence we obtain from equation (8.54b)

$$\frac{\partial \Phi_{ee}}{\partial \bar{G}} = -\frac{1}{T}\bar{F}L\Phi_{r_1r} + \frac{1}{T}(\bar{F}F\Phi_{r_1r_1})^*G = X_1 \tag{8.54c}$$

where X_1 is an unknown function which is analytic in the LHP. From equation (8.54c) and the requirement on X_1, we notice that the partial fraction expansion of $\partial \Phi_{ee}/\partial \bar{G}$ corresponding to poles in the LHP is identically zero, that is,

$$[-\bar{F}L\Phi_{r_1r} + (\bar{F}F\Phi_{r_1r_1})^*G]_+ = 0 \tag{8.55}$$

Because of symmetry, we can write

$$(\bar{F}F\Phi_{r_1r_1})^* = (\bar{F}F\Phi_{r_1r_1})^{*-}(\bar{F}F\Phi_{r_1r_1})^{*+} \tag{8.55a}$$

where ( )$^{*+}$ is analytic in the RHP (or outside the unit circle). Since G is analytic in the RHP (due to physical realizability), we can obtain a function Q defined by

$$Q = G(\bar{F}F\Phi_{r_1r_1})^{*+} \tag{8.55b}$$

which is also analytic in the RHP.

Using equations (8.55a) and (8.55b) in (8.55), we have

$$[-\bar{F}L\Phi_{r_1r} + (\bar{F}F\Phi_{r_1r_1})^{*-}Q]_+ = 0 \tag{8.55c}$$

This equation requires that

$$Q = \left[\frac{\bar{F}L\Phi_{r_1r}}{(\bar{F}F\Phi_{r_1r_1})^{*-}}\right]_+ \tag{8.56}$$

Utilizing this equation, we can write from equation (8.53a)

$$\Phi_{cc} = \frac{1}{T}(FF\Phi_{r_1r_1})^{*+}G\{FF\Phi_{r_1r_1}\}^{*-}\bar{G} = \frac{1}{T}Q\bar{Q} \qquad (8.56a)$$

To obtain a relationship for the mean square error, we have from equations (8.53), (8.53a), and (8.54c)

$$\frac{1}{2\pi j}\int_{-j\infty}^{j\infty}(\Phi_{cc_1} - \Phi_{cc})\,ds = \frac{1}{2\pi j}\int_{-j\infty}^{j\infty}\frac{1}{T}$$

$$\times [\bar{F}\bar{G}L\Phi_{r_1r} - (FF\Phi_{r_1r_1})^{*}\bar{G}G]\,ds$$

$$= \frac{1}{2\pi j}\int_{-j\infty}^{j\infty}\left(-\bar{G}\frac{\partial\Phi_{ee}}{\partial\bar{G}}\right)ds$$

$$= -\frac{1}{2\pi j}\int_{-j\infty}^{j\infty}\bar{G}X_1\,ds \qquad (8.56b)$$

Since both $\bar{G}$ and X_1 are analytic in the LHP, this integral vanishes. Furthermore, changing s into $(-s)$ in equation (8.56b) we obtain the following expression:

$$\frac{1}{2\pi j}\int_{-j\infty}^{j\infty}(\Phi_{c_1c} - \Phi_{cc})\,ds = 0 \qquad (8.56c)$$

From equations (8.51) and (8.51a) we have

$$\overline{[e(t)]^2} = \frac{1}{2\pi j}\int_{-j\infty}^{j\infty}\Phi_{ee}\,ds$$

$$= \frac{1}{2\pi j}\int_{-j\infty}^{j\infty}(\Phi_{c_1c_1} - \Phi_{c_1c} - \Phi_{cc_1} + \Phi_{cc})\,ds \qquad (8.57)$$

This integral can also be written as

$$\overline{[e(t)]^2} = \frac{1}{2\pi j}\int_{-j\infty}^{j\infty}(\Phi_{c_1c_1} - \Phi_{cc})\,ds - \frac{1}{2\pi j}\int_{-j\infty}^{j\infty}(\Phi_{c_1c} - \Phi_{cc})\,ds$$

$$- \frac{1}{2\pi j}\int_{-j\infty}^{j\infty}(\Phi_{cc_1} - \Phi_{cc})\,ds \qquad (8.57a)$$

Noting equations (8.56a) and (8.56c), we finally obtain

$$\overline{[e(t)]^2} = \frac{1}{2\pi j}\int_{-j\infty}^{j\infty}\left(\Phi_{c_1c_1} - \frac{\bar{Q}Q}{T}\right)ds \qquad (8.57b)$$

ILLUSTRATIVE EXAMPLE

This example illustrates a problem of optimum filtering and prediction in the presence of uncorrelated noise.

Referring to Fig. 8.4, assume that

$$c_1(t) = r(t + \alpha) \tag{8.58a}$$

$$L(s) = e^{\alpha s} \tag{8.58b}$$

$$\Phi_{r_1 r}(s) = \frac{2a}{a^2 - s^2} \tag{8.58c}$$

$$\Phi_{r_1 r_1}(s) = \frac{2a}{a^2 - s^2} + \sigma^2 = \frac{\sigma^2(b^2 - s^2)}{a^2 - s^2} \tag{8.58d}$$

where $b^2 = 2a/\sigma^2 + a^2$.

$$F(s) = \frac{b - a}{s + b} \tag{8.58e}$$

We shall determine the optimum $G(s)$ and mean square value of the error as well as the error due to sampling.

From equation (8.56) and the expressions (8.58a–e), we have

$$Q(s) = \left[\frac{(b - a)/(-s + b)e^{\alpha s}(2a)/(a^2 - s^2)}{\left[\frac{(b - a)^2 \sigma^2}{a^2 - s^2} \right]^{*-}} \right]_+ \tag{8.59}$$

From tables of z-transforms (see Table I) we obtain

$$\left[\frac{(b - a)^2 \sigma^2}{a^2 - s^2} \right]^* \triangleq \mathcal{Z}\left[\frac{(b - a)^2 \sigma^2}{a^2 - s^2} \right]$$

$$= \frac{\sigma^2(b - a)^2}{2a} \frac{z(e^{-aT} - e^{+aT})}{z^2 - (e^{aT} + e^{-aT})z + 1} \bigg|_{z = e^{Ts}} \tag{8.59a}$$

This equation can also be written in the following form:

$$\left[\frac{(b - a)^2 \sigma^2}{a^2 - s^2} \right]^* = \left[\quad \right]^{*+} \left[\quad \right]^{*-}$$

$$= \left[\frac{\sigma(b - a)}{\sqrt{2a}} \frac{\sqrt{1 - e^{-2aT}}}{(1 - e^{-aT}e^{-Ts})} \right]$$

$$\times \left[\frac{\sigma(b - a)\sqrt{1 - e^{-2aT}}}{(1 - e^{-aT}e^{Ts})\sqrt{2a}} \right] \tag{8.59b}$$

Substituting the last bracketed term of equation (8.59b) into the expression for $Q(s)$ in equation (8.59), we get

$$Q(s) = \left[\frac{2ae^{\alpha s}\sqrt{2a}}{\sigma(s - b)(s - a)(s + a)} \frac{1 - e^{-aT}e^{Ts}}{\sqrt{1 - e^{-2aT}}} \right]_+$$

$$= \frac{\sqrt{2a}(1 - e^{-2aT})e^{-\alpha a}}{\sigma(a + b)(s + a)} \tag{8.59c}$$

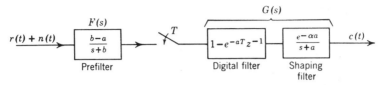

FIGURE 8.5   Block diagram for the optimized sampled-data transmission link.

From equation (8.55b) we finally obtain the optimum $G(s)$ as follows:

$$G_{opt}(s) = \frac{2a}{\sigma^2(b^2 - a^2)} (1 - e^{-aT}e^{-Ts}) \frac{e^{-\alpha a}}{s + a} \tag{8.60}$$

but $2a/\sigma^2 = b^2 - a^2$; hence

$$G_{opt}(s) = (1 - e^{-aT}z^{-1})|_{z=e^{Ts}} \frac{e^{-\alpha a}}{s + a} \tag{8.60a}$$

It is noticed from the preceding that $G(s)$ is composed of a digital filter and a shaping filter. The block diagram of the optimized system is shown in Fig. 8.5.

The mean-square error is given by equation (8.57b), which gives

$$\overline{[e(t)]^2} = 1 - \frac{(b - a)(1 - e^{-2aT})e^{-2\alpha a}}{2aT(b + a)} \tag{8.60b}$$

As T approaches zero, equation (8.60b) gives the result of the Wiener filter, that is,

$$\overline{[e(t)]^2}|_{T=0} = 1 - \frac{b - a}{b + a} e^{-2\alpha} \tag{8.60c}$$

The error due to sampling is given by

$$\overline{[e(t)]^2} - \overline{[e(t)]^2}|_{T=0} = \left(1 - \frac{1 - e^{-2aT}}{2aT}\right)\frac{(b - a)e^{-2\alpha a}}{b + a} \tag{8.61}$$

8.4 z-Transform method applied to problems of economics

National income, consumption, and investment are the three basic fundamentals of any economy. These can be expressed at any given time, $t = nT$, by means of a difference equation and certain constants. Solution of these equations is then found by the z-transform method. Three models of economic systems have been considered and they involve first-, second- and fourth-order difference equations with constant coefficients. Convergence of the solution and stability are also discussed in the following.

Model I

Let y, c, i denote the national income, consumption, and investment, respectively. Considering that time is divided in periods of equal length, say years, we define that at any time $t = nT$ (where n can have integer values 0, 1, 2, . . .) y, c, i have respective values y_n, c_n, i_n.

Since national income is made up of investment and consumption, we can write

$$y_n = c_n + i_n \qquad (8.62)$$

Now we assume that consumption depends linearly on national income but has a constant value even when there is no national income. This is quite logical; therefore we can write

$$c_n = K + my_n \qquad n = 0, 1, 2, \ldots \qquad (8.63)$$

where $K \geq 0$ and $0 < m < 1$.

We must also consider the effect of investment on national income which can be expressed in terms of what the economists call the growth factor r. We can assume the following relationship:

$$y_{n+1} - y_n = ri_n \qquad (8.64)$$

where $r > 0$.

Relations (8.62), (8.63), and (8.64) enable us to determine the desired difference equation. Eliminating i_n and c_n, we get

$$y_{n+1} - y_n = r(y_n - K - my_n) \qquad (8.65)$$

or

$$y_{n+1} + (mr - r - 1)y_n + rK = 0 \qquad n = 0, 1, 2, \ldots \qquad (8.66)$$

Solution of this difference equation can be easily found by taking the z-transform

$$\mathscr{J}[y_{n+1}] + (mr - r - 1)\mathscr{J}[y_n] + \mathscr{J}[rK] = 0 \qquad (8.67)$$

or

$$z[\mathscr{Y}(z) - y_0] + (mr - r - 1)\mathscr{Y}(z) + \frac{rKz}{z - 1} = 0 \qquad (8.68)$$

which gives

$$\mathscr{Y}(z)(z + mr - r - 1) = zy_0 - \frac{rKz}{z - 1} \qquad (8.69)$$

or

$$\mathscr{Y}(z) = \frac{zy_0}{z - (1 + r - mr)} - \frac{rKz}{(z - 1)[z - (1 + r - mr)]} \qquad (8.70)$$

Now $1 + r(1 - m) > 0$. So let $1 + r(1 - m) = a$.

$$\mathcal{Y}(z) = \frac{zy_0}{z - a} + \frac{rKz}{(z - 1)(z - a)}$$

$$= \frac{zy_0 - rKz/(a - 1)}{z - a} - \frac{rKz}{(1 - a)(z - 1)} \tag{8.71}$$

Taking the inverse z-transform of equation (8.71), we get

$$y_n = \left(y_0 - \frac{rK}{a - 1}\right)a^n - \frac{rK}{1 - a} \tag{8.72}$$

or

$$y_n = y_0[1 + r(1 - m)]^n - \frac{K}{1 - m}\{[1 + r(1 - m)]^n - 1\} \tag{8.73}$$

Rewriting,

$$y_n = [1 + r(1 - m)]^n\left(y_0 - \frac{K}{1 - m}\right) + \frac{K}{1 - m} \tag{8.74}$$

This gives the national income for any $n = 0, 1, 2, \ldots$.

Model II

In this model, we define at any time $t = n$ ($n = 0, 1, 2, \ldots$),

y_n = income received
s_n = total savings
i_n = desired investment

We make the following assumptions:

1. Savings during any period is proportional to the income anticipated during the next period which can be mathematically expressed as

$$s_n = Ky_{n+1} \tag{8.75}$$

where K is the proportionality constant

2. Desired investment during any period is equal to a constant multiple g of the increase of the income of that period over the income of the preceding period. This can be expressed mathematically

$$i_{n+1} = g(y_{n+1} - y_n) \tag{8.76}$$

3. Savings in any period is equal to desired investment

$$s_n = i_n \tag{8.77}$$

Equations (8.75), (8.76), and (8.77) can be combined to yield the following difference equation:

$$y_{n+2} - \frac{g}{K} y_{n+1} + \frac{g}{K} y_n = 0, \qquad n \geq 0 \tag{8.78}$$

Taking the z-transform of this equation, we obtain

$$\mathcal{Y}(z) = \frac{z^2 y_0 - (g/K)z y_0 + z y_1}{z^2 - (g/K)z + g/K} \tag{8.79}$$

Using the inverse z-transform integral or tables, we obtain

$$\begin{aligned}
y_n = y_0 &\left\{ \left[\frac{g}{2K} + \sqrt{\left(\frac{g}{2K}\right)^2 - \frac{g}{K}} \right]^{n+1} \right. \\
&\left. - \left[\frac{g}{2K} - \sqrt{\left(\frac{g}{2K}\right)^2 - \frac{g}{K}} \right]^{n+1} \right\} \bigg/ \sqrt{(g/K)^2 - 4(g/K)} \\
&+ \left(y_1 - \frac{g}{K} y_0 \right) \left\{ \left[\frac{g}{2K} + \sqrt{(g/2K)^2 - g/K} \right]^{n} \right. \\
&\left. - \left[\frac{g}{2K} - \sqrt{(g/2K)^2 - g/K} \right]^{n} \right\} \bigg/ \sqrt{(g/K)^2 - 4(g/K)},
\end{aligned}$$
$$n \geq 0 \quad (8.80)$$

For stability or convergence we obtain from the denominator of equation (8.79) $\mathcal{F}(z)$ the following conditions:

1. $\mathcal{F}(1) > 0,$ or $1 > 0$ (8.81)

2. $\mathcal{F}(-1) > 0,$ or $1 + \frac{2g}{K} > 0$ (8.82)

3. $\mathcal{F}(0) < 1,$ or $g < K$ (8.83)

Model III

In this model we obtain, as shown by Tinbergen,[13] the numerical equation for the analysis of economic fluctuations. The numerical equation which is determined from statistical consideration is a fourth-order difference equation, given as[13]

$$y_{n+4} + a y_{n+3} + b y_{n+2} + c y_{n+1} + d y_n = 0 \tag{8.84}$$

where

$$a = -0.398 \qquad b = 0.220 \qquad c = -0.013$$
$$d = -0.027 \tag{8.85}$$

The characteristic equation for (8.84) which can be obtained by taking the z-transform can be expressed as

$$F(z) = z^4 - 0.398z^3 + 0.220z^2 - 0.013z - 0.027 = 0 \qquad (8.86)$$

To determine stability for the system of Model III, we require for the fourth-order case

1. $F(1) > 0,$ that is, $1 - 0.398 + 0.22 - 0.013 - 0.027 > 0$

   $F(-1) > 0,$ that is, $1 + 0.398 + 0.220 + 0.013 - 0.027 > 0$

$$(8.87)$$

which are both satisfied.

2. $(0.027)^2 - 1^2 < - |0.027 \times 0.398 + 0.013 \times 1|,$

   that is, $-0.999 < - |0.02375|$ (8.88)

which is satisfied.

3. $(-0.027)^3 + 2(-0.027)(0.220) + (-0.013)(-0.398)$

   $- (-0.027) - (0.220) - (-0.027)(-0.398)^2 - (-0.027)^2$

   $- (-0.027)^2(0.220) - (-0.013)^2 + 1$

$$+ (-0.027)(-0.013)(0.270) > 0 \quad (8.89)$$

which is also satisfied.

Therefore the system as described by equation (8.84) is stable.

8.5 Linear sequential circuits[14–17,37]

In this section the z-transform method is used to analyze the behavior of linear sequential circuits. Such devices find application, for example, in coding theory, radar detection systems, and computer theory. The underlying mathematical field for analysis is not the field of real or complex numbers; thus the z-transform theory is carefully applied in the following. This discussion is limited, for the most part, to the autonomous behavior of such circuits.

Sequential circuits are devices whose inputs are sequences of numbers belonging to a finite field. When they are linear and have a single input and output, the sequence $x(n)$, its input, and $y(n)$ the output, may be related by the following difference equation:

$$y(n + k) + \alpha_1 y(n + k - 1) + \ldots + \alpha_0 y(n)$$
$$= \beta_0 x(n + k) + \beta_1 x(n + k - 1) + \ldots + \beta_0 x(n) \quad (8.90)$$

In equation (8.90) multiplication and addition are modulo-p and the values of α_i, β_i, y, and x range over the integers $0, 1, 2, 3, \ldots, p - 1$, where p is a prime number. The set of numbers $0, 1, 2, \ldots, p - 1$ with modulo-p arithmetic operations is called a *modular field*.

The following shifting property of the z-transform remains valid when arithmetic operations are carried out modulo-p, that is,

$$\mathscr{Y}[x(n + k)] = z^k \mathscr{X}(z) - z^k \sum_{l=0}^{k-1} x(l) z^{-l} \tag{8.91}$$

Using this equation in obtaining the z-transform of equation (8.90), we get

$$[z^k + \alpha_1 z^{k-1} + \ldots + \alpha_k]\mathscr{Y}(z)$$
$$= [\beta_0 z^k + \beta_1 z^{k-1} + \ldots + \beta_k]\mathscr{X}(z) + I(z) \tag{8.92}$$

where $I(z)$ is a polynomial in z resulting from the initial conditions. Its exact form is not important for the following discussions.

To calculate $y(n)$, we solve for $\mathscr{Y}(z)$ and then calculate its inverse. The usual inversion integrals or tables are not directly applicable in this case because the modular field is not the field of real or complex numbers. Thus it is more convenient to resort to the power series method of finding the inverse z-transform.*

The autonomous behavior of the circuit is determined by letting $x = 0$ in equation (8.90). Thus from equation (8.90) with $x = 0$, it is easy to notice that any k consecutive value of $y(n)$, say $(y_0, y_1, y_2, \ldots, y_{k-1})$, completely determines y for all subsequent n. We may observe that the number of distinct k-tuples $(y_0, y_1, \ldots, y_{k-1})$ is p^k.

Consider the sequence of output symbols $y_0, y_1, y_2 \ldots$. Since the number of distinct k-tuples is finite, there exist indices m and $m + L$ such that $(y_m, y_{m+1}, \ldots, y_{m+k-1})$ is identical to $(y_{m+L}, y_{m+L+1}, \ldots, y_{m+L+k-1})$. Since k consecutive values of y determine all subsequent values of y, the output following $y_{m+L+k-1}$ is identical to that following y_{m+k-1}; hence the output sequence is periodic after y_m. The smallest integer L is called the period of the sequence. The exact period of the sequence may be determined from equation (8.92) with $\mathscr{X}(z)$ set equal to zero.

$$\mathscr{Y}(z) = \frac{I(z)}{z^k + \alpha_1 z^{k-1} + \alpha_2 z^{k-2} + \ldots + \alpha_k} = \frac{I(z)}{P(z)} \tag{8.93}$$

Three cases of $P(z)$ may be distinguished: (1) $P(z)$ is irreducible, (2) $P(z)$ factors into distinct irreducible polynomials, and (3) $P(z)$ factors but not into distinct polynomials. Each of these cases is discussed in the following.

---

* However, with due care in interpretation, the inversion integrals and tables may also be used. Thus a solution in closed form can be.found.

$P(z)$ *Irreducible*

A polynomial with coefficients belonging to a field is said to be irreducible if it is not factorable into polynomials of smaller degree with coefficients belonging to the same field. In this case the coefficients of $P(z)$ belong to a modular field of characteristic p. It is well known that an irreducible polynomial with coefficients in a modular field is a factor of a polynomial $z^L - 1$ for some L that must be a divisor of $p^k - 1$, k being the degree of the polynomial.

Using this fact,

$$z^L - 1 = P(z)R(z) \tag{8.94}$$

where $R(z)$ is a polynomial of degree $L - k$ in z. The smallest L for which equation (8.94) is satisfied is called the period of $P(z)$. Solving for $P(z)$ in (8.94) and substituting in (8.93), we obtain

$$\mathcal{Y}(z) = z^{-L}\frac{I(z)R(z)}{1 - z^{-L}} = z^{-L}I(z)R(z)(1 + z^{-L} + z^{-2L} + \ldots) \tag{8.95}$$

From (8.95) it is clear that $y(k) = y(k + L)$ for all k, therefore the period of $y(n)$ is at most L. (It can be shown that the period must be exactly L.)

When $p^k - 1$ is prime, $L = p^k - 1$. Then, the circuit is said to have maximal period, for $p^k - 1$ is the largest value L may assume. Except for the all-zero k-tuple, every possible k-tuple appears once and only once during each period.

$P(z)$ *factors into nonrepeated factors*

Suppose $P(z)$ factors into distinct nonrepeated factors

$$P(z) = P_1(z)P_2(z) \ldots P_l(z).$$

Then the period of $y(n)$ is a divisor of the least common multiple of the periods of $P_1(z)$, $P_2(z)$, $\ldots$, $P_l(z)$.

To see this, make a partial fraction expansion of equation (8.93),

$$\mathcal{Y}(z) = \frac{q_1(z)}{P_1(z)} + \frac{q_2(z)}{P_2(z)} + \ldots + \frac{q_l(z)}{P_l(z)} \tag{8.96}$$

Each term $q_i(z)/P_i(z)$, $i = 1, 2, 3, \ldots, l$ in equation (8.96), corresponds to a sequence with period that is a divisor of the period of $P_i(z)$. The period of $y(n)$, which is the sum of the sequences corresponding to

$q_i(z)/P_i(z)$, as a consequence, is a divisor of the least common multiple of the periods of $P_1(z)$, $P_2(z)$, ..., $P_l(z)$.

The maximum period of $y(n)$ if $P(z)$ factors is always less than $p^k - 1$. This is so because the period L of $y(n)$ (supposing the degree of $P_i(z)$ is k_i) satisfies the inequality

$$L \leq (p^{k_1} - 1)(p^{k_2} - 1) \ldots (p^{k_l} - 1) < p^{k_1 + k_2 + \cdots + k_l} - 1$$
$$= p^k - 1 \quad (8.97)$$

P(z) Has repeated factors

To compute the period of $y(n)$ for this case, the following lemma which is proved by Elspas[14] is needed.

LEMMA: If $[q(z)]$ is irreducible, $[q(z)]^m$ has period kp^{r_m} where k is the period of $q(z)$ and r_m is the smallest integer satisfying $p^{r_m} \geq m$.

Now, suppose

$$p(z) = p_1^{n_1}(z)\, p_2^{n_2}(z) \ldots p_i^{n_i}(z) \quad (8.98)$$

Thus, just as for the nonrepeated factor case, the period of $y(n)$ is a divisor of the least common multiple of the periods of each factor $p_i^{n_i}(z)$.

In the preceding, it has been tacitly assumed that in equation (8.39) $I(z)$ and $P(z)$ have no common factors. This is always so when $P(z)$ is irreducible. In the last two cases discussed, only upper bounds on the period were established. The reason more precise statements, in general, are not possible is that the periods depend on $I(z)$, that is, the initial conditions.

8.6 Application to discrete Markov processes[18-21]

The z-transform's application in probability theory is well known and often used. This method is referred to as the generating function method and was used by De Moivre and Laplace as early as the nineteenth century. In the following discussion, the z-transform method is used in the solution of the vector difference equation arising in discrete Markov process. Certain features of the process are discussed using this method.

We shall consider the problems of finite-state, discrete Markov process and restrict the discussion to an irreducible, regular Markov process in which there are neither transient states nor absorbing states and the state transition of all persistent states is aperiodic.

We define a set of states

$$S = \{1, 2, 3, \ldots, m\} \quad (8.99)$$

Also, we define a column vector $\mathbf{P}(n)$ and a square matrix $\mathbf{p}(u, t)$ such that

$$\mathbf{P}(n) = \begin{bmatrix} P_1(n) \\ P_2(n) \\ \cdot \\ \cdot \\ \cdot \\ P_m(n) \end{bmatrix} \tag{8.100}$$

$$\mathbf{p}(u, n) = [\ldots p_{ij}(u, n) \ldots], \qquad n \geq u \tag{8.101}$$

where $P_i(n)$ is the absolute probability of state i at time n and $p_{ij}(u, n)$ is the transition probability from a state i at time u to a state j at time n. (Here u and n are taken to be integral numbers.) They have the following properties:

$$\sum_{j=1}^{m} p_{ij}(u, n) = 1, \qquad \text{for all } i \text{ s and for } u,$$
$$n \text{ integers with } n \geq u \geq 0 \tag{8.102}$$

$$p_{ij}(u, n) \geq 0 \tag{8.103}$$

and

$$\sum_{i=1}^{m} P_i(n) = 1 \tag{8.104}$$

Using the matrices of equations (8.100) and (8.101), we can write

$$\mathbf{P}(n) = \mathbf{p}'(u, n)\mathbf{P}(u) \tag{8.105}$$

where the prime indicates the transpose of a matrix. If the process is time-homogeneous, the stochastic matrix $\mathbf{p}(u, n)$ is time-invariant and is given by

$$\mathbf{p}'(u, n) = \mathbf{p}'(n - u) \tag{8.106}$$

Since the process is a Markov one, the Chapman-Kolomogorov equation must be satisfied, that is,

$$\mathbf{p}'(u, n) = \mathbf{p}'(u, u + \tau)\mathbf{p}'(u + \tau, n), \qquad n \geq \tau + u \geq u \tag{8.107}$$

This equation for a time-homogeneous process reduces to

$$\mathbf{p}'(n) = \mathbf{p}'(\tau)\mathbf{p}'(n - \tau) \qquad n \geq \tau \geq 0, \qquad \tau = \text{integer} \tag{8.108}$$

with the knowledge that

$$\mathbf{p}'(0) = \mathbf{I} = \text{identity matrix} \tag{8.109}$$

If we define $\mathbf{p}(1) = \mathbf{p}$, by using equation (8.108) as a recurrence relation we have

$$\mathbf{p}(n) = \mathbf{p}^n, \qquad \text{or } \mathbf{p}'(n) = \mathbf{p}'^n \tag{8.110}$$

Therefore, from equations (8.105) and (8.106), we obtain

$$\mathbf{P}(n + \tau) = \mathbf{p}'(\tau)\mathbf{P}(n) = \mathbf{p}'^{\tau}\mathbf{P}(n) \tag{8.111}$$

In particular, letting $\tau = 1$ in equation (8.111), we obtain the following first-order vector difference equation:

$$\mathbf{P}(n + 1) = \mathbf{p}'\mathbf{P}(n), \qquad n = 0, 1, 2, \ldots \tag{8.112}$$

Application of the z-transform

We shall apply the z-transform to the vector difference equation in (8.112) as follows (with the understanding that the z-transforms of vectors and matrices are obtained by taking the transform of each component in the array).

$$\mathscr{Z}[\mathbf{P}(n)] = \mathscr{P}(z) \triangleq \sum_{n=0}^{\infty} \mathbf{P}(n)z^{-n} \tag{8.113}$$

By the time-translation theorem,

$$\mathscr{Z}[\mathbf{P}(n + 1)] = z[\mathscr{P}(z) - \mathbf{P}(0)] \tag{8.114}$$

Therefore, substituting equations (8.113) and (8.114) into equation (8.112),

$$(z\mathbf{I} - \mathbf{p}')\mathscr{P}(z) = z\mathbf{P}(0)$$
$$\mathscr{P}(z) = z(z\mathbf{I} - \mathbf{p}')^{-1}\mathbf{P}(0) \triangleq \mathscr{G}(z)\mathbf{P}(0) \tag{8.115}$$

where $\mathscr{G}(z)$ is the fundamental matrix of the stochastic matrix $\mathbf{p}'$ such that

$$\mathscr{G}(z) = z(z\mathbf{I} - \mathbf{p}')^{-1} \tag{8.116}$$

Later we shall show the relation between $\mathscr{G}(z)$ and $\mathbf{p}(n)$.

We assume here that there is no multiple pole. Then by the partial fraction expansion of equation (8.116), we have

$$\mathscr{G}(z) = \sum_{k=1}^{m} \frac{z}{z - \lambda_k} \mathbf{G}_k \tag{8.117}$$

where the λ_k's are the eigenvalues of $\mathbf{p}'$, that is the roots of the characteristic equation

$$|\lambda\mathbf{I} - \mathbf{p}'| = 0 \tag{8.118}$$

Then we have the following theorem.

THEOREM 1: For any regular stochastic matrix **p** of a finite-state, discrete-time Markov process

(i) There exists an eigenvalue of **p**′, which is equal to one.

(ii) No eigenvalue of **p**′ exists outside of the unit circle in the complex z-plane.

Proof: Let us consider a determinant

$$|\mathbf{p}' - \mathbf{I}| = \begin{vmatrix} p_{11} - 1 & p_{21} & \cdots & p_{m1} \\ p_{12} & p_{22} - 1 & \cdots & p_{m2} \\ \cdot & \cdot & \cdot & \cdot \\ \cdot & \cdot & \cdot & \cdot \\ \cdot & \cdot & \cdot & \cdot \\ p_{1m} & p_{2m} & \cdots & p_{mm} - 1 \end{vmatrix}$$

If we add all the rows from 2 to m to the first row, all the elements of the first row become zero because

$$\sum_{j=1}^{m} p_{ij} - 1 = 0, \quad \forall i \in S$$

Therefore we have

$$|\mathbf{p}' - \mathbf{I}| = 0 \tag{8.119}$$

Comparing this with equation (8.118), we see that there exists an eigenvalue which is equal to one, which thus proves (i).

The proof of (ii) is shown as follows. Let **X** be an eigenvector of **p** and M be the absolute value of the component of **X** of greatest magnitude. Then from the relation

$$\lambda \mathbf{X} = \mathbf{p} \mathbf{X}$$

we have

$$|\lambda| M \leq M \cdot \sum_{j=1}^{m} p_{ij} = M \tag{8.120}$$

Therefore we get

$$|\lambda| \leq 1 \tag{8.121}$$

Thus, no eigenvalue of equation (8.118) exists outside the unit circle.

In fact, the term in equation (8.117) corresponding to $\lambda_1 = 1$ is the stationary solution of the Markov process. We can verify it in many ways.

If the process is stationary,

$$P(n + 1) = P(n), \quad \forall n; \quad \text{integer}$$

and equation (8.112) can be rewritten as

$$(\mathbf{I} - \mathbf{p}')\mathbf{P}(n) = \mathbf{0} \tag{8.122}$$

where $\mathbf{P}(n)$ is no longer dependent on n. From equation (8.119), we can say that there always exists a nontrivial solution for $\mathbf{P}(n)$ corresponding to the eigenvalue $\lambda_1 = 1$.

Fundamental matrix

We will now study more about the fundamental matrix defined by equation (8.116). If we assume that λ_k's are the simple roots of the characteristic equation, $\mathscr{G}(z)$ from equation (8.117) is expanded by

$$\mathscr{G}(z) = \sum_{k=1}^{m} \frac{z}{z - \lambda_k} \mathbf{G}_k$$

where $\mathbf{G}_k$ is the residue of $\mathscr{G}(z)$ and is

$$\mathbf{G}_k = \lim_{z \to \lambda_k} (z - \lambda_k)(z\mathbf{I} - \mathbf{p}')^{-1} \tag{8.123}$$

We further assume that

$$\lambda_1 = 1, \ |\lambda_k| < 1, \quad \text{for all } k = 2, 3, \ldots, m \tag{8.124}$$

From the final value theorem of the z-transform

$$\mathbf{G}(n)\big|_{n \to \infty} = \lim_{z \to 1} (z - 1) \ \mathscr{G}(z)$$

$$= \lim_{z \to 1} \left(\mathbf{G}_1 + \sum_{k=2}^{m} \frac{z - 1}{z - \lambda_k} \mathbf{G}_k \right) = \mathbf{G}_1 \tag{8.125}$$

We see here again that the first term $\mathbf{G}_1$ corresponding to $\lambda_1 = 1$ is the limiting fundamental matrix of the stationary Markov process. Since $|\lambda_k| < 1$ for $k > 1$, the state transition is always stable and the terms other than the first converge to zero as n increases. This is quite natural because $\mathbf{P}(n)$ itself is bounded by one.

By the inverse z-transform of $\mathscr{G}(z)$, we can find the fundamental matrix in time domain

$$\mathbf{G}(n) = \mathscr{z}^{-1}[\mathscr{G}(z)]$$

$$= \frac{1}{2\pi j} \int_{\Gamma} \mathscr{G}(z) z^{n-1} \, dz$$

$$= \frac{1}{2\pi j} \int_{\Gamma} \sum_{k=1}^{m} \frac{z^n}{z - \lambda_k} \mathbf{G}_k \, dz \tag{8.126}$$

where Γ is taken to be a counterclockwise closed contour on a unit circle in the complex z-plane. This is given by the sum of residues

$$G(n) = \sum_{k=1}^{m} \lambda_k^n G_k \tag{8.127}$$

Since $|\lambda_k| < 1$ for all $k(2, 3, \ldots, m)$, the terms from 2 to m converge to zero as $n \to \infty$. When λ_k is a complex root, the kth term is an oscillatory attenuating term, that is, denoting

$$\lambda_k = a_k + jb_k = e^{-(\alpha_k - j\omega_k)}. \tag{8.128}$$

the attenuating constant α_k and the frequency ω_k are given by

$$\alpha_k = -\tfrac{1}{2} \ln (a_k^2 + b_k^2) = -\ln |\lambda_k|$$

$$\omega_k = \tan^{-1}\left(\frac{a_k}{b_k}\right) = \text{ang } \lambda_k \tag{8.129}$$

Since λ_k is in the unit circle, α_k should always be positive.

By the inverse z-transform of equation (8.115), we have

$$P(n) = G(n)P(0) \tag{8.130}$$

In general,

$$P(n + \tau) = G(\tau)P(n)$$

Comparing this with equation (8.111), we note that

$$G(n) = p'(n) \tag{8.131}$$

$$\mathcal{G}(z) = \mathcal{Y}[p'(n)] \tag{8.132}$$

The initial value of $G(n)$ is

$$G(n)\big|_{n=0} = \lim_{z \to \infty} \mathcal{G}(z) = I \tag{8.133}$$

Furthermore, from equation (8.125),

$$G_1 = \lim_{n \to \infty} G(n) = \lim_{n \to \infty} p'^n \tag{8.134}$$

Therefore G_1 is the limit of the nth power of the transpose of the transition matrix.

REFERENCES

1. Jury, E. I., *Sampled-Data Control Systems*, John Wiley and Sons, New York, 1958.

2. Tsypkin, Y. Z. *Theory of Pulse Systems*, Physico-Mathematical Literature, Moscow, 1958.

3. Jury, E. I., "Contribution to the Modified z-Transform Method," *J. Franklin Inst.*, Vol. 270, No. 2, August 1960, pp. 119–129.

4. Jury, E. I., and M. A. Pai, "Convolution z-Transform Method Applied to Certain Nonlinear Discrete Systems," *IRE, PGAC*, Vol. AC-7, No. 1, January 1962.

5. Pai, M. A., "The Analysis of Nonlinear Feedback Sampled-Data Systems," Ph.D. Thesis, September 1961, University of California, Berkeley.

6. Montel, P., *Leçons sur les Recurrences et leur Applications*, Gauthier-Villars, Paris, 1957.

7. Schelkunoff, S. A., "A Mathematical Theory of Linear Arrays," *Bell System Tech. J.*, Vol. 22, January 1943, pp. 80–107.

8. Cheng, D. K., and M. T. Ma, "A New Mathematical Approach for Linear Array Analysis," *IRE Trans. Antennas and Propagation*, Vol. AP-8, No. 3, 1960.

9. Cheng, D. K., and M. T. Ma, "A Critical Study of Linear Arrays with Equal Side Lobes," *IRE International Convention Record*, Part 1, 1961, pp. 110–122.

10. Stone, W. M., "A List of Generalized Laplace Transforms," *Iowa State College Journal of Science*, Vol. 22, April 1948, pp. 215–225.

11. Goldberg, S., *Introduction to Difference Equations*, John Wiley and Sons, New York, 1958.

12. Samuelson, P. A., "Conditions that Roots of a Polynomial Be Less than Unity in Absolute Value," *Annals of Math. Stat.*, Vol. 12, 1941, p. 360.

13. Tinbergen, J., *Business Cycles in the United States*, 1919–1932, League of Nations, 1939, pp. 126–150 (Economics Intelligence Service, Geneva, Switzerland).

14. Elspas, B., "The Theory of Autonomous Linear Sequential Networks," *IRE Trans. Circuit Theory*, Vol. CT-6, No. 1, March 1959, pp. 45–60.

15. Friedland, B., "Linear Modular Sequential Circuits," *Ibid.*, pp. 61–69.

16. Hartmanis, J., "Linear Multivalued Sequential Coding Networks," *Ibid.*, pp. 69–74.

17. Huffman, D. A., "The Synthesis of Linear Sequential Coding Networks, *Proceedings of the Symposium on Information Theory*, London, England, 1955, pp. 77–95.

18. Feller, W., *An Introduction to Probability Theory and its Applications*, John Wiley and Sons, New York, Vol. 1, 1960.

19. Sittler, P. W., "System Analysis of Discrete Markov Process," *IRE PGCT*, Vol. CT-3, No. 4, December 1956, pp. 237–266.

20. Howard, R. A., *Dynamic Programming and Markov Processes*, MIT Press and John Wiley and Sons, New York, 1960.

21. Bellman, R., *Introduction to Matrix Analysis*, McGraw-Hill Book Co., New York, 1960.

22. Van der Waerdon, B. L., *Modern Algebra*, Vol. 1, F. Ungar Publishing Co., New York, 1945.

23. Meschkowski, H., *Differenzengleichungen*, Gottingen, Vandenhoeck and Ruprecht, 1959.

24. Murphy, G. J., and J. F. Egan, "The Analysis of Demodulating Compensating Networks," *IRE Trans. Automatic Control*, Vol. AC-4, December 1959, pp. 71–79.

25. Brulé, John D., "Polynomial Extrapolations of Sampled-Data with an Analog Computer," *IRE Trans. Automatic Control*, Vol. AC-7, January 1962, pp. 76–77.

26. Cattermole, K. W., "Efficiency and Reciprocity in Pulse-Amplitude Modulation," *Proc. IEE*, Part B, September 1958, pp. 449–462.

27. Chang, S. S. L., *Synthesis of Optimum Control Systems*, McGraw-Hill Book Co.' New York, 1961, Ch. 6.

28. Jury, E. I., "Optimization Procedure for Sampled-Data and Digital Control Systems," *Scientia Electrica*, Zurich, Switzerland, Vol. VII, Part 1, 1961, pp. 16–26.

29. De Russo, P. M., "Optimum Linear Filtering of Signals Prior to Noise," *AIEE Trans.*, Part II, Vol. 79, 1960, pp. 549–555.

30. Thellier, P. L., "Optimization et Auto-Optimisation des systémes de Commande à Données Échantillonnées, en Présence de Saturations," Doctor of Science Thesis, 1962, Faculté des Sciences de L'université de Grenoble, Paris Impremiere Nationale, 1962.

31. Nishimura, T., "On the Modified z-Transform of Power Spectral Densities," *IRE Trans. Automatic Control*, July 1962, pp. 55–56.

32. Nishimura, T. and E. I. Jury, "Contribution to Statistical Design of Sampled-Data Control Systems," Institute of Engineering Research Report, Series 60, No. 210, July 1958, University of California, Berkeley.

33. Budnicki, Zdzislaw, "Input Impedance and Transfer Function of Ladder Network," *IEEE, PGCT*, Vol. CT-10, No. 2, June 1963, pp. 286–287.

34. Urkowitz, H., "Analysis and Synthesis of Delay Line Periodic Filters," *IRE, PGCT*, No. 2, Vol. CT-4, June 1957, pp. 41–53.

35. Robinson, E. A., "External Properties of the Wold Decomposition," *J. Math. Analysis and Applications*, Vol. 6, February 1963, pp. 75–85.

36. Murphy G. J., "The Analysis and Design of Production and Inventory Control Systems", *Proc. National Electronics Conference*, Vol. 19, 1963.

37. Iwens, R. P., "Application of the z-Transform to Sequential Circuits," Master of Science Project, Dept. of Electrical Engineering, University of California, Berkeley, January 1964.

38. Higgins, T. J. and J. K. Shah, "Basic Theory, and Application in Circuit Analysis of the Finite Alternate z-Transform," IEEE Conference paper No. CP 63–1467, Presented at Chicago, Illinois, October 28–30, 1963.

39. Higgins, T. J. and Robert E. Osterlei, "General Theory of Finite z-Transforms and Applications to Analysis of Discrete Systems," IEEE Conference paper No. CP 63–970, Presented at Toronto, Ont., Canada, June 16–21, 1963.

40. Christiansen, Peter L., "On the Closed Form of the Array Factor for Linear Arrays," *IEEE Trans. on Antennas and Propagation*, Vol. AP-11, No. 2, p. 198, March 1963.

APPENDIX

TABLE I. z-TRANSFORM PAIRS

Number	Discrete Time-Function $f(n),\ n \geq 0$	z-Transform $\mathscr{F}(z) = \mathscr{z}[f(n)],\ \lvert z \rvert > R$ $= \displaystyle\sum_{n=0}^{\infty} f(n)z^{-n}$
1	$u(n) = \begin{cases} 1, & \text{for } n \geq 0 \\ 0, & \text{otherwise} \end{cases}$	$\dfrac{z}{z-1}$
2	$e^{-\alpha n}$	$\dfrac{z}{z - e^{-\alpha}}$
3	n	$\dfrac{z}{(z-1)^2}$
4	n^2	$\dfrac{z(z+1)}{(z-1)^3}$
5	n^3	$\dfrac{z(z^2 + 4z + 1)}{(z-1)^4}$
6	n^4	$\dfrac{z(z^3 + 11z^2 + 11z + 1)}{(z-1)^5}$
7	n^5	$\dfrac{z(z^4 + 26z^3 + 66z^2 + 26z + 1)}{(z-1)^6}$
8	$n^{k}**$	$(-1)^k D^k \left(\dfrac{z}{z-1} \right);\quad D = z\dfrac{d}{dz}$

9	$u(n-k)$	$\dfrac{z^{-k+1}}{z-1}$
10	$e^{-\alpha n}f(n)$	$\mathscr{F}(e^{\alpha}z)$
11	$n^{(2)} = n(n-1)$	$2\dfrac{z}{(z-1)^3}$
12	$n^{(3)} = n(1-1)(n-2)$	$3!\dfrac{z}{(z-1)^4}$
13	$n^{(k)} = n(n-1)(n-2)\ldots(n-k+1)$	$k!\dfrac{z}{(z-1)^{k+1}}$
14	$n^{[k]}f(n), n^{[k]} = n(n+1)(n+2)\ldots(n+k-1)$	$(-1)^k z^k \dfrac{d^k}{dz^k}[\mathscr{F}(z)]$
15	$(-1)^k n(n-1)(n-2)\ldots(n-k+1)f_{n-k+1}$†	$z\mathscr{F}^{(k)}(z), \ \mathscr{F}^{(k)}(z) = \dfrac{d^k}{dz^k}\mathscr{F}(z)$
16	$-(n-1)f_{n-1}$	$\mathscr{F}^{(1)}(z)$
17	$(-1)^k(n-1)(n-2)\ldots(n-k)f_{n-k}$	$\mathscr{F}^{(k)}(z)$
18	$nf(n)$	$-z\mathscr{F}^{(1)}(z)$
19	$n^2 f(n)$	$z^2\mathscr{F}^{(2)}(z) + z\mathscr{F}^{(1)}(z)$
20	$n^3 f(n)$	$-z^3\mathscr{F}^{(3)}(z) - 3z^2\mathscr{F}^{(2)}(z) - z\mathscr{F}^{(1)}(z)$
21	$\dfrac{c^n}{n!}$	$e^{c/z}$
22	$\dfrac{(\ln c)^n}{n!}$	$c^{1/z}$

* Table IV represents entries for k up to 10.
† It may be noted that f_n is the same as $f(n)$

TABLE I (*Continued*)

Number	Discrete Time-Function $f(n)$, $n \geq 0$	z-Transform $\mathcal{F}(z) = \mathcal{Z}[f(n)], \|z\| > R$ $= \sum_{n=0}^{\infty} f(n) z^{-n}$
23	$\binom{k}{n} c^n a^{k-n}$, $\quad \binom{k}{n} = \dfrac{k!}{(k-n)! \, n!}$, $\quad n \leq k$	$\dfrac{(az + c)^k}{z^k}$
24	$\binom{n+k}{k} c^n$	$\dfrac{z^{k+1}}{(z-c)^{k+1}}$
25	$\dfrac{c^n}{n!}$, $\quad (n = 1,3,5,7,\ldots)$	$\sinh\left(\dfrac{c}{z}\right)$
26	$\dfrac{c^n}{n!}$, $\quad (n = 0,2,4,6,\ldots)$	$\cosh\left(\dfrac{c}{z}\right)$
27	$\sin(\alpha n)$	$\dfrac{z \sin \alpha}{z^2 - 2z \cos \alpha + 1}$
28	$\cos(\alpha n)$	$\dfrac{z(z - \cos \alpha)}{z^2 - 2z \cos \alpha + 1}$
29	$\sin(\alpha n + \psi)$	$\dfrac{z^2 \sin \psi + z \sin(\alpha - \psi)}{z^2 - 2z \cos \alpha + 1}$
30	$\cosh(\alpha n)$	$\dfrac{z(z - \cosh \alpha)}{z^2 - 2z \cosh \alpha + 1}$
31	$\sinh(\alpha n)$	$\dfrac{z \sinh \alpha}{z^2 - 2z \cosh \alpha + 1}$

32	$\dfrac{1}{n}$, $\quad n > 0$	$\ln\dfrac{z}{z-1}$
33	$\dfrac{1 - e^{-\alpha n}}{n}$	$\alpha + \ln\dfrac{z - e^{-\alpha}}{z - 1}$, $\quad \alpha > 0$
34	$\dfrac{\sin \alpha n}{n}$, $\quad n > 0$	$\alpha + \tan^{-1}\dfrac{\sin \alpha}{z - \cos \alpha}$, $\quad \alpha > 0$
35	$\dfrac{\cos \alpha n}{n}$, $\quad n > 0$	$\ln\dfrac{z}{\sqrt{z^2 - 2z\cos \alpha + 1}}$
36	$\dfrac{(n+1)(n+2)\dots(n+k-1)}{(k-1)!}$	$\left(1 - \dfrac{1}{z}\right)^{-k}$, $\quad k = 2,3,\dots$
37	$\displaystyle\sum_{m=1}^{n}\dfrac{1}{m}$	$\dfrac{z}{z-1}\ln\dfrac{z}{z-1}$
38	$\displaystyle\sum_{m=0}^{n-1}\dfrac{1}{m!}$	$\dfrac{e^{1/z}}{z-1}$
39	$\dfrac{(-1)^{(n-p)/2}}{2^n\left(\dfrac{n-p}{2}\right)!\left(\dfrac{n+p}{2}\right)!}$, $\quad$ for $n \geq p$ and $n - p = $ even $= 0,$ $\quad$ for $n < p$ or $n - p = $ odd $\quad (m = 0,1,2,\dots)$	$J_p(z^{-1})$
40	$\begin{cases}\dbinom{\alpha}{n\mid k} b^{n/k}, & n = mk, \quad (m = 0,1,2,\dots)\\ = 0, & n \neq mk\end{cases}$	$\left(\dfrac{z^k + b}{z^k}\right)^{\alpha}$
41	$a^n P_n(x) = \dfrac{a^n}{2^n n!}\left(\dfrac{d}{dx}\right)^n (x^2 - 1)^n$	$\dfrac{z}{\sqrt{z^2 - 2xaz + a^2}}$

TABLE I (Continued)

Number	Discrete Time-Function $f(n),\ n \geq 0$	z-Transform $\mathscr{F}(z) = \mathscr{z}[f(n)],\ \|z\| > R$ $= \displaystyle\sum_{n=0}^{\infty} f(n)z^{-n}$
42	$a^n T_n(x) = a^n \cos(n \cos^{-1} x)$	$\dfrac{z(z - ax)}{z^2 - 2xaz + a^2}$
43	$\dfrac{L_n(x)}{n!} = \displaystyle\sum_{r=0}^{\infty} \binom{n}{r} \dfrac{(-x)^r}{r!}$	$\dfrac{z}{z-1}\, e^{-x/(z-1)}$
44	$\dfrac{H_n(x)}{n!} = \displaystyle\sum_{k=0}^{[n/2]} \dfrac{(-1)^{n-k} x^{n-2k}}{k!\,(n-2k)!\,2^k}$	$e^{-x/z - 1/2z^2}$
45	$a^n P_n^m(x) = a^n(1 - x^2)^{m/2}\left(\dfrac{d}{dx}\right)^m P_n(x),\qquad m = \text{integer}$	$\dfrac{(2m)!}{2^m m!}\, \dfrac{z^{m+1}(1 - x^2)^{m/2} a^m}{(z^2 - 2xaz + a^2)^{m+1/2}}$
46	$\dfrac{L_n^m(x)}{n!} = \left(\dfrac{d}{dx}\right)^m \dfrac{L_n(x)}{n!},\qquad m = \text{integer}$	$\dfrac{(-1)^m z}{(z-1)^{m+1}}\, e^{-x/(z-1)}$
47	$-\dfrac{1}{n}\,\mathscr{z}^{-1}\left[z\,\dfrac{\mathscr{F}'(z)}{\mathscr{F}(z)} - z\,\dfrac{\mathscr{G}'(z)}{\mathscr{G}(z)}\right]$, where $\mathscr{F}(z)$ and $\mathscr{G}(z)$ are rational polynomials in z of the same order	$\ln\dfrac{\mathscr{F}(z)}{\mathscr{G}(z)}$
48	$\dfrac{1}{m(m+1)(m+2)\dots(m+n)}$	$(m-1)!\,z^m\left[e^{1/z} - \displaystyle\sum_{k=0}^{m-1} \dfrac{1}{k!\,z^k}\right]$
49	$\dfrac{\sin(\alpha n)}{n!}$	$e^{\cos\alpha/z} \cdot \sin\left(\dfrac{\sin\alpha}{z}\right)$

50	$\dfrac{\cos(\alpha n)}{n!}$	$e^{\cos \alpha/z} \cdot \cos\left(\dfrac{\sin \alpha}{z}\right)$
51	$\displaystyle\sum_{k=0}^{n} f_k g_{n-k}$	$\mathscr{F}(z)\mathscr{G}(z)$
52	$\displaystyle\sum_{k=0}^{n} k f_k g_{n-k}$	$-\mathscr{F}^{(1)}(z)\mathscr{G}(z),\ \mathscr{F}^{(1)}(z) = \dfrac{d\mathscr{F}(z)}{dz}$
53	$\displaystyle\sum_{k=0}^{n} k^2 f_k g_{n-k}$	$\mathscr{F}^{(2)}(z)\mathscr{G}(z)$
54	$\dfrac{\alpha^n + (-\alpha)^n}{2\alpha^2}$	$\dfrac{1}{z^2 - \alpha^2}$
55	$\dfrac{\alpha^n - \beta^n}{\alpha - \beta}$	$\dfrac{z}{(z-\alpha)(z-\beta)}$
56	$(n+k)^{(k)}$	$k!\, z^k\ \dfrac{z}{(z-1)^{k+1}}$
57	$(n-k)^{(k)}$	$k!\, z^{-k}\ \dfrac{z}{(z-1)^{k+1}}$
58	$\dfrac{(n \mp k)^{(m)}}{m!}\, e^{\alpha(n-k)}$	$\dfrac{z^{1 \mp k}\, k\, e^{m\alpha}}{(z - e^\alpha)^{m+1}}$
59	$\dfrac{1}{n}\sin\dfrac{\pi}{2}n$	$\dfrac{\pi}{2} + \tan^{-1}\dfrac{1}{z}$
60	$\dfrac{\cos\alpha(2n-1)}{2n-1},\quad n>0$	$\dfrac{1}{4\sqrt{z}}\ln\dfrac{z + 2\sqrt{z}\cos\alpha + 1}{z - 2\sqrt{z}\cos\alpha + 1}$

TABLE I (Continued)

Number	Discrete Time-Function $f(n)$, $n \geq 0$	z-Transform $\mathcal{F}(z) = \mathfrak{z}[f(n)], \|z\| > R$ $= \displaystyle\sum_{n=0}^{\infty} f(n) z^{-n}$
61	$\dfrac{\gamma^n}{(\gamma - 1)^2} + \dfrac{n}{1 - \gamma} - \dfrac{1}{(1 - \gamma)^2}$	$\dfrac{z}{(z - \gamma)(z - 1)^2}$
62	$\dfrac{\gamma + a_0}{(\gamma - 1)^2}\gamma^n + \dfrac{1 + a_0}{1 - \gamma}n + \left(\dfrac{1}{1 - \gamma} - \dfrac{a_0 + 1}{(1 - \gamma)^2}\right)$	$\dfrac{z(z + a_0)}{(z - \gamma)(z - 1)^2}$
63	$a^n \cos \pi n$	$\dfrac{z}{z + a}$
64	$e^{-\alpha n} \cos an$	$\dfrac{z(z - e^{-\alpha} \cos a)}{z^2 - 2ze^{-\alpha} \cos a + e^{-2\alpha}}$
65	$e^{-\alpha n} \sinh (an + \psi)$	$\dfrac{z^2 \sinh \psi + ze^{-\alpha} \sinh (a - \psi)}{z^2 - 2ze^{-\alpha} \cosh a + e^{-2\alpha}}$
66	$\dfrac{\gamma^n}{(\gamma - \alpha)^2 + \beta^2} + \dfrac{(\alpha^2 + \beta^2)^{n/2} \sin (n\theta + \psi)}{\beta[(\alpha - \gamma)^2 + \beta^2]^{1/2}}$ $\quad\quad\quad \theta = \tan^{-1} \dfrac{\beta}{\alpha}$ $\quad\quad\quad \psi = \tan^{-1} \dfrac{\beta}{\alpha - \gamma}$	$\dfrac{z}{(z - \gamma)[(z - \alpha)^2 + \beta^2]}$
67	$\dfrac{n\gamma^{n-1}}{(\gamma - 1)^3} - \dfrac{3\gamma^n}{(\gamma - 1)^4} + \dfrac{1}{2}\left[\dfrac{n(n - 1)}{(1 - \gamma)^2} - \dfrac{4n}{(1 - \gamma)^3} + \dfrac{6}{(1 - \gamma)^4}\right]$	$\dfrac{z}{(z - \gamma)^2(z - 1)^3}$
68	$\displaystyle\sum_{\nu=0}^{k} (-1)^\nu \binom{k}{\nu}\dfrac{(n + k - \nu)^{(k)}}{k!}e^{\alpha(n-\nu)}$	$\dfrac{z(z - 1)^k}{(z - e^\alpha)^{k+1}}$

No.		
69	$\dfrac{f(n)}{n}$	$\displaystyle\int_z^\infty p^{-1}\mathcal{F}(p)\,dp + \lim_{n\to 0}\frac{f(n)}{n}$
70	$\dfrac{f_{n+2}}{n+1},\quad f_0 = 0,\quad f_1 = 0$	$\displaystyle z\int_z^\infty \mathcal{F}(p)\,dp$
71	$\dfrac{1+a_0}{(1-\gamma)[(1-\alpha)^2+\beta^2]} + \dfrac{(\gamma+a_0)\gamma^n}{(\gamma-1)[(\gamma-\alpha)^2+\beta^2]}$ $+\dfrac{[\alpha^2+\beta^2]^{n/2}[(a_0+\alpha)^2+\beta^2]^{1/2}}{\beta[(\alpha-1)^2+\beta^2]^{1/2}[(\alpha-\gamma)^2+\beta^2]^{1/2}}\sin(n\theta+\psi+\lambda),$ $\psi = \psi_1 + \psi_2,\quad \psi_1 = -\tan^{-1}\dfrac{\beta}{\alpha-1},\quad \theta = \tan^{-1}\dfrac{\beta}{\alpha}$ $\psi_2 = -\tan^{-1}\dfrac{\beta}{\alpha-\gamma}$ $\lambda = \tan^{-1}\dfrac{\beta}{a_0+\alpha},$	$\dfrac{z(z+a_0)}{(z-1)(z-\gamma)[(z-\alpha)^2+\beta^2]}$
72	$(n+1)e^{\alpha n} - 2ne^{\alpha(n+1)} + e^{\alpha(n-2)}(n-1)$	$\left(\dfrac{z-1}{z-e^\alpha}\right)^2$
73	$(-1)^n\dfrac{\cos\alpha n}{n},\quad n>0$	$\ln\dfrac{z}{\sqrt{z^2+2z\cos\alpha+1}}$
74	$\dfrac{(n+k)!}{n!}f_{n+k},\quad f_n = 0,\ \text{for } 0\le n<k$	$(-1)^k z^{2k}\dfrac{d^k}{dz^k}[\mathcal{F}(z)]$
75	$\dfrac{f(n)}{n+h},\quad h>0$	$\displaystyle z^h\int_z^\infty p^{-(1+h)}\mathcal{F}(p)\,dp$
76	$-na^n\cos\dfrac{\pi}{2}n$	$\dfrac{2a^2z^2}{(z^2+a^2)^2}$

TABLE I (Continued)

Number	Discrete Time-Function $f(n), n \geq 0$	z-Transform $\mathscr{F}(z) = \mathfrak{z}[f(n)], \; |z| > R$ $= \sum_{n=0}^{\infty} f(n)z^{-n}$
77	$na^n \dfrac{1 + \cos \pi n}{2}$	$\dfrac{2a^2 z^2}{(z^2 - a^2)^2}$
78	$a^n \sin \dfrac{\pi}{4} n \cdot \dfrac{1 + \cos \pi n}{2}$	$\dfrac{a^2 z^2}{z^4 + a^4}$
79	$a^n \left(\dfrac{1 + \cos \pi n}{2} - \cos \dfrac{\pi}{2} n \right)$	$\dfrac{2a^2 z^2}{z^4 - a^4}$
80	$\dfrac{P_n(x)}{n!}$	$e^{xz^{-1}} J_0(\sqrt{1 - x^2 z^{-1}})$
81	$\dfrac{P_n^{(m)}(x)}{(n+m)!}, \quad m > 0, \quad P_n^m = 0, \quad$ for $n < m$	$(-1)^m e^{xz^{-1}} J_m(\sqrt{1 - x^2 z^{-1}})$
82	$\dfrac{1}{(n+\alpha)^\beta}, \; \alpha > 0, \; \operatorname{Re} \beta > 0$	$\Phi(z^{-1}, \alpha, \beta), \quad$ where $\Phi(1, \beta, \alpha) = \zeta(\beta, \alpha)$ = generalized Rieman-Zeta function
83	$a^n \left(\dfrac{1 + \cos \pi n}{2} + \cos \dfrac{\pi}{2} n \right)$	$\dfrac{2z^4}{z^4 - a^4}$
84	$\dfrac{c^n}{n}, \quad (n = 1,2,3,4, \ldots)$	$\ln z - \ln(z - c)$
85	$\dfrac{c^n}{n}, \quad n = 2,4,6,8, \ldots$	$\ln z - \tfrac{1}{2} \ln(z^2 - c^2)$

86	$n^2 c^n$	$\dfrac{cz(z+c)}{(z-c)^3}$
87	$n^3 c^n$	$\dfrac{cz(z^2+4cz+c^2)}{(z-c)^4}$
88	$n^k c^n$	$-\dfrac{d\mathscr{F}(z/c)}{dz}, \quad \mathscr{F}(z) = \mathfrak{z}[n^{k-1}]$
89	$-\cos\dfrac{\pi}{2}n \displaystyle\sum_{i=0}^{(n-2)/4}\binom{n/2}{2i+1}a^{n-2-4i}(a^4-b^4)^i$	$\dfrac{z^2}{z^4+2a^2z^2+b^4}$
90	$n^k f(n), \quad k>0$ and integer	$-z\dfrac{d}{dz}\mathscr{F}_1(z), \quad \mathscr{F}_1(z) = \mathfrak{z}[n^{k-1}f(n)]$
91	$\dfrac{(n-1)(n-2)(n-3)\ldots(n-k+1)}{(k-1)!}a^{n-k}$	$\dfrac{1}{(z-a)^k}$
92	$\dfrac{k(k-1)(k-2)\ldots(k-n+1)}{n!}$	$\left(1+\dfrac{1}{z}\right)^k$
93	$na^n \cos bn$	$\dfrac{[(z/a)^3 + z/a]\cos b - 2(z/a)^2}{[(z/a)^2 - 2(z/a)\cos b + 1]^2}$
94	$na^n \sin bn$	$\dfrac{(z/a)^3\sin b - (z/a)\sin b}{[(z/a)^2 - 2(z/a)\cos b + 1]^2}$
95	$\dfrac{na^n}{(n+1)(n+2)}$	$\dfrac{z(a-2z)}{a^2}\ln\left(1-\dfrac{a}{z}\right) - \dfrac{2}{a}z$
96	$\dfrac{(-a)^n}{(n+1)(2n+1)}$	$2\sqrt{z/a}\tan^{-1}\sqrt{a/z} - \dfrac{z}{a}\ln\left(1+\dfrac{a}{z}\right)$

TABLE I *(Continued)*

Number	Discrete Time-Function $f(n),\ n \geq 0$	z-*Transform* $\mathscr{F}(z) = \mathfrak{z}[f(n)],\ |z| > R = \sum\limits_{n=0}^{\infty} f(n)z^{-n}$
97	$\dfrac{a^n \sin \alpha n}{n+1}$	$\dfrac{z \cos \alpha}{a} \tan^{-1} \dfrac{a \sin \alpha}{z - a \cos \alpha}$ $+ \dfrac{z \sin \alpha}{2a} \ln \dfrac{z^2 - 2az \cos \alpha + a^2}{z^2}$
98	$\dfrac{a^n \cos (\pi/2)\, n \sin \alpha(n+1)}{n+1}$	$\dfrac{z}{4a} \ln \dfrac{z^2 + 2az \sin \alpha + a^2}{z^2 - 2az \sin \alpha + a^2}$
99	$\dfrac{1}{(2n)!}$	$\cosh(z^{-1/2})$
100	$\dbinom{-\frac{1}{2}}{n}(-a)^n$	$\sqrt{z}/(z - a)$
101	$\dbinom{-\frac{1}{2}}{\frac{n}{2}} a^n \cos \dfrac{\pi}{2}\, n$	$\dfrac{z}{\sqrt{z^2 - a^2}}$
102	$\dfrac{B_n(x)}{n!}$ $B_n(x)$ are Bernoulli polynomials	$\dfrac{e^{x/z}}{z(e^{1/z} - 1)}$
103	$W_n(x) \triangleq$ Tchebycheff polynomials of the second kind	$\dfrac{z^2}{z^2 - 2xz + 1}$
104	$\left| \sin \dfrac{n\pi}{m} \right|,\qquad m = 1, 2, \ldots$	$\dfrac{z \sin \pi/m}{z^2 - 2z \cos \pi/m + 1} \dfrac{1 + z^{-m}}{1 - z^{-m}}$

TABLE II. PAIRS OF MODIFIED z-TRANSFORMS†

$G(s)$	$\mathscr{G}(z, m)$‡
	Simple Forms of $G(s)$
$\dfrac{1}{s}$	$\dfrac{1}{z-1}$ (A.1)
$\dfrac{1}{s+a}$	$\dfrac{e^{-amT}}{z - e^{-aT}}$ (A.2)
	Quadratic Denominators of $G(s)$
$\dfrac{1}{s^2}$	$\dfrac{mT}{z-1} + \dfrac{T}{(z-1)^2}$ (A.3)
$\dfrac{1}{(s+a)^2}$	$Te^{-amT}\left[\dfrac{m}{z - e^{-aT}} + \dfrac{e^{-aT}}{(z - e^{-aT})^2} \right]$ (A.4)
$\dfrac{1}{(s+a)(s+b)}$	$\dfrac{1}{b-a}\left(\dfrac{e^{-amT}}{z - e^{-aT}} - \dfrac{e^{-bmT}}{z - e^{-bT}} \right)$ (A.5)
$\dfrac{s+a_0}{(s+a)(s+b)}$	$\dfrac{1}{b-a}\left[\dfrac{(a_0 - a)e^{-amT}}{z - e^{-aT}} - \dfrac{(a_0 - b)e^{-bmT}}{z - e^{-bT}} \right]$ (A.6)
$\dfrac{1}{(s+\alpha)^2 + \beta^2}$	$\dfrac{e^{-\alpha mT}}{\beta} \dfrac{z \sin m\beta T + e^{-\alpha T} \sin[(1-m)\beta T]}{z^2 - 2ze^{-\alpha T}\cos \beta T + e^{-2\alpha T}}$ (A.7)
$\dfrac{s+a_0}{(s+\alpha)^2 + \beta^2}$	$e^{-\alpha mT} \sec \phi \, \dfrac{z \cos (m\beta T + \phi) - e^{-\alpha T} \cos [(1-m)\beta T - \phi]}{z^2 - 2ze^{-\alpha T}\cos \beta T + e^{-2\alpha T}}$ (A.8)

$$\tan \phi = \dfrac{\alpha - a_0}{\beta}$$

TABLE II (*Continued*)

$G(s)$	$\mathscr{G}(z, m)$	
$\dfrac{1}{s^2 + \beta^2}$	$\dfrac{1}{\beta}\dfrac{z \sin m\beta T + \sin(1-m)\beta T}{z^2 - 2z \cos \beta T + 1}$	(A.9)
$\dfrac{1}{s^2 - \beta^2}$	$\dfrac{1}{\beta}\dfrac{z \sinh m\beta T + \sinh[(1-m)\beta T]}{z^2 - 2z \cosh \beta T + 1}$	(A.10)
$\dfrac{s}{s^2 + \beta^2}$	$\dfrac{z \cos m\beta T - \cos[(1-m)\beta T]}{z^2 - 2z \cos \beta T + 1}$	(A.11)
$\dfrac{s}{s^2 - \beta^2}$	$\dfrac{z \cosh m\beta T - \cosh(1-m)\beta T}{z^2 - 2z \cosh \beta T + 1}$	(A.12)
$\dfrac{s + a_0}{s^2 + \beta^2}$	$\dfrac{\sqrt{a_0^2 + \beta^2}\; z \cos(m\beta T - \phi) - \cos[(1-m)\beta T + \phi]}{\beta^2 \quad z^2 - 2z \cos \beta T + 1}$	(A.13)

$$\tan \phi = \frac{a_0}{\beta}$$

Some special forms of G(s)

$G(s)$	$\mathscr{G}(z, m)$
$\dfrac{k\pi/T}{s^2 + (k\pi/T)^2}$	$\dfrac{\sin mk\pi}{z + (-1)^{k+1}}$
$\dfrac{\pi/T}{s^2 + (\pi/T)^2}$	$\dfrac{\sin m\pi}{z + 1}$
$\dfrac{\pi/T}{(s+\alpha)^2 + (\pi/T)^2}$	$\dfrac{e^{-\alpha m T} \sin m\pi}{z + e^{-\alpha T}}$
$\dfrac{(s+\alpha)}{(s+\alpha)^2 + (\pi/T)^2}$	$\dfrac{e^{-\alpha m T} \cos m\pi}{z + e^{-\alpha T}}$

$F(s)$	z-transform	
$\dfrac{s+a}{(s+\alpha)^2+(\pi/T)^2}$	$\dfrac{e^{-\alpha mT}}{z+e^{-\alpha T}}\left[\dfrac{T(a-\alpha)}{\pi}\sin m\pi+\cos m\pi\right]$	(A.14)

Cubic Denominators of $G(s)$

$F(s)$	z-transform	
$\dfrac{1}{s^3}$	$\dfrac{T^2}{2}\left[\dfrac{m^2}{z-1}+\dfrac{2m+1}{(z-1)^2}+\dfrac{2}{(z-1)^3}\right]$	(A.15)
$\dfrac{1}{(s+a)^3}$	$\dfrac{T^2 e^{-amT}}{2}\left[\dfrac{m^2}{z-e^{-aT}}+\dfrac{(2m+1)e^{-aT}}{(z-e^{-aT})^2}+\dfrac{2e^{-2aT}}{(z-e^{-aT})^3}\right]$	(A.16)
$\dfrac{s+a_0}{s^2(s+\alpha)}$	$\dfrac{1}{\alpha}\left[\dfrac{a_0-\alpha}{\alpha}\dfrac{e^{-\alpha mT}}{(z-e^{-\alpha T})}+\dfrac{a_0 T}{(z-1)^2}+\left(a_0 mT+1-\dfrac{a_0}{\alpha}\right)\dfrac{1}{z-1}\right]$	(A.17)
$\dfrac{s^2+a_1 s+a_0}{s^2(s+\alpha)}$	$\dfrac{1}{\alpha}\left[\dfrac{a^2-a_1\alpha+a_0}{\alpha}\dfrac{e^{-\alpha mT}}{z-e^{-\alpha T}}+\dfrac{a_0 T}{(z-1)^2}+\left(a_0 mT+a_1-\dfrac{a_0}{\alpha}\right)\dfrac{1}{z-1}\right]$	(A.18)
$\dfrac{1}{s(s+a)(s+b)}$	$\dfrac{1}{ab(z-1)}+\dfrac{e^{-amT}}{a(a-b)(z-e^{-aT})}+\dfrac{e^{-bmT}}{b(b-a)(z-e^{-bT})}$	(A.19)
$\dfrac{s+a_0}{s(s+a)(s+b)}$	$\dfrac{a_0}{ab}\dfrac{1}{z-1}+\dfrac{a_0-a}{a(a-b)}\dfrac{e^{-amT}}{z-e^{-aT}}+\dfrac{a_0-b}{b(b-a)}\dfrac{e^{-bmT}}{z-e^{-bT}}$	(A.20)
$\dfrac{s^2+a_1 s+a_0}{s(s+a)(s+b)}$	$\dfrac{a_0}{ab}\dfrac{1}{z-1}+\dfrac{a^2-a_1 a+a_0}{a(a-b)}\dfrac{e^{-amT}}{z-e^{-aT}}+\dfrac{b^2-a_1 b+a_0}{b(b-a)}\dfrac{e^{-bmT}}{z-e^{-bT}}$	(A.21)

TABLE II (Continued)

$G(s)$	$\mathscr{G}(z, m)$
	Cubic Denominators of $G(s)$ (Continued)

$$\frac{1}{(s+a)(s+b)(s+c)} \qquad \frac{1}{(b-a)(c-a)}\frac{e^{-amT}}{z-e^{-aT}} + \frac{1}{(a-b)(c-b)}\frac{e^{-bmT}}{z-e^{-bT}} + \frac{1}{(a-c)(b-c)}\frac{e^{-cmT}}{z-e^{-cT}} \tag{A.22}$$

$$\frac{s+a_0}{(s+a)(s+b)(s+c)} \qquad \frac{a_0-a}{(b-a)(c-a)}\frac{e^{-amT}}{z-e^{-aT}} + \frac{a_0-b}{(a-b)(c-b)}\frac{e^{-bmT}}{z-e^{-bT}} + \frac{a_0-c}{(a-c)(b-c)}\frac{e^{-cmT}}{z-e^{-cT}} \tag{A.23}$$

$$\frac{s^2+a_1 s+a_0}{(s+a)(s+b)(s+c)} \qquad \frac{a^2-aa_1+a_0}{(c-a)(b-a)}\frac{e^{-amT}}{z-e^{-aT}} + \frac{b^2-ba_1+a_0}{(a-b)(c-b)}\frac{e^{-bmT}}{z-e^{-bT}} + \frac{c^2-ca_1+a_0}{(a-c)(b-c)}\frac{e^{-cmT}}{z-e^{-cT}} \tag{A.24}$$

$$\frac{1}{s(s+\alpha)^2} \qquad \frac{1}{\alpha^2}\left\{ \frac{1}{z-1} - e^{-\alpha mT}\left[\frac{1+\alpha mT}{z-e^{-\alpha T}} + \frac{\alpha Te^{-\alpha T}}{(z-e^{-\alpha T})^2} \right]\right\} \tag{A.25}$$

$$\frac{s+a_0}{s(s+\alpha)^2} \qquad \frac{1}{\alpha^2}\left\{ \frac{a_0}{z-1} + e^{-\alpha mT}\left[\frac{m\alpha T(a_0-\alpha)-a_0}{z-e^{-\alpha T}} + \frac{(a_0-\alpha)\alpha Te^{-\alpha T}}{(z-e^{-\alpha T})^2} \right]\right\} \tag{A.26}$$

$$\frac{s^2+a_1 s+a_0}{s(s+\alpha)^2} \qquad \frac{1}{\alpha^2}\left\{ \frac{a_0}{z-1} + e^{-\alpha mT}\left[\frac{\alpha^2-a_0+mT\alpha(a_1\alpha-\alpha^2-a_0)}{z-e^{-\alpha T}} + \frac{\alpha T(a_1\alpha-\alpha^2-a_0)e^{-\alpha T}}{(z-e^{-\alpha T})^2} \right]\right\} \tag{A.27}$$

$$\frac{1}{(s+b)(s+\alpha)^2} \qquad \frac{1}{(\alpha-b)^2}\left\{ \frac{e^{-bmT}}{z-e^{-bT}} + e^{-\alpha mT}\left[\frac{mT(\alpha-b)-1}{z-e^{-\alpha T}} + \frac{(\alpha-b)Te^{-\alpha T}}{(z-e^{-\alpha T})^2} \right]\right\} \tag{A.28}$$

$$\frac{s+a_0}{(s+b)(s+\alpha)^2} \qquad \frac{1}{(b-\alpha)^2}\left\{ \frac{(a_0-b)e^{-bmT}}{z-e^{-bT}} + e^{-\alpha mT}\left[\frac{(b-a_0)+(a_0-\alpha)(b-\alpha)mT}{z-e^{-\alpha T}} + \frac{(a_0-\alpha)(b-\alpha)Te^{-\alpha T}}{(z-e^{-\alpha T})^2} \right]\right\} \tag{A.29}$$

$$\frac{s^2 + a_1 s + a_0}{(s+b)(s+\alpha)^2}$$

$$\frac{1}{(b-\alpha)^2}\left\{(b^2 - a_1 b + a_0)\frac{e^{-bmT}}{z - e^{-bT}} + (\alpha^2 - 2\alpha b + a_1 b - a_0)\frac{e^{-\alpha mT}}{z - e^{-\alpha T}}\right.$$
$$\left. + (\alpha^2 - a_1\alpha + a_0)(b-\alpha)Te^{-\alpha mT}\left[\frac{m}{z - e^{-\alpha T}} + \frac{e^{-\alpha T}}{(z - e^{-\alpha T})^2}\right]\right\} \tag{A.30}$$

$$\frac{1}{s[(s+\alpha)^2 + \beta^2]}$$

$$\frac{1}{\alpha^2 + \beta^2}\left(\frac{1}{z-1} - e^{-\alpha mT}\sec\phi\,\frac{z\cos(m\beta T + \phi) - e^{-\alpha T}\cos[(1-m)\beta T - \phi]}{z^2 - 2ze^{-\alpha T}\cos\beta T + e^{-2\alpha T}}\right) \tag{A.31}$$

$$\tan\phi = \frac{-\alpha}{\beta}$$

$$\frac{s + a_0}{s[(s+\alpha)^2 + \beta^2]}$$

$$\frac{a_0}{\alpha^2 + \beta^2}\left(\frac{1}{z-1} - e^{-\alpha mT}\sec\phi\,\frac{z\cos(m\beta T + \phi) - e^{-\alpha T}\cos[(1-m)\beta T - \phi]}{z^2 - 2ze^{-\alpha T}\cos\beta T + e^{-2\alpha T}}\right) \tag{A.32}$$

$$\tan\phi = \frac{\alpha^2 + \beta^2 - \alpha a_0}{a_0\beta}$$

$$\frac{1}{(s+b)[(s+\alpha)^2 + \beta^2]}$$

$$\frac{1}{(\alpha-b)^2 + \beta^2}\left\{\frac{e^{-bmT}}{z - e^{-bT}} - e^{-\alpha mT}\sec\phi\,\frac{z\cos(m\beta T + \phi) - e^{-\alpha T}\cos[(1-m)\beta T - \phi]}{z^2 - 2ze^{-\alpha T}\cos\beta T + e^{-2\alpha T}}\right\} \tag{A.33}$$

$$\tan\phi = \frac{b - \alpha}{\beta}$$

$$\frac{s^2 + a_1 s + a_0}{s[(s+\alpha)^2 + \beta^2]}$$

$$\frac{1}{\alpha^2 + \beta^2}\left\{\frac{a_0}{z-1} + (\alpha^2 + \beta^2 - a_0)e^{-\alpha mT}\sec\phi\,\frac{z\cos(m\beta T + \phi) - e^{-\alpha T}\cos[(1-m)\beta T - \phi]}{z^2 - 2ze^{-\alpha T}\cos\beta T + e^{-2\alpha T}}\right\} \tag{A.34}$$

$$\tan\phi = \frac{\alpha - a_1}{\beta} - \frac{a_0(2\alpha - a_1)}{\beta(\alpha^2 + \beta^2 - a_0)}$$

$$\frac{s + a_0}{(s+b)[(s+\alpha)^2 + \beta^2]}$$

$$\frac{a_0 - b}{(\alpha - b)^2 + \beta^2}\left\{\frac{e^{-bmT}}{z - e^{-bT}} - e^{-\alpha mT}\sec\phi\,\frac{z\cos(m\beta T + \phi) - e^{-\alpha T}\cos[(1-m)\beta T - \phi]}{z^2 - 2ze^{-\alpha T}\cos\beta T + e^{-2\alpha T}}\right\} \tag{A.35}$$

$$\tan\phi = \frac{(a_0 - \alpha)(b - \alpha) - \beta^2}{(a_0 - b)\beta}$$

TABLE II (Continued)

$G(s)$	$\mathscr{G}(z, m)$	
$\dfrac{s^2 + a_1 s + a_0}{(s + b)[(s + \alpha)^2 + \beta^2]}$	$\dfrac{1}{(\alpha - b)^2 + \beta^2}\left\{(b^2 - a_1 b + a_0)\dfrac{e^{-bmT}}{z - e^{-bT}} + (\alpha^2 + \beta^2 - 2\alpha b + a_1 b - a_0)e^{-\alpha_m T}\sec\phi\ \dfrac{z\cos[m\beta T + \phi] - e^{-\alpha T}\cos[(1 - m)\beta T - \phi]}{z^2 - 2ze^{-\alpha T}\cos\beta T + e^{-2\alpha T}}\right\}$ $\tan\phi = \dfrac{\alpha + \dfrac{(\alpha^2\beta^2)(b - a_1) + 2a_0\alpha - a_0 b}{\alpha^2 + \beta^2 - 2\alpha b + a_1 b - a_0}}{\beta}$	(A.36)
$\dfrac{1}{s(s^2 + \beta^2)}$	$\dfrac{1}{\beta^2}\left\{\dfrac{1}{z - 1} - \dfrac{z\cos m\beta T - \cos[(1 - m)\beta T]}{z^2 - 2z\cos\beta T + 1}\right\}$	(A.37)
$\dfrac{s + a_0}{s(s^2 + \beta^2)}$	$\dfrac{a_0}{\beta^2}\left\{\dfrac{1}{z - 1} - \sec\phi\ \dfrac{z\cos(m\beta T - \phi) - \cos[(1 - m)\beta T + \phi]}{z^2 - 2z\cos\beta T + 1}\right\}$ $\tan\phi = \dfrac{a_0}{\beta}$	(A.38)
$\dfrac{s^2 + a_1 s + a_0}{s(s^2 + \beta^2)}$	$\dfrac{1}{\beta^2}\left\{\dfrac{a_0}{z - 1} + (\beta^2 - a_0)e^{-\alpha_m T}\sec\phi\ \dfrac{z\cos(m\beta T - \phi) - e^{-\alpha T}\cos[(1 - m)\beta T + \phi]}{z^2 - 2ze^{-\alpha T}\cos\beta T + e^{-2\alpha T}}\right\}$ $\tan\phi = \dfrac{a_1\beta}{\beta^2 - a_0}$	(A.39)
$\dfrac{s + a_0}{(s + b)(s^2 + \beta^2)}$	$\dfrac{a_0 - b}{\beta^2 + b^2}\left\{\dfrac{e^{-bmT}}{z - e^{-bT}} - \sec\phi\ \dfrac{z\cos(m\beta T + \phi) - \cos[(1 - m)\beta T - \phi]}{z^2 - 2z\cos\beta T + 1}\right\}$ $\tan\phi = \dfrac{a_0 b - \beta^2}{(a_0 - b)\beta}$	(A.40)

$$\frac{s^2 + a_1 s + a_0}{(s+b)(s^2+\beta^2)}$$

$$\frac{1}{\beta^2+b^2}\left\{(b^2 - a_1 b + a_0)\frac{e^{-bmT}}{z-e^{-bT}}\right.$$
$$\left. + (\beta^2 + a_1 b - a_0)\sec\phi\,\frac{z\cos(m\beta T + \phi) - \cos[(1-m)\beta T - \phi]}{z^2 - 2z\cos\beta T + 1}\right\} \quad (A.41)$$

$$\tan\phi = \frac{\beta^2(b - a_1) - a_0 b}{\beta(\beta^2 a_1 b - a_0)} \quad (A.42)$$

Biquadratic Denominators of G(s)

$$\frac{1}{s^4}$$

$$\frac{T^3}{6}\left[\frac{m^3}{z-1} + \frac{3m^2+3m+1}{(z-1)^2} + \frac{6m+6}{(z-1)^3} + \frac{6}{(z-1)^4}\right] \quad (A.43)$$

$$\frac{1}{s^3(s+a)}$$

$$\frac{1}{a}\left[\frac{T^2m^2/2 - mT/a + 1/a^2}{z-1} + \frac{T^2(m+1/2) - T/a}{(z-1)^2} + \frac{T^2}{(z-1)^3} - \frac{1}{a^2}\frac{e^{-amT}}{z - e^{-aT}}\right] \quad (A.44)$$

$$\frac{1}{s^2(s+a)^2}$$

$$\frac{1}{a^2}\left[\frac{mT - 2/a}{z-1} + \frac{T}{(z-1)^2} + \frac{e^{-amT}(mT + 2/a)}{z - e^{-aT}} + \frac{Te^{-aT(m+1)}}{(z-e^{-aT})^2}\right]$$

$$\frac{1}{(s+a)^2(s^2+\beta^2)}$$

$$\frac{1}{a^2+\beta^2}\left\{e^{-amT}\left[\frac{\frac{2a}{a^2+\beta^2}+mT}{z-e^{-aT}} + \frac{Te^{-aT}}{(z-e^{-aT})^2}\right] + \frac{1}{\beta}\frac{\cos[(1-m)\beta T+\phi] - z\cos(m\beta T-\phi)}{z^2-2z\cos\beta T+1}\right\}$$

$$\tan\phi = \frac{\beta^2 - a^2}{2a\beta} \quad (A.45)$$

$$\frac{1}{s^2(s^2+\beta^2)}$$

$$\frac{1}{\beta^2}\left\{\frac{mT}{z-1} + \frac{T}{(z-1)^2} - \frac{1}{\beta}\frac{z\sin\beta T + \sin[(1-m)\beta T]}{z^2-2z\cos\beta T+1}\right\} \quad (A.46)$$

TABLE II (Continued)

$G(s)$	$\mathscr{G}(z,m)$
$\dfrac{1}{s^2[(s+\alpha)^2+\beta^2]}$	$\dfrac{2\alpha}{(\alpha^2+\beta^2)^2}\left\{\dfrac{[T(\alpha^2+\beta^2)/2\alpha]}{(z-1)^2}+\dfrac{[mT(\alpha^2+\beta^2)/2\alpha]-1}{z-1}\right.$ $\left.+\sec\phi\,e^{-\alpha mT}\dfrac{z\cos(m\beta T+\phi)-e^{-\alpha T}\cos[(1-m)\beta T-\phi]}{z^2-2ze^{-\alpha T}\cos\beta T+e^{-2\alpha T}}\right\}$ $\tan\phi=\dfrac{\beta^2-\alpha^2}{2\alpha\beta}\qquad\text{(A.47)}$
$\dfrac{s+a_0}{s^2[(s+\alpha)^2+\beta^2]}$	$\dfrac{1}{\beta_0^4}\left\{\dfrac{\beta_1^2+a_0\beta_0^2 mT}{z-1}+\dfrac{a_0\beta_0^2 T}{(z-1)^2}-\beta_1^2 e^{-\alpha mT}\sec\phi\,\dfrac{z\cos(m\beta T+\phi)-e^{-\alpha T}\cos[(1-m)\beta T-\phi]}{z^2-2ze^{-\alpha T}\cos\beta T+e^{-2\alpha T}}\right\}$ $\beta_0^2=\alpha^2+\beta^2;\quad\beta_1^2=\beta_0^2-2\alpha a_0$ $\tan\phi=-\dfrac{\alpha\beta_1^2+a_0\beta_0^2}{\beta\beta_1^2}$ $\text{When }a_0=\alpha,\ \tan\phi=-\dfrac{2\alpha\beta}{\beta^2-\alpha^2}\qquad\text{(A.48)}$

E. I. Jury, "Additions to the Modified z-Transform Method," *I.R.E. Wescon Convention Record*, Part IV, August 21, 1957, pp. 136–156. Similar tables of modified z-transform are presented by R. H. Barker, "The Pulse Transfer Function and Its Applications to Sampling Servo Systems," *Proc. I.E.E. (London)*, Vol. 99, Part IV, 1952, pp. 302–307.

† A few entries of Barker's table (British Crown Copyright) in a modified form have been included in the table above for which the permission of the Controller of Her Britannic Majesty's Stationary Office has been obtained.

‡ It should be noted that $\mathscr{G}(z)$ can be obtained by multiplying $\mathscr{G}(z,m)$ by z and letting m go to zero.

TABLE III   TOTAL SQUARE INTEGRALS

A solution of the integral

$$I_n = \frac{1}{2\pi j} \oint_{\substack{\text{unit} \\ \text{circle}}} \mathscr{F}(z, m)\mathscr{F}(z^{-1}, m)z^{-1}\, dz$$

is presented in this table.

Let

$$\mathscr{F}(z, m) = \frac{B(z)}{A(z)}$$

where

$$A(z) = \sum_{r=0}^{n} a_r z^{n-r}, \qquad a_0 \neq 0$$

$$B(z) = \sum_{r=0}^{n} b_r z^{n-r}, \quad \text{and} \quad \text{the } b_r\text{'s are bounded functions of } m,$$
$$0 \leq m \leq 1$$

and the coefficients $a_r, 0 < r \leq n$, and $b_r, 0 \leq r \leq n$ are not necessarily nonzero.

The integral I_n is equivalent to the ratio of two determinants as follows:

$$I_n = \frac{|\Omega_1|}{a_0 |\Omega|}$$

where Ω is the following matrix:

$$\Omega \triangleq \begin{bmatrix} a_0 & a_1 & a_2 & a_3 & \cdots & a_n \\ a_1 & a_0 + a_2 & a_1 + a_3 & a_2 + a_4 & \cdots & a_{n-1} \\ a_2 & a_3 & a_0 + a_4 & a_1 + a_5 & \cdots & a_{n-2} \\ \vdots & & & & & \\ a_n & 0 & 0 & 0 & \cdots & a_0 \end{bmatrix}$$

and Ω_1 is the matrix formed from Ω by replacing the first column by

$$\begin{bmatrix} \sum_{i=0}^{n} b_i^2 \\ 2 \sum b_i b_{i+1} \\ 2 \sum b_i b_{i+2} \\ \vdots \\ 2 \sum b_i b_{i+n-1} \\ 2 b_0 b_n \end{bmatrix}$$

TABLE III   (*Continued*)

Tabulated values of the integral I_n

$$I_n = \frac{1}{2\pi j} \oint_{\substack{\text{unit} \\ \text{circle}}} \frac{B(z)}{A(z)} \frac{B(z^{-1})}{A(z^{-1})} z^{-1} \, dz$$

1. $\mathscr{F}(z) = \dfrac{b_0 z + b_1}{a_0 z + a_1} = \dfrac{B(z)}{A(z)}$

$$I_1 = \frac{(b_0^2 + b_1^2)a_0 - 2b_0 b_1 a_1}{a_0(a_0^2 - a_1^2)}$$

2. $\mathscr{F}(z) = \dfrac{b_0 z^2 + b_1 z + b_2}{a_0 z^2 + a_1 z + a_2}$

$$I_2 = \frac{B_0 a_0 e_1 - B_1 a_0 a_1 + B_2(a_1^2 - a_2 e_1)}{a_0[(a_0^2 - a_2^2)e_1 - (a_0 a_1 - a_1 a_2)a_1]}$$

$B_0 = b_0^2 + b_1^2 + b_2^2$

$B_1 = 2(b_0 b_1 + b_1 b_2)$

$B_2 = 2b_0 b_2$

$e_1 = a_0 + a_2$

3. $\mathscr{F}(z) = \dfrac{b_0 z^3 + b_1 z^2 + b_2 z + b_3}{a_0 z^3 + a_1 z^2 + a_2 z + a_3}$

$$I_3 = \frac{a_0 B_0 Q_0 - a_0 B_1 Q_1 + a_0 B_2 Q_2 - B_3 Q_3}{[(a_0^2 - a_3^2)Q_0 - (a_0 a_1 - a_2 a_3)Q_1 + (a_0 a_2 - a_1 a_3)Q_2]a_0}$$

$B_0 = b_0^2 + b_1^2 + b_2^2 + b_3^2$

$B_1 = 2(b_0 b_1 + b_1 b_2 + b_2 b_3)$

$B_2 = 2(b_0 b_2 + b_1 b_3)$

$B_3 = 2b_0 b_3$

$Q_0 = (a_0 e_1 - a_3 e_2)$

$Q_1 = (a_0 a_1 - a_2 a_3)$

$Q_2 = (a_1 e_2 - a_2 e_1)$

$Q_3 = (a_1 - a_3)(e_2^2 - e_1^2) + a_0(a_0 e_2 - a_3 e_1)$

$e_1 = a_0 + a_2$

$e_2 = a_1 + a_3$

TABLE III (*Continued*)

4. $\mathcal{F}(z) = \dfrac{b_0 z^4 + b_1 z^3 + b_2 z^2 + b_3 z + b_4}{a_0 z^4 + a_1 z^3 + a_2 z^2 + a_3 z + a_4}$

$I_4 = \dfrac{a_0 B_0 Q_0 - a_0 B_1 Q_1 + a_0 B_2 Q_2 - a_0 B_3 Q_3 + B_4 Q_4}{a_0[(a_0^2 - a_4^2)Q_0 - (a_0 a_1 - a_3 a_4)Q_1 \\ \qquad\qquad + (a_0 a_2 - a_2 a_4)Q_2 - (a_0 a_3 - a_1 a_4)Q_3]}$

$B_0 = b_0^2 + b_1^2 + b_2^2 + b_3^2 + b_4^2, \qquad B_3 = 2(b_0 b_3 + b_1 b_4)$

$B_1 = 2(b_0 b_1 + b_1 b_2 + b_2 b_3 + b_3 b_4), \qquad B_4 = 2 b_0 b_4$

$B_2 = 2(b_0 b_2 + b_1 b_3 + b_2 b_4)$

$Q_0 = a_0 e_1 e_4 - a_0 a_3 e_2 + a_4(a_1 e_2 - e_3 e_4)$

$Q_1 = a_0 a_1 e_4 - a_0 a_2 a_3 + a_4(a_1 a_2 - a_3 e_4)$

$Q_2 = a_0 a_1 e_2 - a_0 a_2 e_1 + a_4(a_2 e_3 - a_3 e_2)$

$Q_3 = a_1(a_1 e_2 - e_3 e_4) - a_2(a_1 e_1 - a_3 e_3) + a_3(e_1 e_4 - a_3 e_2)$

$Q_4{}^* = a_0[e_2(a_1 a_4 - a_0 a_3) + e_5(a_0^2 - a_4^2)] \\ \qquad\qquad + (e_2^2 - e_5^2)[a_1(a_1 - a_3) + (a_0 - a_4)(e_4 - a_2)]$

$e_1 = a_0 + a_2$

$e_2 = a_1 + a_3$

$e_3 = a_2 + a_4$

$e_4 = a_0 + a_4$

$e_5 = a_0 + a_2 + a_4$

---

* For ease of calculations Q_4 and Q_3 of I_3 can be respectively written

$$Q_4 = -a_4 Q_0 + a_3 Q_1 - a_2 Q_2 + a_1 Q_3$$
$$Q_3 = a_3 Q_0 - a_2 Q_1 + a_1 Q_2$$

The author is grateful to Dr. Paul Le Fevre of Paris, France for pointing out these relationships.

TABLE IV CLOSED FORMS OF THE FUNCTION $\sum\limits_{n=0}^{\infty} n^r x^n$, $x < 1$

r	$\sum\limits_{n=0}^{\infty} n^r x^n$
0	$\dfrac{1}{1-x}$
1	$\dfrac{x}{(1-x)^2}$
2	$\dfrac{x^2 + x}{(1-x)^3}$
3	$\dfrac{x^3 + 4x^2 + x}{(1-x)^4}$
4	$\dfrac{x^4 + 11x^3 + 11x^2 + x}{(1-x)^5}$
5	$\dfrac{x^5 + 26x^4 + 66x^3 + 26x^2 + x}{(1-x)^6}$
6	$\dfrac{x^6 + 57x^5 + 302x^3 + 302x^4 + 57x^2 + x}{(1-x)^7}$
7	$\dfrac{x^7 + 120x^6 + 1191x^5 + 2416x^4 + 1191x^3 + 120x^2 + x}{(1-x)^8}$
8	$\dfrac{x^8 + 247x^7 + 4293x^6 + 15619x^5 + \ldots + x}{(1-x)^9}$
9	$\dfrac{x^9 + 502x^8 + 14608x^7 + 88234x^6 + 156190x^5 + \ldots + x}{(1-x)^{10}}$
10	$\dfrac{x^{10} + 1013x^9 + 47840x^8 + 455192x^7 + 1310354x^6 + \ldots + x}{(1-x)^{11}}$

The missing terms are apparent since the numerator polynomials are symmetric in the coefficients.

PROBLEMS

Chapter 1

PROBLEM 1.1   Prove equations: (1.50), (1.51), and (1.52).

PROBLEM 1.2   Prove equations: (1.97)–(1.105) and (1.107)–(1.109).

PROBLEM 1.3   The basic Fibonacci sequence f_n has the following recurrence relationship

$$f_{n+2} = f_{n+1} + f_n, \qquad \text{where } f_0 = 0, f_1 = 1.$$

Let $\phi_n = f_{2n}$ and $\psi_n = f_{2n+1}$. Obtain the z-transforms of

(a) $\Phi(z) = \jmath[\phi_n]$,   and   (b) $\Psi(z) = \jmath[\psi_n]$

(c) Find the relationship between $\Psi(z)$ and $\Phi(z)$.

PROBLEM 1.4   Show that

$$z\left[\frac{1}{(s+a)^n}\right] = \frac{T^{n-1}}{(n-1)!}$$

$$\cdot x\left[\frac{1 + x^{n-2} + a_1^n(x + x^{n-3}) + a_2^n(x^2 + x^{n-4}) + \ldots + a_k^n(x^k + x^{n-2-k})}{(1-x)^n}\right]$$

where

$$x = e^{-aT}z^{-1}$$

and

$$a_p^n = c_n^0(p+1)^{n-1} - c_n^1 p^{n-1} + \ldots + (-1)^q c_n^q(p-q+1)^{n-1}$$
$$+ \ldots + (-1)^p c_n^p$$

$$c_n^p = \frac{n!}{p!\,(n-p)!}$$

PROBLEM 1.5   A sampled-data control system is shown in Fig. 1.5. Given

$$G(s) = \frac{1}{s+1} e^{-1.35sT}$$

$$H(s) = \frac{1}{s+2} e^{-2.8sT}$$

$$T = 1, \quad R(s) = \frac{1}{s}$$

(a) Obtain $\mathscr{C}(z, m)$.

(b) Find the continuous response.

(c) Indicate how to obtain from (b) the response at sampling instants.

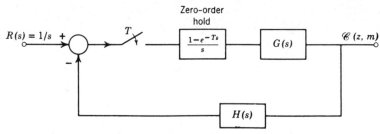

FIGURE PROB. 1.5

PROBLEM 1.6   For the delayed sampler operation of system in Fig. 1.6, obtain the modified z-transform of the output and the actual output $c(n,m)T = c(t)$.

FIGURE PROB. 1.6

PROBLEM 1.7   If

$$\mathscr{J} \frac{B_n(x)}{n!} = \frac{e^{x/z}}{z[e^{1/z} - 1]}, \qquad \text{where } B_n(x) \text{ are the Bernoulli polynomials}$$

show

(a) $B_0(x) = 0! (1) = 1$

$B_1(x) = 1! (x - \frac{1}{2}) = x - \frac{1}{2}$

$\cdot$

$\cdot$

$\cdot$

$B_3(x) = 3! \left(\frac{x^3}{6} - \frac{x^2}{4} + \frac{x}{12} \right) = x^3 - \frac{3}{2} x^2 + \frac{x}{2}$

(b) $B_{2n+1} = 0$, $\quad n = 1, 2, 3, \ldots$, $\quad$ where $B_n \equiv B_n(0) = $ Bernoulli numbers

(c) $B_1(1) = \frac{1}{2}$, $B_n(1) = B_n$, $\quad n = 0, 2, 3, 4, \ldots$

(d) $\dfrac{B_p(x)}{p!} = \sum_{n=0}^{p} B_n \dfrac{x^{p-n}}{n!\,(p-n)!} = \dfrac{1}{p!} \sum_{n=0}^{p} \binom{p}{n} B_n x^{p-n}$

PROBLEM 1.8   Show that

$$\sum_{x=1}^{N-1} x^p = \frac{1}{p+1}[B_{p+1}(N) - B_{p+1}(1)]$$

when $p = 5$, we get

$$\sum_{x=1}^{N-1} x^5 = \frac{1}{6}[N^6 - 3N^5 + \tfrac{5}{2}N^4 - \tfrac{1}{2}N^2 + \tfrac{1}{42} - \tfrac{1}{42}]$$

PROBLEM 1.9   Show that

$$\sum_{n=1}^{\infty} \frac{1}{n^{2p}} = \frac{(2\pi)^{2p}(-1)^{p-1}}{2(2p)!} B_{2p}, \quad p = 1, 2, 3, \ldots$$

Hint: (a) Show first that $2y \coth y = 2y/(e^{2y} - 1) + 2y/(1 - e^{-2y})$

(b) Using the generating function of Bernoulli's numbers, obtain*

$$y \coth y = \sum_{p=0}^{\infty} B_{2p} \frac{(2y)^{2p}}{(2p)!}$$

PROBLEM 1.10   Show that

$$B_n(1 - x) = (-1)^n B_n(x)$$

PROBLEM 1.11   Obtain the steady-state response v_{ss} of the voltage across the resistor for the initially unexcited circuit shown in Fig. 1.11a in response to a periodic input shown in Fig. 1.11b.

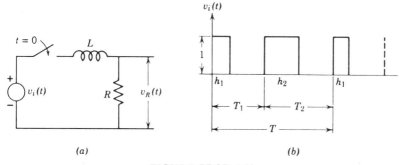

(a)   (b)

FIGURE PROB. 1.11

---

* The generating function of $f(n)$ is defined by $\displaystyle\sum_{n=0}^{\infty} f(n)z^n$.

PROBLEM 1.12   Show that

$$\int_0^\infty f(t)\,dt\Bigr] = T\int_0^1 \mathcal{F}(z, m)\Bigr|_{z=1}\,dm$$

$$\int_0^\infty f(t)^2\,dt\Bigr] = \frac{T}{2\pi j}\int_\Gamma\int_0^1 p^{-1}\mathcal{F}\,(p, m)\,\mathcal{F}(p^{-1}, m)\,dm\,dp$$

PROBLEM 1.13   Show that

$$\frac{1}{T}\sum_{k=-\infty}^{\infty} F\left(jk\,\frac{2\pi}{T}\right) = \mathcal{F}(z, m)\Bigr|_{z=1, m=1},\qquad \text{for } f(0^+) = 0$$

PROBLEM 1.14   Show that

$$\mathcal{Z}_m[F(s)\bigr|_{s=0}] = T\int_0^1 \mathcal{F}(1, m)\,dm$$

PROBLEM 1.15   Show that

$$\mathcal{Z}_m[F(s)G(s)] = Tz\int_0^m \mathcal{F}(z, m - \lambda)\mathcal{G}(z, \lambda)\,d\lambda$$
$$+ T\int_m^1 \mathcal{F}(z, 1 + m - \lambda)\mathcal{G}(z, \lambda)\,d\lambda$$

and

$$\mathcal{Z}_m[F(s)G(-s)] = T\int_0^m \mathcal{F}(z, m - \lambda)\mathcal{G}(z^{-1}, 1 - \lambda)\,d\lambda$$
$$+ Tz^{-1}\int_m^1 \mathcal{F}(z, 1 + m - \lambda)\mathcal{G}(z^{-1}, 1 - \lambda)\,d\lambda$$

Chapter 2

PROBLEM 2.1   In the example of Section 2.1, let V be a d-c voltage source of 10 volts and R = 1 ohm. Find the current in the 10th loop (i.e., n = 9), if the end loop (i.e., 10th) is short-circuited.

PROBLEM 2.2   For the ladder network with capacitors shown in Fig. 2.2, assuming zero initial conditions,

(a) Write the equation of the $(n + 1)$st loop.
(b) Obtain the expression for $\mathcal{I}(z, s) \triangleq \mathcal{Z}[I(n, s)]$, and $I(n, s) = \mathcal{L}_t[i(n, t)]$.
(c) Obtain $I(n, s)$
(d) Show how to obtain $i(n, t)$.

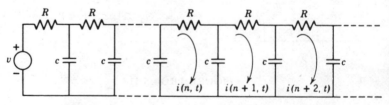

FIGURE PROB. 2.2.   Ladder network with capacitors.

PROBLEM 2.3 Consider a series in which the first r terms are all positive, the next r all negative, the next r all positive, and so on. This can be expressed as follows
The sequence u_n is

$$1, 1, \ldots, 1, \quad -1, -1, \ldots, -1, \quad 1, 1, \ldots$$

$$\underbrace{}_{r \text{ terms}} \quad \underbrace{}_{r \text{ terms}} \quad \underbrace{}_{}$$

Obtain the factor u_n which must be introduced into the nth term to allow for such fluctuation of sign.

PROBLEM 2.4 Given the Fibonacci's numbers as follows:

$$0, 1, 1, 2, 3, 5, 8, 13, 21, 34, \ldots$$

(Each of these numbers is the sum of the two numbers immediately preceding it.)
(a) Obtain the difference equation which describes the general term f_n.
(b) Solve the difference equation in (a) by the z-transform method and show that the solution for f_n can be presented by the following formula:

$$f_n = \frac{1}{2^{n-1}} \left[\binom{n}{1} + \binom{n}{3} 5 + \binom{n}{5} 5^2 + \ldots + \binom{n}{2m+1} 5^m + \ldots \right]$$

PROBLEM 2.5 Given the following constant coefficient difference equation:

$$a_l y(n) + a_{l-1} y(n-1) + \ldots + a_0 y(n-l)$$
$$= b_{l_1} x(n-l+l_1) + b_{l_1-1} x(n-l+l_1-1) + \ldots + b_0 x(n-l)$$

For zero initial condition show that $y(n)$ can be represented as follows:

$$y(n) = \frac{1}{a_l} \left\{ \sum_{v=0}^{l_1} b_{l_1-v} x(n-l+l_1-v) - \sum_{v=1}^{l} a_{l-v} y(n-v) \right\}$$

PROBLEM 2.6 Find the solution $x(t)$ for the following difference-differential equation:
$$x'(t) + 2x(t-1) + x(t) = f(t)$$

if $x \equiv 0$ for $t \leq 0$, and $f(t) =$ unit step and unit ramp.

PROBLEM 2.7 For a periodically varying sampling rate system shown in Fig. 2.7a obtain the response for a step input. T_n is represented as follows (shown

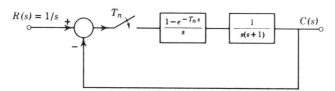

FIGURE PROB. 2.7a

graphically in Fig. 2.7b):

$$
T_n = \begin{cases} 0.5 \text{ second} & n = 0, 4, 8, 12, \ldots \\ 0.5 \text{ second} & n = 1, 5, 9, 13, \ldots \\ 1.0 \text{ second} & n = 2, 6, 10, 15, \ldots \\ 1.0 \text{ second} & n = 3, 7, 11, 15, \ldots \end{cases}
$$

The total period $T = 3.0$ seconds.

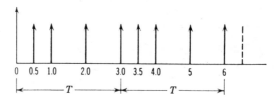

FIGURE PROB. 2.7b The sampling pattern of system of Fig. 2.7a.

PROBLEM 2.8   For the time-varying sampled-data system shown in Fig. 2.8, given the following values:

$$d_n = 1 + e^{-n}$$

$$\mathscr{G}(z) = \frac{1}{z - 1}, \; T = 1, \; \mathscr{R}(z) = \frac{z}{z - 1}$$

(a) Obtain the equation for the z-transform of the output $\mathscr{C}(z)$.
(b) Show that the solution c_n of the equation obtained in (a) is

$$c(n) = 1 - (-1)^n e^{-(1/2)n(n-1)}$$

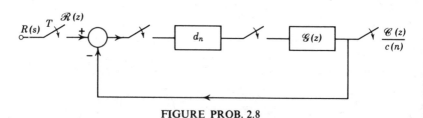

FIGURE PROB. 2.8

PROBLEM 2.9   A square of side n units is subdivided into n^2 (see Fig. 2.9) unit squares by parallels to the sides. The diagonal OA is drawn and also the diagonals which are parallel to OA of all the unit squares.
Obtain the number of paths by which one may travel from O to A keeping to

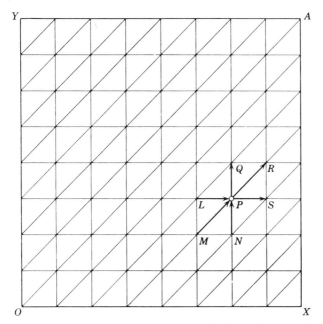

FIGURE PROB. 2.9   A square of side n units.

the lines of the figure.   It is understood that at junctions such as P, a path may proceed in one of the directions PQ, PR, or PS only.

PROBLEM 2.10   Find the eigenvalues of the following matrix:

$$
A = \begin{bmatrix}
0 & 1 & 0 & . & . & . & 0 \\
1 & 0 & 1 & 0 & & & . \\
0 & 1 & 0 & 1 & 0 & & . \\
 & . & . & . & . & . & \\
 & . & . & . & . & . & . \\
 & . & . & . & . & . & \\
 & . & & . & . & . & 0 \\
 & . & & . & . & . & \\
 & . & & 0 & 1 & 0 & 1 \\
0 & . & . & . & 0 & 1 & 0
\end{bmatrix}
$$

by using a recurrence relationship in the computation of the required determinants.

Chapter 3

PROBLEM 3.1   Check for the number of roots inside the unit circle for the following polynomials:

(a) $F_1(z) = 12z^6 + 16z^5 + 20z^4 + 14z^3 + 9z^2 + 3z + 1$

(b) $F_2(z) = 6z^6 + 8z^5 + 19z^4 + 19z^3 + 15z^2 + 6z + 2$

PROBLEM 3.2   If the determinant $|X_k + Y_k|$ is expanded as follows:

$$|X_k + Y_k| = \begin{vmatrix} a_0 + b_{n-k+1} & a_1 + b_{n-k+2} & \cdots & a_{k-1} + b_n \\ & b_{n-k+2} & a_0 + b_{n-k+3} & \cdots & a_{k-2} \\ & \vdots & & & \\ & & \Delta_2 & & \Delta_1 \\ & b_n & & \cdots & & a_0 \end{vmatrix}$$

$$= a_0 \Delta_1 \mp b_n \Delta_2$$

Then if Δ_1 is expanded, the expansion of the second determinant, Δ_2, can be written from the first, Δ_1, by replacing a_k by b_{n-k} and b_k by a_{n-k}.

PROBLEM 3.3   Given the following fourth-order real polynomial,

$$F(z) = a_0 + a_1 z + a_2 z^2 + a_3 z^3 + a_4 z^4, \qquad \text{with } a_4 = 1$$

(a) Show that the conditions for the roots to be real are

$$D_0 = a_1^2 - 2a_0 a_2 > 0$$

$$D_1 = \begin{vmatrix} a_1^2 - 2a_0 a_2 & a_1 a_2 - 3a_0 a_3 \\ a_1 a_2 - 3a_0 a_3 & 2a_2 - 4a_0 - 2a_1 a_3 \end{vmatrix} > 0$$

$$D_2 = \begin{vmatrix} & D_1 & & a_1 a_3 - 4a_0 \\ & & & 2a_2 a_3 - 3a_1 \\ a_1 a_3 - 4a_0 & 2a_2 a_3 - 3a_1 & 3a_3^2 - 2a_2 \end{vmatrix} > 0$$

and

$$D_3 = \begin{vmatrix} & & & a_1 \\ & D_2 & & 2a_2 \\ & & & 3a_3 \\ a_1 & 2a_2 & 3a_3 & 4 \end{vmatrix} > 0$$

(*b*) For the real roots to lie between zero and unity we require the following additional conditions:

$$1 + a_3 + a_2 + a_1 + a_0 > 0$$
$$a_3 + 2a_2 + 3a_1 + 4a_0 < 0$$
$$a_2 + 3a_1 + 6a_0 > 0$$
$$a_1 + 4a_0 < 0$$
$$a_0 > 0$$

PROBLEM 3.4   Show that for an aperiodic system (discrete or continuous), the maximum number of extrema is $n - 1$, where the order of the system is n.

Hint: Show this for a second-order system and by induction for the *n*th order system.

PROBLEM 3.5   Obtain the number of roots inside, outside, and on the unit circle for the following real polynomial:

$$F(z) = z^6 + 0.7z^5 + 0.4z^4 - 8.5z^3 - 5.6z^2 - 3.2z + 4$$

PROBLEM 3.6   Show that a necessary condition for the roots of $F(z) = 0$ to lie inside the unit circle is:

$$\frac{n!}{(n - r)!} |a_n| > r! |a_r|, \qquad (r = 0, 1, 2, \ldots, n - 1)$$

For a fifth-order polynomial this yields

$$|a_0| < 1, \ |a_1| < 5, \ |a_2| < 10, \ |a_3| < 10, \ |a_4| < 5, \qquad \text{with } a_5 = 1$$

Hint: Show that every circle K (or polygon) encircling all roots of a polynomial $F(z) = 0$ also encircles the roots of the derivatives $F^{(k)}(z) = 0$.

PROBLEM 3.7   If the roots of $F(z)$ (with $a_n = 1$) are all inside the unit circle, show that the maximum modulus of the roots, r, can be obtained from the following relationship:

$$r^2 < 1 - \frac{(A_{n-1} - B_{n-1})^2 F(1) F(-1)(-1)^{n(n-1)}}{2^{n(n-1)}}$$

or

$$|r| < 1 - \frac{(-1)^{n(n-1)}(A_{n-1} - B_{n-1})^2 F(1) F(-1)}{2^{n^2 - n + 1}}$$

Hint: Use equations (3.68) through (3.70) to verify this inequality.

PROBLEM 3.8   Obtain the root distribution of the following polynomial:

$$F(z) = z^5 - 3.5714z^4 + 5.7755z^3 - 5.303z^2 + 2.6405z - 0.5414$$

PROBLEM 3.9   Obtain the root distribution of the following polynomials:

(*a*) $F(z) = 4 + 3z^3 + 2z^{10}$

(*b*) $F(z) = -2 + 4z + 5z^2 - 6z^3 + 2z^4 + 6z^5 - 4z^6 - 2z^7 + z^8$

Chapter 4

PROBLEM 4.1 If $\mathscr{F}(z) = \jmath[f]$ and $\mathscr{G}(z) = \jmath[g]$ are both analytic for $|z| > R_0$, show that the function $\mathscr{H}(z) = \jmath[fg]$ is obtainable from $\mathscr{F}(z)$ and $\mathscr{G}(z)$ as follows:

$$\mathscr{H}(z) = \frac{1}{2\pi j} \oint_{|\zeta| = R_1} \mathscr{F}(\zeta)\mathscr{G}\left(\frac{z}{\zeta}\right)\frac{d\zeta}{\zeta}$$

for $|z| > R_0 R_1$, where $R_1 > R_0$. (The path of integration can be chosen as a simple closed curve Γ.)

PROBLEM 4.2 For a multirate error-sampled feedback system shown in Fig. 4.2, obtain the modified z-transform of the output $\mathscr{C}(z_{T_2}, m)$; n is an integer larger than one.

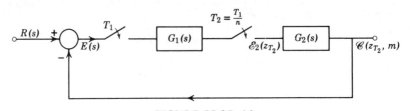

FIGURE PROB. 4.2

PROBLEM 4.3 Let $F_r = \sum\limits_{n=0}^{\infty} n^r x^n$; show that

(a) $F_r' = \dfrac{dF_r}{dx} = \dfrac{F_{r+1}}{x}$, with $F_0 = \dfrac{1}{1-x}$, $x < 1$

(b) Show by induction that

$$F_r = \frac{S_r(x)}{(1-x)^{r+1}}, \qquad x < 1$$

where

$$S_r(x) = \sum_{i=1}^{r} S_{r,i}x^i, \qquad r > 0$$

(c) Using $S_r(x)$ in F_r of (b), differentiating and using (a), show that

$$S_{r+1} = \sum_{i=1}^{r+1} S_{r+1,i}x^i = \sum_{i=1}^{r} [ix^i + (r+1-i)x^{i+1}]S_{r,i}$$

(d) From (c) by equating coefficients, show

$$S_{r+1,i} = iS_{r,i} + (r+2-i)S_{r,i-1}$$

(e) If $r = 3$, obtain the value of

$$\sum_{n=0}^{\infty} n^3 x^n, \qquad \text{for} \qquad x < 1$$

PROBLEM 4.4 Let $F_{r,n}(x) = \sum_{i=0}^{n-1} i^r x^i$ and $T_{r,n}(x) = \sum_{i=n}^{\infty} i^r x^i$; show from the results of the preceding problem that

(a) $F_{r,n}(x) = F_r(x) - T_{r,n}(x)$

(b) By a change of variable show that

$$T_{r,n}(x) = \sum_{i=0}^{\infty} (n+i)^r x^{n+i} = \sum_{i=0}^{\infty} \sum_{j=0}^{r} \binom{r}{j} i^j n^{r-j} x^{n+i} = \sum_{j=0}^{r} \binom{r}{j} n^{r-j} x^n F_j(x)$$

(c) Show that

$$F_{r,n}(x) = S_r(x) - \sum_{j=0}^{r} \binom{r}{j} n^{r-j} x^n S_j(x), \qquad \text{for all } x$$

(d) Show that the finite sum $\sum_{i=1}^{n-1} i^r$ is a known result in terms of Bernoulli numbers.

PROBLEM 4.5 Let $\mathscr{H}(z) = \dfrac{z^2 + b_1 z}{z^2 + a_1 z + a_2} = \dfrac{z^2 + b_1 z}{(z - p_1)(z - p_2)}$

where

$$a_1 = -(p_1 + p_2), \qquad a_2 = p_1 p_2$$

Using the residue method, show that

(a) $N_s = \dfrac{1}{2\pi j} \oint_\Gamma \mathscr{H}(z)\mathscr{H}(z^{-1}) \dfrac{dz}{z} = \dfrac{(b_1^2 + 1)(1 + p_1 p_2) + 2b_1(p_1 + p_2)}{(1 - p_1^2)(1 - p_2^2)(1 - p_1 p_2)}$

(b) Show that N_s in (a) is the same as obtained from Table III of the Appendix when $n = 2$ and $b_0 = 1$, $b_2 = 0$, $a_0 = 1$.

PROBLEM 4.6 Given the following expressions for the sampled spectral density $\Phi_{1,2}(z)$.

(a) $\dfrac{1}{(1 + 0.5z^{-1})(1 + 0.5z)}$, (b) $\dfrac{z + 1}{(z + 0.5)(z - 2)}$

Determine $\phi_{12}(nT)$ for each case.

PROBLEM 4.7 For the error-sampled data feedback system shown in Fig. 4.7,

(a) Obtain the total squared error for a step input.

(b) Obtain the discrete square error (that is, the sampled square error).

$$G(s) = \frac{27.8(s + 1)}{s[(s + 3)^2 + (2\pi)^2]}$$

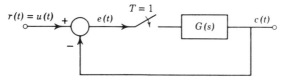

FIGURE PROB. 4.7 Error sampled feedback system.

Chapter 5

PROBLEM 5.1   A saturating amplifier sampled-data feedback system is given in Fig. 5.1; also given is the form of $h(n)$ as follows:

$$h(n) = \begin{cases} 40 & e(n) \geq 40 \\ e(n) & -40 \leq e(n) \leq 40 \\ -40 & e(n) \leq -40 \end{cases}$$

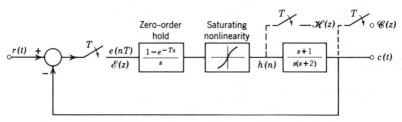

FIGURE PROB. 5.1   Saturating amplifier sampled-data feedback system.

The power series representation of this nonlinearity over the interval $-65 \leq e(n) \leq 65$ is

$$h(n) = 1.111e(n) - 0.1234 \ 0.10^{-3}[e(n)]^3$$
$$r(n) = 60 \text{ volts}$$
$$e(0) = 60, \ e(1) = 32, \ T = 1$$

(a) Obtain the nonlinear difference equation which describes the error $e(n)$.

(b) Solve the preceding equation using the convolution z-transform to obtain $e(n)$.

PROBLEM 5.2   Given a nonlinear discrete system as shown in Fig. 5.2. If

$$h(n) = m_1 e(n) + m_3 e(n)^3, \quad \text{with } m_3 = 0.1, \ m_1 = 1$$

and

$$r(n) = \text{unit step}, \quad \text{and } T = 1$$

obtain

(a) The nonlinear difference equation which describes the output $c(n)$.

(b) Solve the preceding equation using the convolution z-transform, and obtain $c(n)$.

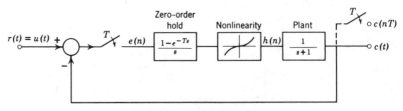

FIGURE PROB. 5.2   Nonlinear discrete system.

(c) Compare a few values of $c(n)$ from (b) with the exact solution using (a) as a recurrence relationship.

Chapter 6

PROBLEM 6.1 Given a nonlinear sampled-data feedback system as shown in Fig. 6.1a and the type of nonlinearity shown in Fig. 6.1b.
(a) Show that the limit cycle $+1$, $+1$, -1, -1, exists.
(b) Show that the limit cycle 0, $+1$, -1, 0, does not exist.

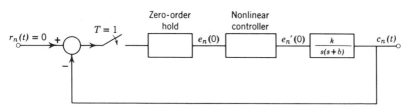

FIGURE PROB. 6.1a

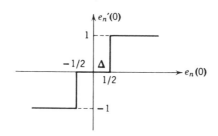

FIGURE PROB. 6.1b

PROBLEM 6.2 For the example in Section 6.6, if the relay output is -1, -1, $+1$, $+1$, obtain the possible values of c_0, c_1, c_2, c_3 to maintain a limit cycle of period 4.

PROBLEM 6.3 The nonlinear difference equation describing a PWM system which is in a limit cycle of period two is given as follows:

$$c_{n+1} = \gamma(n)\frac{k}{b^2}(bh_n - e^{-b(T-h_n)} + e^{-bT}) + c_n + \frac{1 - e^{-bT}}{b}\dot{c}_n$$

$$= f(c_n, \dot{c}_n)$$

$$\dot{c}_{n+1} = \gamma(n)\frac{k}{b}[e^{-b(T-h_n)} - e^{-bT}] + e^{-bT}\dot{c}_n = g(c_n, \dot{c}_n)$$

If,

$$h_n = \alpha|r_n - c_n|, \qquad r_n = 1$$

and

$$\gamma(0) = +1, \gamma(1) = -1, h_n = h_0 \text{ and } c_n|_{h_n=h_0} = c_{0s}, \dot{c}_n|_{h_n=h_0} = \dot{c}_{0s}$$

(a) Obtain the elements of the matrix $[A_G]$.

(b) Find the characteristic equation of the matrix which can be tested for the roots inside the unit circle.

(c) Obtain conditions on the stability of the limit cycle.

(d) Show that the solution for $h = 0$, and $\alpha k < (\alpha k)_c = 2b \dfrac{1 + e^{-bT}}{1 - e^{-bT}}$, is always stable.

PROBLEM 6.4   For a relay sampled-data system given in Fig. 6.1a and b, the following are given:

$$b = 1, \qquad k = 1, \qquad T = 1$$

(a) Show that the continuous response at the limit cycle is given by

$$c_0(mT) = -\left\{ \tfrac{1}{2}(1 - 2m)T + \frac{1 + e^{-2T} + e^{-mT} - e^{-(1+m)T}}{1 + e^{-2T}} \right\},$$

$$0 \le m \le 1$$

$$c_1(mT) = \frac{T}{2} - \frac{(1 - e^{-T})e^{-mT}}{1 + e^{-2T}}, \qquad 0 \le m \le 1$$

Hint: Note that when $m = 0$, the response at sampling instants is obtained.

(b) Show that the postulated sequence $+1, 0, -1, 0$ can exist if $c_0 = -0.245$ and $c_1 = 0.166$ and half the dead zone $\Delta = 0.2$.

Chapter 7

PROBLEM 7.1   (a) Find the approximate solution of the following differential equation using the z-forms method and assuming $T = 0.2$ second.

$$\frac{d^3y}{dt^3} + 2\frac{d^2y}{dt^2} + 2\frac{dy}{dt} + y = 1, \qquad y(0) = \dot{y}(0) = \ddot{y}(0) = 0$$

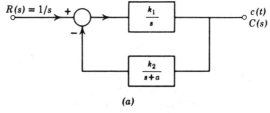

(a)

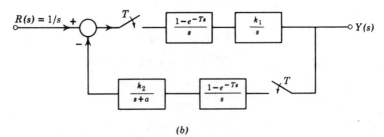

(b)

FIGURE PROB. 7.2

(b) Compare this solution with the exact solution and comment on the choice of T.

PROBLEM 7.2   Compare the exact step response of Fig. 7.2a with the approximate model of Fig. 7.2b for the following values:

(a) $T = \frac{1}{25}$ second, $k_1 = 3.2$, $k_2 = 555$, $a = 50$ radians per second.

(b) Repeat (a) with $T = \frac{1}{75}$ second.

PROBLEM 7.3   The z-transforms of the input and output of a discrete filter are given as follows:

$$\mathcal{F}_i(z) = 1 + 3z^{-1} + 5z^{-1}$$

$$\mathcal{F}_0(z) = 4 + 14z^{-1} + 27z^{-2} + 13z^{-3} + 5z^{-4}$$

(a) Determine the z-transform of the filter $\mathcal{H}(z)$.

(b) If a small disturbance is made in the measurement of the output such that the leading term of $\mathcal{F}_0(z)$, that is, 4, becomes 3, determine the z-transform of the filter for this case $\mathcal{H}^*(z)$.

(c) Using the substitution

$$z^{-1} = \lambda + 1$$

obtain $\mathcal{H}_1(\lambda)$ for (a).

(d) Determine $\mathcal{H}_1^*(\lambda)$ for (b).

(e) If we truncate the series for $\mathcal{H}_1^*(\lambda)$ after the second (or after the third) term, determine $\mathcal{H}^*(z)$ for these cases and compare with (b).

(f) Comment on the value of the transformation in c.

PROBLEM 7.4   To obtain the z-forms for a double integrator $(1/s^2)$, the following second-order difference equation is used to approximate $i_2(t) = \int\int y(t)\, dt$:

$$Ai_2(t + 2T) + Bi_2(t + T) + Ci_2(t)$$
$$= Dy(t + 2T) + Ey(t + T) + Fy(t) \tag{1}$$

where the coefficients A, B, C, D, E, and F are to be determined.

(a) Using the following relationship in equation (1),

$$\mathcal{L}[i(t + nT)] = e^{nTs}\mathcal{L}[i(t)]$$

and

$$\mathcal{L}[i_2(t)] = \frac{1}{s^2}\,\mathcal{L}[y(t)]$$

obtain the Laplace transform of the difference equation.

(b) If the exponential operators in (a) are expanded in a Taylor's series, and we equate the same powers of s on both sides of the difference equation, show that difference equation for a second-order integration is

$$i_2(t + 2T) - 2i_2(t + T) + i_2(t)$$
$$= \frac{T^2}{12}y(t + 2T) + \frac{10T^2}{12}y(t + T) + \frac{T^2}{12}y(t) \tag{2}$$

(c) Show that the z-transform of (2), neglecting initial conditions, is given by the following z-form of $1/s^2$

$$\frac{\mathscr{I}_2(z)}{\mathscr{Y}(z)} = \frac{T^2}{12} \frac{z^2 + 10z + 1}{(z-1)^2}$$

(d) If initial conditions are not zero, and if $y(T)$ and $i_2(T)$ are expressed as follows:

$$y(T) = y(0) + Ty'(0) + \frac{T^2}{2!} y''(0) + \ldots$$

$$i_2(T) = y^{(-2)}(0) + Ty^{(-1)}(0) + \frac{T^2}{2!} y(0) + \ldots$$

show that $\mathscr{I}_2(z)$ is given by

$$\mathscr{I}_2(z) = \frac{T^2}{12} \frac{z^2 + 10z + 1}{(z-1)^2} \mathscr{Y}(z) + \frac{z}{z-1} y^{(-2)}(0) + \frac{Tz}{(z-1)^2} y^{(-1)}(0)$$

$$- \frac{T^2}{12} \frac{z(z+5)}{(z-1)^2} y(0) + \frac{T^3}{12} \frac{z}{(z-1)^2} y'(0) - \frac{T^5}{180} \frac{z}{(z-1)^2} y'''(0) + \ldots$$

(e) Similarly, for one integration, show that

$$\mathscr{I}_1(z) = \frac{T}{2} \frac{z+1}{z-1} \mathscr{Y}(z) - \frac{Tz}{2(z-1)} y(0) + \frac{z}{z-1} y^{(-1)}(0),$$

$$\text{where } y^{(-1)}(0) = \int y \, dt\Big|_{t=0}$$

PROBLEM 7.5 Using the z-forms obtained in (7.4) and the z-transform, compare the approximate solution of the following differential equation with the exact solution:

$$\frac{d^2y}{dt^2} + 3\frac{dy}{dt} + 2y = 0, \qquad y(0) = 3, \qquad y'(0) = -4$$

Choose $T = 0.1$ second.

PROBLEM 7.6 If the exact solution of the following time-varying equation

$$\frac{d^2}{dt^2}[(t^2 - 1)y] - \frac{d}{dt}[2ty] - 6y = 0, \qquad y(0) = -0.5, \qquad y'(0) = 0$$

is

$$y(t) = 0.5(3t^2 - 1), \qquad 0 \le t \le 1$$

Obtain the approximate solution for $T = 0.1$ using the z-forms and the z-transform and compare with the exact solution.

Chapter 8

PROBLEM 8.1 In the analysis of one-way transmission channels, sampling of information is used. Figure 8.1a shows the elements of a connection containing a unilateral repeater which isolates the two media (modems) and provides each with a matching termination.

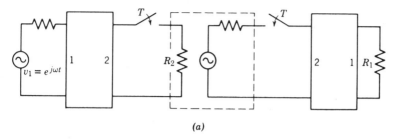

(a)

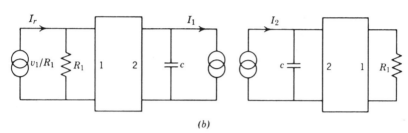

(b)

FIGURE PROB. 8.1

(a) If the pulse length h is assumed much less than the sampling period T, show that the circuit in Fig. 8.1a is equivalent to Fig. 8.1b, where

$$I_r = c \sum_{n=0}^{\infty} e^{j\omega t} F_r(j\omega)\delta(t - nT)$$

and $F_r(j\omega)$ is an impedance ratio function of the frequency (ω).

(b) If the voltage ratio $2v_2/v_1$ produced by insertion of the whole system is denoted as $T(j\omega)$ and we assume that the intervening network (1–2) is eliminated, show that the modulus of transmission is

$$|T(j\omega)| = \frac{4\alpha e^{-\alpha}(\cosh \alpha - \cos y)}{\alpha^2 + y^2}$$

where $\alpha = T/R_1 c$, and $y = \omega T$.

(c) Plot the modulus of transmission $|T(j\omega)|$ for various values of α as a function of f_m/f_r = ratio between modulating and sampling frequencies.

Hint: See reference 26 of Chapter 8.

PROBLEM 8.2   The circuit of a periodically switched network which produces a phase lag is shown in Fig. 8.2a. The actuation of the sampler is such that the left-hand loop is closed for $kT \leq t < (k + \delta)T$ and open for $(k + \delta)T \leq t < (k + 1)T$, and that the right-hand loop is closed for $(k + 0.5)T \leq t < (k + 0.5 + \delta)T$ and open for $kT \leq t < (k + 0.5)T$ and $(k + 0.5 + \delta)T \leq t < (k + 1)T$, where $0 < \delta \leq 0.5$ and $k = 0, 1, 2, \ldots$. The input to the network is a carrier-suppressed amplitude-modulated sinusoid given by

$$e_1(t) = e_i(t) \cos (\Omega t + \phi), \qquad \Omega = \frac{2\pi}{T}$$

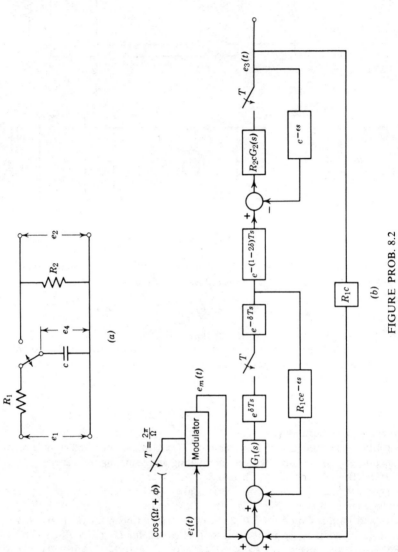

FIGURE PROB. 8.2

(a) Show that the circuit system in Fig. 8.2a is equivalent to the block diagram Fig. 8.2b, where ε is an infinitely small quantity

$$G_1(s) = \frac{1}{R_1cs + 1}, \qquad G_2(s) = \frac{1}{R_2cs + 1}$$

(b) If $e_i(t)$ is a step function of magnitude E_0, show that the response is

$$e_3(t) = \frac{kE_0[1 - e^{-(k+1)\delta T/R_\xi c}][e^{-[t-(k+0.5)T]/R_2c}]}{1 - e^{-\delta T/R_\xi c}}$$

$$\{u[t - (k + 0.5)]T - u[t - (k + \delta + 0.5)]T\}$$

where $u(t)$ is a unit step and

$$R_\xi = \frac{1}{1/R_1 + 1/R_2}$$

$$k = \frac{\Omega R_1 c \sin(\Omega\delta T + \phi) + \cos(\Omega\delta T + \phi)}{\Omega^2 R_1^2 c^2 + 1}$$

PROBLEM 8.3 Sometimes inventory control problems can be represented as staggered sampled-data feedback systems. One such problem is that concerned with the maintenance of a certain quantity of parts in a storage location. This system can be represented in a simplified form as shown in Fig. 8.3. If

$$aT = \tfrac{1}{3}, \qquad 0 \le \delta_1 \le 1$$

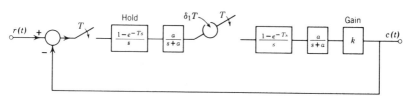

FIGURE PROB. 8.3

(a) Determine the value of δ_1 (the sampler phasing) that yields the maximum gain k for stability limit.

(b) Compare the gain obtained in (a) with the maximum gain for $\delta_1 = 0$ and $\delta_1 = 1$.

PROBLEM 8.4 THE TOYMAKER PROBLEM*

The toymaker is involved in the toy business. He may be in either of two states. He is in the first state if his toy is in favor and in the second state if his toy is out of favor with the public. Suppose that when he is in state 1 there is a 50% chance of a transition to state 2. When he is in state 2, he experiments with new toys and he may return to state 1 after a week with probability $\tfrac{2}{5}$ or remain unprofitable in state 2 with probability $\tfrac{3}{5}$.

---

* This problem is obtained from Reference (20), Chapter 8.

(a) Find the transition matrix P which describes the discrete Markov process

$$P = [P_{ij}] = \begin{bmatrix} P_{11} & P_{12} \\ P_{21} & P_{22} \end{bmatrix}$$

Define a state probability $\pi_i(n)$, the probability that the system will occupy state i after n transitions if its state at $n = 0$ is known.

(b) Write the vector difference equation which describes the probability that the system occupies each of its states after n moves; that is, the probability to be in state 1 after n weeks if we know he is in state 1 at the beginning of the n-week period, $n = 0, 1, 2, \ldots$.

(c) Apply the z-transform to the vector difference equation of (b). Assume P is given as in (a).

(d) Find $H(n)$ the inverse transform of $(I - zP)^{-1}$. I is the identity matrix.

(e) Obtain the state-probability vector at time n, knowing the initial state probability vector.

(f) If the toymaker starts in the successful state 1, obtain $\pi(0)$, the initial state. Also obtain (c) for this particular initial state.

(g) Show that when $n \to \infty$, the state probability components approach the limiting state probabilities of the process.

INDEX

321